THE CACTUS
HANDBOOK

Erik Haustein

THE CACTUS HANDBOOK

CHARTWELL
BOOKS, INC.

Acknowledgments

The publishers wish to thank the following for their permission to reproduce their photographs: Andreae (10), Artia (Crkal/Riha) (217), Barthlott (6), Buining (11), Fröhlich (21), Haager (1), Haugg (36), Krähenbühl (3), Krainz (2), Kretschmer (2), Milkuhn (5), Polka (1), Rauh, Walter (24), Rauh, Werner (113), Schäfer (1), Schreier (26), Sommer (10), Stauch (1), Stiglmayr (3) and Supthut (1).

The publishers are grateful to Dr David Hunt for his assistance in the preparation of this edition.

Published in 1988 by
Chartwell Books, Inc.
A Division of Book Sales, Inc.
110 Enterprise Avenue
Secaucus, New Jersey 07094

© 1986 Franckh'sche Verlagshandlung, W. Keller & Co
Kosmos-Verlag, Stuttgart

© 1986 English translation Ridgmount Books Limited

ISBN 1 55521 206 9

Original title: *Der Kakteenführer*

Translated by Pamela Marwood, MIL

Printed in Czechoslovakia

54267

CONTENTS

FOREWORD

This book is intended not only for the countless cactus lovers who would like to add to the sheer pleasure they derive from their own cacti by learning more about the cactus family, but also for all plant enthusiasts who are interested in the beauty of the plant world in all its extraordinary complexity, of which the cactus family is a particularly impressive part.

For the experienced cactophile the first section describes in detail the special characteristics that so strikingly distinguish cacti from all other plant families. It shows how these peculiarities, such as the thick, fleshy, ribbed and often very prickly body or the remarkable flowers, can be related to the general basic form of flowering plants. The interesting pollination systems are discussed, as well as the various ways in which cacti are used.

Cactus enthusiasts who want practical information for successful cultivation can turn to the end of this section where there is a comprehensive introduction to all aspects of caring for and propagating cacti.

The main colour-illustrated section of the book is a broad survey of all the genera of cacti, in which the individual genera are arranged according to their natural affinities — as far as these have been determined to date — so that their similarities may be compared. Special attention has been paid to the choice of species featured; each one is illustrated by a colour photograph, often taken in the original habitat, and is accompanied by a detailed description. Some 500 of the approximately 2000 known species are included and with their help it should at least be possible for the reader to ascertain to which genus an unknown species belongs.

The book ends with advice on recognizing and dealing with diseases and pests which attack cacti, as well as a helpful glossary of technical terms and an index of all the species mentioned.

CACTUS STRUCTURE AND DEVELOPMENT

VEGETATIVE STRUCTURES

Most cacti grow in areas with low rainfall, long dry periods and intense sunlight. Certain highly characteristic adaptations make it possible for them to endure these extreme environmental conditions without damage. In spite of vast differences in form, all cacti share a common underlying groundplan. Visually, the typical cactus is characterized by three features: stem succulence, reduction of leaves, and absence or sparsity of lateral branching. In most cases, there is also the production of spines, which gives the plants their exceptional appearance

The most primitive group of cacti, the Pereskioideae, demonstrates the transition from the familiar appearance of a flowering plant, divided into shoot, leaf and root to what we think of as a cactus. Pereskias are freely-branching shrubs or small trees, erect and spreading or climbing, in one case with the help of claw-like spines. Their stems are woody and non-succulent and bear normal, broad and flat, slightly fleshy, foliage-leaves that are shed at the end of the growing season (Figs. 1 and 2). In this group, apart from

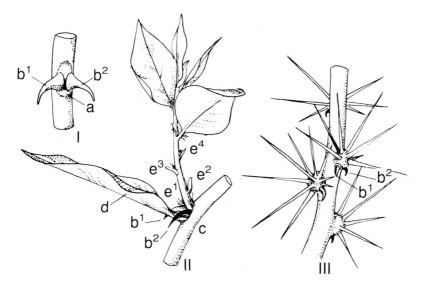

Fig. 1
Pereskia aculeata, **I** part of a shoot with leaf-scar *a* in its axil, the areole with 2 prophyll spines *b¹*, *b²*; **II** part of a shoot at later stage, with areoles further developed, having produced prickly leaf-spines above the 2 prophyll spines *b¹*, *b²*; **III** part of a shoot *c* with leaf *d*. Here the areole has developed a long-shoot; *e¹–e⁴* are scaly lower leaves with broad leaves above; *b¹*, *b²* are prophyll spines. (After Troll.)

7

Fig. 2
Pereskia sacharosa, the foliage leaves on the main axis having fallen, the areoles have grown new leaves, after first producing spines. (After Britton and Rose.)

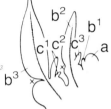

Fig. 3
Opuntia ficus-indica, stem-tip in longitudinal section; *a* growing-point, b^1–b^3 first leaf rudiments, c^1–c^3 rudimentary spines. (After Goebel.)

the flowers, it is only the buds in the axils of the leaves which are typically cactus-like. In the first year, these buds appear almost dormant, producing a small tuft or cushion of woolly felt, call the 'areole', and sometimes a few spines, which are in fact modified leaves. In *Pereskia aculeata*, a pair of claw-like spines also develops early on, (Fig. 1), which correspond to prophylls, that is the first, rudimentary leaves which develop at the base of a side-shoot in other dicotyledonous plants. The areole is in fact a very complex and condensed structure, analogous to the short-shoots or spurs found in some other families; it is unique to the cactus family and one of its universal and most important hallmarks.

In *Pereskia*, the areoles can remain active in the second year, producing more spines and, in some species, foliage leaves. They may also, however, grow out into normal leafy shoots, particularly if the tip of the main shoot is cut off. Finally, the areoles can also bear flowers (indeed, in all cacti the flowers always arise from an areole). In botanical terms, of course, the flower itself is actually no more than a highly modified, leafy shoot.

The next major group of cacti, the Opuntioideae, shows the transition to stem succulence and, at the same time, reduction of the leaves. The Opuntioideae have cylindrical to awl-shaped leaves, with the exception of the genera *Pereskiopsis* and *Quiabentia* which have retained flat leaves.

Leaves first appear at the growing-point of the stem as hemispherical protrusions (Fig. 3) which soon differentiate into a base and a more vigorously growing tip, separated by a constriction of the side facing away from the axis. This constriction forms the dividing line between the upper leaf which will become the leaf-blade (or leaf proper) and the lower leaf which is united with the axis to form the leaf-base, usually more or less protruding, and often termed 'podarium' (plural, podaria). On its upper side, each podarium carries an areole, developed from an axillary bud as in *Pereskia*. In some species of *Opuntia*, the podaria are also readily recognizable by their rhombic outline.

In cacti, water storage tissue in the stem is formed from the outer layers, or cortex, whereas other succulent plants use their central pith or medullary zone. Many cacti, however, can also make use of the pith to store additional water (for example, *Carnegiea gigantea*).

Leaf development and stem succulence seem to be related; *Opuntia subulata* can have leaves 5–12 cm long and 3–4 years old, while stem succulence is still only moderately developed. In *Opuntia cylindrica*, however, with leaves only 10–13 mm long and caducous, the stem succulence is much more marked. The leaves are even more reduced and the stems more succulent in the Cactoideae, the group with the greatest variety of forms. While leaves are still evident as small tubercles on the growing-point, differentiation into upper and lower leaf does not occur and their development is in fact halted, so that they are no longer visible at all at later stages. The primordium of the side-shoot, the areole, moves to the subtending leaf itself, the meristematic region being transferred from the reduced upper-leaf to the leaf-base. In some genera, this grows to a teat-like protrusion, or mamilla (Fig. 4). Mamillae, therefore, are simply succulent leaf-bases with completely reduced upper-leaves, carrying spine-bearing areoles on their tips.

The position of the leaves (or the podaria) on the stem follows the general laws of leaf-arrangement, in which two possibilities are distinguished: the growing tip either produces several leaf-primordia simultaneously, or leaf-primordia form consecutively. The first type is known as 'verticillate', where consecutive leaf-whorls alternate and the angles between each two sets of leaves are equal. In the second type the leaf-position is 'alternate': the consecutive leaves are connected by an imaginary spiral running round the stem and here, too, the angles between two consecutive leaves are equal. If these angles are expressed not in degrees but in fractions of the stem-circumference, the following values are often found: 1/2, 1/3, 2/5, 3/8, 5/13. The angle 2/5, for example, means that by spiralling twice around a stem, starting from a certain leaf, the fifth leaf will be exactly above or below the leaf started from. Certain leaves are positioned in 'orthostichies — or straight lines — so in the 2/5 position there would be five lines. This sequence of angles is also referred to as the 'Fibonacci genes', which is formulated so that the numerator of a fraction equals the sum of the two previous numerators, and the same with the denominator, until the divergence limit is reached at 137°, 30'.

However, the significance of these divergence values should not be overestimated.

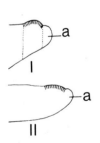
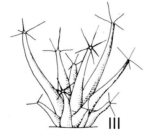

Fig. 4
I–II Development of mammillae; a leaf-primordium rudimentary leaf, shaded area indicates areole position (further explanation in text). III–V *Leuchtenbergia principis.* III young plant; IV a tip of tubercle; V flowering areole, a leaf-rudiment. (I–III after Troll, IV after Buxbaum.)

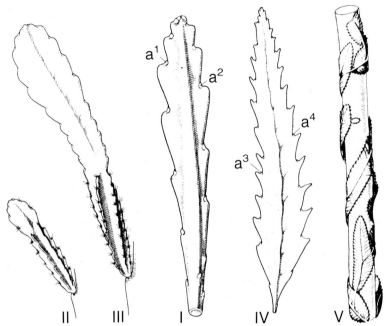

Fig. 5

I–III *Nopalxochia phyllanthoides*, I part of a normal shoot, a^1, a^2 scale-leaves with areoles in their axils; II–III reverted shoots, arising from areoles of old stock, lower part multi-ribbed, with spine-bearing areoles; IV *Rhipsalis* *houlletiana*, a^3, a^4 scale-leaves with undeveloped areoles in their axils; V shoot of *Strophocactus wittii* climbing up a support. (I–IV after Troll, V after Schumann.)

During the course of ontogenesis several divergences may occur consecutively and overlap each other. In addition, the position of leaves or mamillae also depends on the relationship of the younger leaf-buds to the older ones in the course of progressing round the basic spiral. The possibility of contact between the leaf primordia depends on their relative size and the circumference of the meristem. Depending on the kind of contact made in each case, the number of the 'parastichies' — or oblique lines — will emerge. These can be observed particularly well with Mammillarias.

If we return to the first set of values, taking 2/5, 3/8 will find the leaves or mamillae in five and eight straight lines above each other respectively. The relationships between leaves in the verticillate position are simpler; here the number of straight lines is twice the number of components in a given whorl. Depending on the space available, this can lead to the formation of continuous ribs, where tubercles that were originally separated from each other develop along a communal base. In such cases, the tubercle-structure has an increasing tendency to form a ridge and the sooner displacement occurs between the tubercles, the stronger the tendency is. Such transitional forms are, for example, found in the genus *Gymnocalycium*, where *G. schickendantzii* retains almost intact tubercles, whereas in *G. megalothelos* diagonal incisions on the ribs make it just possible to recognize their development from tubercles. If the leaf-arrangement is verticillate, there are

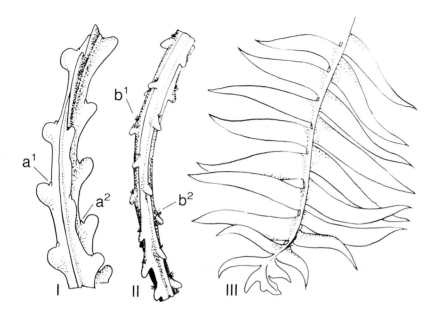

Fig. 6
Part of a shoot of **I** *Hylocereus calcaratus*, a^1, a^2
scale-leaves; **II** *Selenicereus hamatus*, b^1, b^2
areoles; **III** *Epiphyllum chrysocardium*. (I after
Britton and Rose, II after Troll, III after
Buxbaum.)

often four-parted whorls, which will result in the development of eight ribs. Similarly, five, six and eight-parted whorls will become shoots with 10, 12, and 16 ribs. Whorls with only two or three components are rarer; they lead to four or six ridges, for example, in *Cereus jamacaru*. If the leaf-arrangement is alternate the 2/5 or more commonly the 3/8 formation is observed which results in five and eight ribs as in *Astrophytum myriostigma* and *A. asterias*.

It can be said, then, that the number of ribs is determined initially by leaf arrangement. During the course of development this can, however, change: under favourable nutritional and light conditions, the rib number may increase with the plant's vigour, new ribs being inserted between the existing ones. Under poor conditions they can also decrease. Thus rib-formation has a certain autonomy to which tubercle-position is subordinate. In contrast to the cases just described, favourable food and light conditions can also result in a *decrease* of ribs, as seen in the example of the so-called 'leaf-cacti' (*Epiphyllum* and allied genera). Here the seedlings and the young side-shoots are many-ribbed with clearly formed angles (Fig. 5). During the course of development the superfluous ribs fuse in one by one, so that towards the top they disappear. After the growing-point has modified and changed to the two-ranked leaf-arrangement, only two narrow ribs are retained, which consequently gives the shoot a leaf-like appearance.

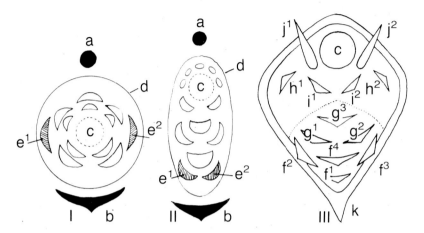

Fig. 7

I–II Areole development in *Opuntia*; *a* main axis, *b* subtending leaf, *c* growing-point, producing the axillary areole, *d* limit of areole, e^1, e^2 prophylls, followed by further leaf rudiments; III *Leuchtenbergia principis*, developmental sequence of spines: seedlings develop only spines f^1-f^1; older areoles, not yet capable of flowering, develop spines g^1-g^3 as far as the dotted line; h^1-h^2, i^1-i^2 spines develop at flowering areole only; j^1 and j^2 are short, subulate spines; *k* leaf-rudiment of subtending leaf, *c* growing-point. (I and II after Troll, III after Buxbaum.)

Two-winged, leaf-like shoots are also found among some members of the genus *Rhipsalis* such as *R. houlletiana*, in *Wittia amazonica* and *Strophocactus wittii* and other genera of the Hylocereeae.

The physical structure of ribs varies a great deal. All transitions are found, from shallow elevations only divided from each other by sharp incisions, as in *Haageocereus*, to the fine, gill-like ribbing of *Stenocactus*, or the two-ribbed *Epiphyllum* and *Rhipsalis* species already mentioned.

Longitudinally these ribs or ridges run in straight lines, only interrupted by the evenly placed areoles. They may, however, be divided by cross-furrows into shallow, hexagonal tubercles, as in *Trichocereus thelegonus*. The development of part of a rib can be distorted, forming, for example, chin-like protrusions below the areoles; this is the case in *Neoporteria ebenacantha*, in the three-ribbed *Hylocereus calcaratus* or in *Selenicereus hamatus* (Fig. 6) which has backward-pointing hooks that serve the same purpose as the climbing spines in other scrambling or climbing cacti. In the leaf-like shoots of *Epiphyllum* and *Rhipsalis* species, there is a similar exaggeration of the rib-construction between the areoles, resulting in a more or less sinuate appearance. The most extreme case of this can be seen in *Epiphyllum chrysocardium*, with 'leaves' so deeply indented that they seem pinnate. The areoles in all these examples are found in the notches.

Those areoles found on tubercles or ribs are short-shoots, mostly capable of only

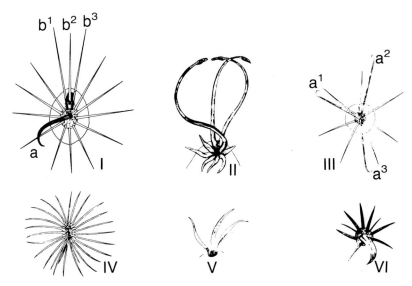

Fig. 8
Areoles with various types of spine: **I**
Hamatocactus setispinus with porrect, hook-shaped central spine *a*, 3 upward-pointing central spines *b¹–b³* and a gland spine *c*; **II**
Pelecyphora strobiliformis with 3 active gland spines; **III** *Neolloydia odorata* with 3 hooked spines a^1–a^3, and needle-shaped spines; **IV**
Neolloydia sp. with comb-shaped (pectinate) spine arrangement; **V** *Opuntia papyracantha* with papery spines, interspersed with tufts of glochids; **VI** *Ferocactus latispinus* with several subulate spines and one tongue-shaped spine. (After Buxbaum.)

limited growth; the growing-point only becomes active under certain conditions, such as the formation of side-shoots. Only in very few cases are the areoles regularly structured; they generally elongate in the direction of the subtending leaf (Figs. 7 and 8) and at the same time the growing-point moves to the side facing the shoot (adaxial side). Leaf-primordia are almost always formed on the side of the areole pointing away from the shoot (abaxial side). The growth tissue on the upper end of the areole remains capable of development for a long time and may produce a flower, or, more rarely, a side-branch. The areole has differentiated into an upper area with flowers and leaves and a lower spiny area.

Among many cacti with tubercles this development goes still further: the areole is extended lengthwise on the upper side of the tubercle, and the sites for spine and flower formation move further and further apart. The spines will grow from the tip of the mamilla, the flowers from the lower end of the extended areole. Between them normally runs a hair-lined furrow that runs from the tip of the mamilla to the flower. The developmental trend reaches its conclusion when the division into two independent growing-points is complete, and the furrow on the upper side of the mamilla disappears. This is known as serial division of the growing-point (Figs. 10 and 11): the tip of the mamilla bears the outer growing-point that will in most cases produce strong spines, while at the base of the mamilla (in its 'axil') is the spineless growing-point that will only produce flowers or side-shoots. The axil will also produce a large number of hairs.

13

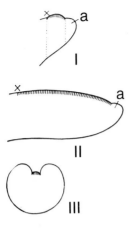

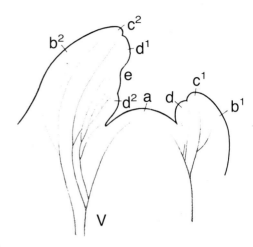

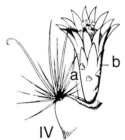

Fig. 9
Tubercle development; **I–III** schematic diagrams, *a* leaf primordium
or rudiment, shaded area indicates position of areole (detailed
explanation in the text); **IV** *Ancistrocactus brevihamatus*, tubercle,
a hairy furrow, *b* flower at base of furrow; **V** longitudinal section
through the vegetative apex of *Coryphantha sp.*, showing serial
division of the areolar growing-point, *a* shoot apex, *b¹* older, *b²*
young tubercles, *c¹, c²* leaf-rudiments, *d* still undivided part of
areolar growing-point on *b¹*, on *b² d¹* outer part (later spiny), *e*
rudimentary furrow, *d²* inner part (axil rudiment) of rudimentary
areole after division. (**I–IV** after Troll, **V** after Ganong.)

The shape of the completely formed tubercle is frequently four-cornered or round-ish. In many cases the mamillae may be flattened, becoming hatchet-shaped if flattened lengthwise with the shoot (as in *Pelecyphora aselliformis*), and scale- or leaf-like if flattened transversely. The similarity to leaves is enhanced by the fact that leaf-like tubercles unfold outwards from an initially upright position. Well-known examples of this are *Obregonia denegrii* and species of *Ariocarpus*, particularly *A. retusus* and *A. agavoides*. If unfolding does not take place, as in *Pelecyphora (Encephalocarpus) strobiliformis* the tubercles overlap each other like scales in their adult state, too, causing the whole plant to look deceptively like a conifer.

Other remarkable structures are the tubercles of *Leuchtenbergia principis* which are up to 12.5 cm long. Their flattened upper surface makes them look exactly like the succulent leaves of *Agave iophantha*, which occurs in the same area.

Apart from the leaf-primordia that give rise to spines, the areole produces abundant felt and bristly hairs, presenting itself as a spine-bearing hairy tuft.

The number of spines produced by areoles varies greatly but is fairly constant within each species. Young areoles often have fewer spines than older ones. The individual spines can be very diverse on one areole; one or several strong central spines are frequently surrounded by weaker radial spines. In *Pereskia* the two frontal leaf-primordia (prophylls) become strong hooked spines.

Spines are extraordinarily varied in size, shape and colour. The wide diversity of

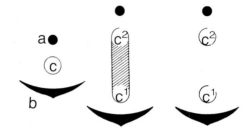

Fig. 10
Serial bud formation; *a* main axis, *b* subtending leaf, *c* growing-point arising out of axil and producing the serial growing-points c^1 and c^2. (After Troll.)

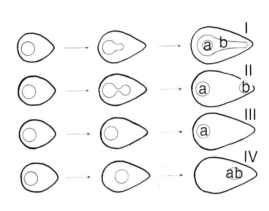

Fig. 11
Development of areoles in *Ariocarpus*; *a* flower-bearing part, *b* spine-bearing part;
I subgenus *Roseocactus*;
II *Ariocarpus retusus*;
III *Ariocarpus trigonus* and *Ariocarpus scapharostrus*;
IV *Ariocarpus agavoides*.
(After Anderson.)

cactus form already made possible by the wealth of shapes the stem can assume is endlessly increased by their spination. This varies from the bristling armour of *Ferocactus uncinatus* to the soft, silky, woolly-hair coat of *Cephalocereus senilis* (Fig. 9), and from weak bristles only a few millimetres long to the bone-hard spines of certain Melocacti that will pierce the thickest leather, with every variation in between. Some spines are straight, others like fish-hooks, some even twisted like a goat's horn, as in *Astrophytum capricorne*. Some spines are needle-shaped, others have edges or are flattened ribbon-like, many have lengthways grooves or are ribbed across. Spines can be white, yellow, brown, red or black, the tip often different from the rest. Young spines are often brighter, the older ones tending to go grey.

Characteristic of the Opuntioideae are their barbed bristles, known as 'glochids' which are produced in large numbers along with other spines; they are fragile and brittle and will break at the slightest touch and penetrate the skin in bundles, their barbed hooks making it very hard to remove them. Some Opuntias such as *O. tunicata* have in addition a number of sheathed-spines which have a parchment like cover (tunica) that pulls off. Finally, there are the 'nectar' or 'gland' spines which are either full of sap or hold it just in their swollen tips. They also secrete nectar.

Hair-like spines, such as those of *Cephalocereus senilis* can be up to 30 cm long. There is also real hair which occurs freely around the flowering region in many species (for example, *Echinocactus*, *Parodia*) but most profusely on cephalia where it appears as a dense, woolly felt as in *Melocactus*, or as highly developed hair-tufts on species with pseudocephalia. Hairs are sometimes also found quite independently of areoles or flowers. For instance, as fine, short flakes on the epidermis of the *Astrophytum* species making the plants appear almost pure white (as in *A. myriostigma*).

JUVENILE STAGES

Cacti develop according to how the fully developed plant is organized, (Fig. 12). Seedlings of the leafy, non-succulent *Pereskia* do not differ from those of familiar plants. Their cotyledons and the leaves that follow are broad and their elongate hypocotyl is not succulent. Only the areoles in the leaf-axils are evidence that these plants belong to the family Cactaceae.

In the Opuntioideae the succulent leaves are reduced in size and the shoots are already distinctly succulent. Seedlings develop accordingly: cotyledons are well developed, the leaves that follow are mostly rudimentary and the shoots are fleshy, but the hypocotyl region is not thickened.

In the most highly developed Cactoideae the hypocotyl is fleshy and turgid. Although in some cases it still has clearly recognizable fleshy cotyledons, these are usually modified to short teeth or hemispherical bumps on the almost globose hypocotyl. During further development the hypocotyl will in these cases grow considerably larger to provide the characteristic tuberous rootstock. The cotyledons are far less important now. Generally in the Cactoideae the reduction of the cotyledons is never quite so complete as that of the later leaves. Independent of their eventual shape, tubercled or ribbed, all go through a mamilate juvenile stage. After this ribbed cacti form ribs, whereas tuberculate cacti retain their juvenile form. There are only isolated cases of rib development from the very beginning (for example, *Astrophytum asterias*).

ADULT GROWTH FORMS

The growth form of cacti depends on a number of factors, the manner of branching being of particular importance. Shrubby growth occurs if the primary axis produces side-shoots from the base as is characteristic of Pereskioideae, many Opuntias and also Cactoideae. Tree forms, which occur predominantly among the columnar cacti, arise when a long trunk grows and forms a branching crown. The appearance of both these forms is determined by the number and relative position of side branches, and the angle formed between the primary shoot and side branches. If the side branches begin in a curve then run vertically upwards, the result is either like a candelabra or organ-pipes, or can be tufted. Gradual suppression of the side branches leads from the candelabra-form to the solitary columnar stem. Short columnar stems, globose forms and sometimes flat, disc-shaped growth will result if the ratio between growth in height and growth in girth is reduced. The capacity for lateral branching is, however, retained by globose forms, which leads to the distinctive clump-forming typical of Mammillarias. Extreme cases of this are to be found in the high-altitude forms of Tephrocacti, with their freely-branching shoots that remain short and form enormous hemispherical clumps. In some cases clustered growth can also be the result of true dichotomous (forked) division of the vegetative apex. Here the consecutive planes of division stand vertically one above the other, as in *Mammillaria parkinsonii, M. perbella* and a few other species. A special, rare kind of lateral branching is the development of subterranean runners or stolons. These stolons are usually rather short, (for example, *Notocactus ottonis*) but may grow up to 50 cm long (as in *Erdisia meyenii*). It is noteworthy, however, that in *Erdisia meyenii* the shoots above ground that have developed from the ends of stolons seem to die off after their seeds have ripened.

Another factor determining the adult form is the longitudinal symmetry of main shoot and side shoot, often manifesting itself in marked periodicity of the primary growing

16

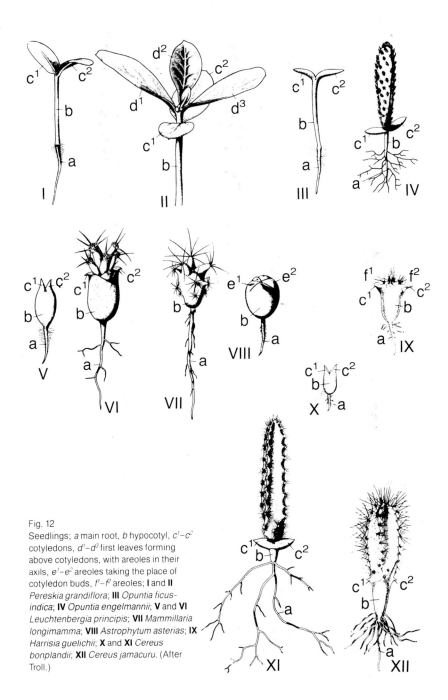

Fig. 12
Seedlings; a main root, b hypocotyl, c^1–c^2 cotyledons, d^1–d^3 first leaves forming above cotyledons, with areoles in their axils, e^1–e^2 areoles taking the place of cotyledon buds, f^1–f^2 areoles; **I** and **II** *Pereskia grandiflora*; **III** *Opuntia ficus-indica*; **IV** *Opuntia engelmannii*; **V** and **VI** *Leuchtenbergia principis*; **VII** *Mammillaria longimamma*; **VIII** *Astrophytum asterias*; **IX** *Harrisia guelichii*; **X** and **XI** *Cereus bonplandii*; **XII** *Cereus jamacuru*. (After Troll.)

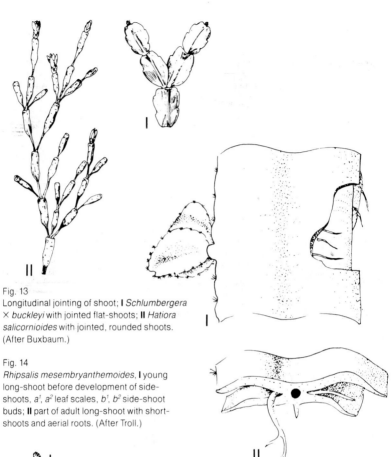

Fig. 13
Longitudinal jointing of shoot; **I** *Schlumbergera × buckleyi* with jointed flat-shoots; **II** *Hatiora salicornioides* with jointed, rounded shoots. (After Buxbaum.)

Fig. 14
Rhipsalis mesembryanthemoides, **I** young long-shoot before development of side-shoots, a^1, a^2 leaf scales, b^1, b^2 side-shoot buds; **II** part of adult long-shoot with short-shoots and aerial roots. (After Troll.)

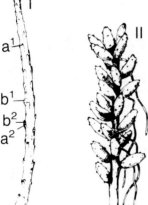

Fig. 15
Selenicereus testudo, **I** view from above, on the right the uppermost rib removed to show the adventitious roots arising between the ribs; **II** cross-section through climbing shoot. (After Troll.)

point. When this happens, the axis becomes segmented, which means that each season's growth is sharply separated from the next by a constriction, (for example, *Jasminocereus*). Opuntias show this particularly well, for each stem-segment can be elongate and cylindric (Cylindropuntias) or flattened and leaf-like (Platyopuntias). Equally clearly segmented is the axis of the flat-stemmed *Schlumbergera* or the clavate-cylindric shoots of *Hatiora* (Fig. 13).

Conspicuous adult forms are found among many epiphytic cacti, that is species which grow on other plants for support, mainly on trees. Above all, species of the *Rhipsalinae* group form freely-branching, pendent shrubs, with long central shoots and clusters of simulated whorls, which are sub-divided into a profusion of joints of second and third order. *Rhipsalis mesembryanthemoides* (Fig. 14) has spindly short-shoots arising from the areoles of each long-shoot,,which could easily be mistaken for the succulent leaves of *Mesembryanthemum* after which this species is named.

Of the epiphytic species *Selenicereus (Deamia) testudo* and *Strophocactus wittii* should also be mentioned. Shoots of *S. testudo* which are pendent or climbing with aerial roots, have 5–8 wing-like, flat ribs (Fig. 15). The pendent shoots are more or less symmetrical, whereas the climbing ones are compressed, and the rib nearest the supporting trunk is much reduced. The climbing stem clings firmly on to its support by adventitious roots which arise from between the ribs. *Strophocactus* is a freely-branching, multi-jointed shrub with leaf-like, crenate shoots that carry roots on their underside, with which they lie close against their support and climb high up tree-trunks (Fig. 5, V).

ROOT SYSTEMS

Studies of the root systems of cacti in their natural habitat have hitherto been rather inadequate but some typical forms of development are known. Many cacti growing in extremely dry areas are decidedly shallow-rooted, with a highly developed root-system close to the surface, which enables it to absorb the slightest trace of moisture, such as from dew or mist.

There are also a number of cacti with a tuberous rootstock, which takes on the task of water storage. To be precise, these plants ought to be called 'root-succulents' (Fig. 16). It is notable in *Pterocactus tuberosus*, for example, that there is a remarkable difference between the slender shoots above the ground and the massive size of the root, which can grow up to 12 cm thick, while the root of *Peniocereus greggii* with a diameter of 15–20 or even 60 cm and weighing 30–50 kg contrasts even more strikingly with the finger-sized shoots it forms above ground.

As well as the shrubby species, there are a number of tuberous-root cacti with only a single stem (Fig. 17). In the case of *Neolloydia (Rapicactus) mandragora*, a neck-like extension separates the shoot from the root; in *Neoporteria napina*, a dwarf plant with a globose stem, 2–9 cm high, there is no such extension, but a division between stem and root is formed by a constriction. In *Opuntia subterranea* the stem above ground continues uninterruptedly into the ordinary branched root. Where shoot and root increase considerably in thickness, but only slightly in length, forms such as *Ariocarpus* result.

Opuntia chaffeyi occupies a special position among tuberous-root cacti because here the shoots above ground die off annually and are replaced from subterranean buds at the beginning of every growth period.

The task of water storage in cacti can be performed by root tubers, as well as by tap roots. Root tubers are roots which have been transformed into storage organs and have largely or completely lost their root characteristics. Tubers are generally adventitious, which means that they are not attached to roots but to subterranean stem-sections. *Opuntia pottsii* has roots up to 3 cm thick, that are not smooth, but have bead-like swellings. *Opuntia macrorhiza* has thick, fleshy root tubers, that are somewhat unusual, as they grow at the tip into many-branched, thin, feeder roots (Fig. 18). Similar to *Ptero-*

cactus tuberosus or *Peniocereus greggii* are the *Wilcoxia* species, but these have adventitious storage roots instead of a tuberous root. Water is stored in enlarged roots at the base of the stems. The roots are replaced by new ones when their stored reserves are used up.

Epiphytic and climbing cacti, such as many *Hylocereus* and particularly *Rhipsalis* species, have adapted to their specific living conditions by developing large numbers of aerial roots to serve as feeders and climbing aids in addition to the root system evolved from the primary root. As in ivy, these aerial roots only develop on the shaded side of the stems. They usualy arise along the centre of the flat side, or, in two-winged cacti such as *Strophocactus wittii*, out of the rib. Occasionally roots will form next to areoles, as in species of *Rhipsalis*.

Another noteworthy habis is that certain tree-like cerei can produce buds and massive shoots from roots spreading far underground, and these are already densely spiny, a feature typical of the upper branches, and not found in seedlings. A well-known example of this root-sprouting occurs in *Myrtillocactus geometrizans*.

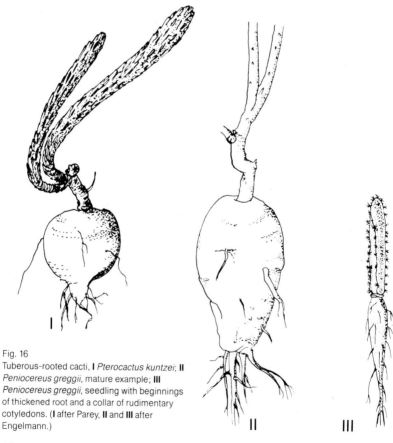

Fig. 16
Tuberous-rooted cacti, **I** *Pterocactus kuntzei*; **II** *Peniocereus greggii*, mature example; **III** *Peniocereus greggii*, seedling with beginnings of thickened root and a collar of rudimentary cotyledons. (**I** after Parey, **II** and **III** after Engelmann.)

ANATOMY

The ability that cacti have to adapt to their specific environment can be attributed partly to their anatomy. Their epidermis is covered by a thick layer (the cuticle) made of cutin, a wax-like substance secreted by the cells. The epidermis adjusts to the plant's growth by continuous division, a process that may go on for many years and even decades. In some species, every epidermal cell encapsulates a druse of calcium oxalate, in others the calcium oxalate crystals are found deeper in the cortex, in regular or irregular groups, often even forming a layer below the epidermis, sometimes accompanied by mucilage cells. The arrangement of the crystals and their relationship with the mucilage cells are genus-specific.

Compared to the number of stomata in the stems of most herbaceous plants, the number in cacti is high, but it is much lower than that in the foliage of other plants. The stomata are often recessed, resulting in decreased water loss; they may run at right angles or parallel to the axis, or completely irregularly, but are largely constant within each genus and therefore taxonomically significant (taxonomy being systematic classification into family, genus, species, and so on).

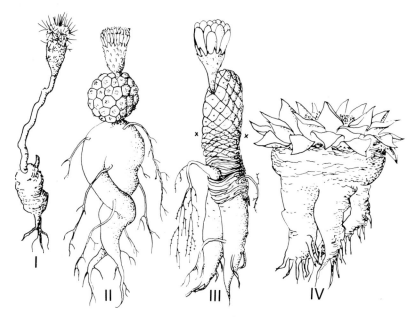

Fig. 17
Tuberous-rooted cacti, **I** *Neolloydia subterranea*, older plant; **II** *Neoporteria napina*, flowering plant; the constriction between root and sprouting stem marks the position of the cotyledons; **III** *Opuntia subterranea*, the upper part of the root has contracted strongly, pulling the shoot into the ground as far as point x–x; **IV** *Ariocarpus retusus*, the dividing line between shoot and tuberous root is marked by the constriction visible in the centre of the drawing. (**I** after Buxbaum, **II** from *Gartenflora* Vol. 21, **III** after Fries, **IV** after Troll.)

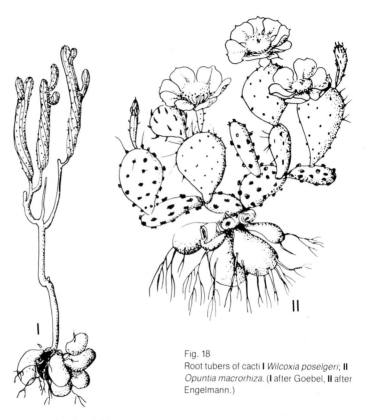

Fig. 18
Root tubers of cacti I *Wilcoxia poselgeri*; II
Opuntia macrorhiza. (I after Goebel, II after
Engelmann.)

In many species, in addition to the cuticle the epidermis is also covered in a layer of wax which appears as an attractive grey or white bloom on young shoots. Periodic changes in the production of this wax layer can produce markings resembling a pointed arch.

Below the epidermis is a continuous layer of collenchyma, 2–3 cells or more thick. Collenchyma is a supportive tissue of living cells with unevenly thickened walls. The only interruptions in this tissue are for air-chambers, one below each stoma. The strongly developed cortex, carrying chlorophyll, lies below the layers of collenchyma and consists mainly of round, colourless, basic tissue-cells full of mucilage.

All stem-tissues retain the capacity for cell division over a relatively long period, a major factor in the stem's increase in thickness. This also explains why cuttings take root or can be grafted so easily.

Mammillarias have latex ducts which are important for systematic classification; they contain a rather thick, white fluid, that seeps out in drops upon the slightest damage to the plant, hardens and gradually turns yellow. Chemically it is a mixture of resin and rubbery substances. Deep inside the plant the ducts are sparsely distributed, becoming more numerous towards the outside, forming a network in the basic cortical tissue and extending to immediately below the outer skin. Ducts are also present in the basic cortical tissue of the roots.

The vascular bundles have no unusual features. In young shoots they are arranged in a circle and often remain divided by broad medullary rays for many years. It takes a long time in most species to unite the separate bundles into one continuous ring by means of interfascicular bundles. Some species have additional isolated bundles in medulla or cortex.

Secondary wood is formed from the same elements as primary wood. (Secondary wood is the tissue that develops on the inside of the cambium, the cylinder of tissue beneath the cortex capable of cell division indefinitely). The wood of the massive tree-like cerei is very hard and durable, so much so that it is used in northern Venezuela for furniture production or as a building material. The epidermis, which has a capacity for cell division and growth over a long period, is eventually replaced by a secondary tissue, the periderm. The periderm can develop in the epidermis or in the hypodermis (the layer below the epidermis) or in the basic tissue. This can lead to the build-up of thick layers of cork and finally bark.

Although up to 90 per cent or more of the body of a *Cereus* may consist of thin-walled basic tissue cells even when it is 20 years old, these cacti are mechanically very resilient. In species with a non-woody body, the high turgidity of the mucilage-filled tissue cells gives them a similar strength, which is assisted by marked thickening of the epidermis. Rib-development is also of considerable importance in increasing structural resilience.

FLOWERS

The cactus flower is held in a beaker-shaped floral axis elongated into a tube called the receptacle-tube. In the most primitive forms of Pereskioideae such as *P. aculeata* the floral axis is distinctly broadened, forming a disc-shaped receptacle slightly conical in the centre, with a superior ovary formed from five fused carpels (Fig. 19). The ovary is free-standing, encircled by an extension of the floral axis which carries stamens and perianth-segments. In *P. sacharosa* the raised central cone has disappeared and the receptacle somewhat depressed; the ovary is still free-standing.

In all more highly developed species of the Opuntioideae and Cactoideae the ovary has become inferior, that is the other floral parts are inserted above the ovary, and at the same time the flower axis is elongated into a definite tube. It is now possible to distinguish between the free portion above the ovary which is still called the receptacle-tube, the lower portion that actually encases the ovary which is called the pericarpel and the area below that, which is known as the pedicellate zone.

The leaves and areoles on the pericarpel and receptacle-tube make it obvious that they derive from axis tissue (Fig. 20). In *Pereskia* the leaves are reduced to leaf-like scales. As a flower axis is not fundamentally different from a vegetative axis, the areoles of the leaf scales can occasionally produce secondary flowers; the flower is said to proliferate. An apical flower, such as that of *Pereskia grandiflora*, can repeatedly proliferate and form an inflorescence.

The flowers of the Opuntioideae also reveal their axial nature by frequent proliferation. Sometimes a vegetative shoot will also produce an apical flower. The leaves are scale-like and often identical to reduced foliage.

The Pereskioideae and Opuntioideae do not have well-formed receptacle-tubes, or only rarely, unlike the Cactoideae, where the receptacle-tube distinctly overlaps the pericarpel (Fig. 21). The receptacle-tube can be tubular, bell-shaped or funnel-shaped (Fig. 22).

In the Pereskioideae and Opuntioideae the receptacle-tube is distinctly marked off from the flowering parts it subtends and its leaves are all more or less the same, the transition to perianth-segments being achieved without intermediate stages (Fig. 23). In the Cactoideae, on the other hand, not only is the receptacle-tube externally modified into a tube, but its structure has largely been integrated into that of the flower as a whole.

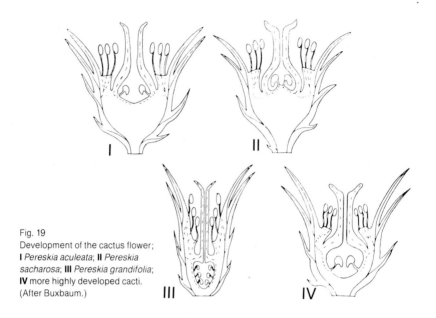

Fig. 19
Development of the cactus flower;
I *Pereskia aculeata*; II *Pereskia sacharosa*; III *Pereskia grandifolia*;
IV more highly developed cacti.
(After Buxbaum.)

Fig. 20
The axial nature of pericarpel and receptacle-tube; I fruit of *Pereskia bahiensis* with foliage leaves; II proliferating fruit of *Pereskia sacharosa*; III terminal flower out of a flat shoot of *Opuntia lemaireana*; IV bud of *Opuntia subulata*. (I and II after Britton and Rose, III after W. Lange, IV after Buxbaum.)

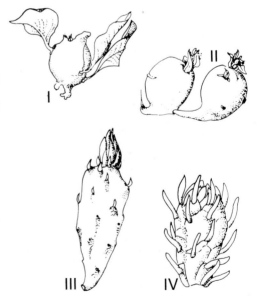

Only the pericarpel retains its purely vegetative character. The podaria it carries are more in evidence and closer together, the scales smaller and the areoles less reduced. The scales on the receptacle-tube, by contrast, are more distant and on less noticeable podaria, they grow wider towards the tip, and in size and colour merge imperceptibly into the outer perianth-segments. Likewise its areoles frequently produce spines and so forth, that are rudimentary compared with those on the pericarpel.

In the Pereskioideae, there is a transition from superior ovary to inferior, as mentioned above, and at the same time the number and position of the ovules inside it changes (Fig. 19). The four or five ovules of *Pereskia aculeata* lie at the bottom of the upright ovary. As the receptacle-tube becomes depressed in the middle, the ovules move further out, and, in species where the ovary is completely submerged and inferior, as in the Opuntioideae and Cactoideae they are attached to the outer walls of the ovary. This gives more space to the placenta, that is the ovary wall tissue on which the ovules form and their number can consequently increase to several hundred. Where ovules are

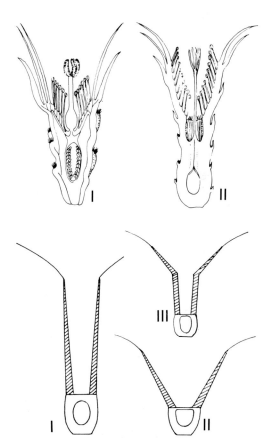

Fig. 21
I *Opuntia rafinesquei*, receptacle-tube only slightly developed; II *Carnegieia gigantea*, receptacle-tube well-developed. (After Buxbaum.)

Fig. 22
Development of the receptacle-tube in Cactoideae; I tubular; II bell-shaped (campanulate); III funnel-shaped. (After Buxbaum.)

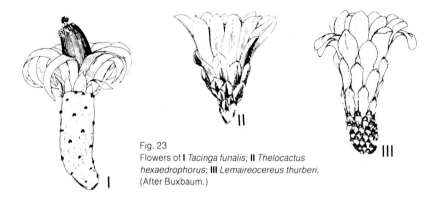

Fig. 23
Flowers of **I** *Tacinga funalis*; **II** *Thelocactus hexaedrophorus*; **III** *Lemaireocereus thurberi*. (After Buxbaum.)

few in number and have limited space, they are merely attached to the ovary wall with short funicles. In most cases, however, they are on longer funicles joined in bunches at the bottom (Fig. 24), the funicles often being actually branched.

The ovules themselves are campylotropous or more rarely anatropous, usually curving towards their funicle, which widens out opposite the micropyle and wraps it in a fold. Upward-pointing papillae are sometimes found along the side of the funicle, conjecturally cilia for the pollen-tube. Often the funicle is wrapped around the ovule several times, enveloping it in its widened folds.

Primitive flowers such as those of *Pereskia sacharosa* do not have completely fused carpels, but otherwise cactus flowers have the typical columnar style ending in 2-∞ rays (Fig. 25). The individual rays of the stigma are as a rule covered in close-set papillae over the upper surface and along the edges. In some cases, as in the large-flowered Hylocereeae where the number of carpels and stigmas is vastly greater, all surfaces are

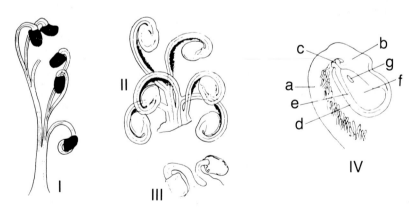

Fig. 24
I Branching funicles of *Opuntia spinosissima*; **II** false branching of funicles of *Epiphyllum crenatum*; **III** non-branching funicles of *Echinopsis campylacantha*; **IV** ovule of

Weberocereus tunilla, *a* funicle, *b* chalaza, *c* micropyle, *d* outer integument, *e* inner integument, *f* nucellus, *g* embryo sac. (After Buxbaum.)

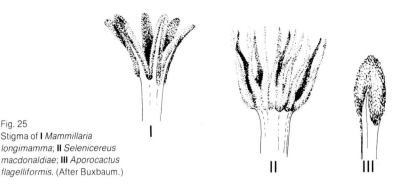

Fig. 25
Stigma of **I** *Mammillaria*
longimamma; **II** *Selenicereus*
macdonaldiae; **III** *Aporocactus*
flagelliformis. (After Buxbaum.)

covered in papillae both inside and out. Occasionally the stigmatic rays do not open out and then capitate stigmas are formed, as in *Schlumbergera* and *Aporocactus*.

The style is not infrequently a hollow tube, its channel clad with papillate epidermal cells, but the pollen-tubes can also make their way through the conducting tissue of the wall of the style tube.

In the Pereskioideae the stamens are found on the flat upper rim of the circular extension that surrounds either the superior or inferior ovary. In all the more highly evolved Opuntioideae and in Cactoideae where the receptacle-tube is more or less elongate-tubular, the numerous stamens are on its inner wall. Right inside, closest to the ovary and style and usually on a raised area of the axis, are the stamens that developed first; consecutive circles of stamens are developed centrifugally outward, following the extended receptacle-tube either in a regular spiralling pattern or distributed in clusters (fascicles). There is often an empty space above a lower fascicle or spiral, and shorter stamens are usually in a circle around the receptacle-tube rim. Usually the number of stamens is very large, almost always more than 10. The anthers are attached to the filaments by their base or their back, opening by longitudinal slits that point inwards or laterally. The pollen grains have three furrows (colpi) and are globose with 6-∞ round pores. They are usually very small and, like the pollen grains of other Centrospermae, contain three cell-nuclei. The exine, the extremely tough outermost layer of the pollen grain, has a honeycomb structure with fine spines and tiny cavities. In numerous genera, such as *Opuntia*, *Echinopsis*, and *Echinocereus*, the filaments are extremely sensitive, twisting towards the stigma as soon as they are touched.

The first row of stamens is usually found on a ridge inside the receptacle-tube and often exserted. Between its base and the ovary is a nectar chamber of varying shape containing a honey-sweet secretion. The Opuntioideae have the least complicated structure (Fig. 26): their receptacle-tube is primitive and so the nectary takes up the more or less funnel-shaped wall-section between the ovary or style and the primary stamens. This is called the nectar-furrow, or, where it is extensive, the nectar-chamber. The nectar-chamber can occasionally be loosely closed by the ridge on which the primary stamens are situated.

The Cactoideae are more complex. Essentially, three main types can be distinguished:

1. The nectar-furrow type, where the nectary occupies a furrow between the style base and receptacle-tube wall, rather as in Opuntioideae.

2. The very variable nectar-chamber type which differs from the furrow type in that here the upper surface of the ovary forms the bottom of the nectar-chamber. Its floor is

wide, even where the upper surface of the ovary is covered by the receptaculum. It can be open at the top or closed tightly round the style by the ridge that carries the primary stamens or by the enlarged bases of the primary stamens themselves. There are numerous subtypes of taxonomic importance, that will not be discussed here. One particular way of closing the nectar-chamber should however be mentioned, namely plugging it with dense, curly hair which may be true hair or modified hair derived from reduced stamens.

3. The disc-type of nectar chamber is the third form. The receptacle-tube in some species such as those of the *Rhipsalidinae* is reduced to such an extent that, only an extended flower axis remains, justifying comparison with the most primitive Pereskioideae. Here the nectar tissues are found on a disc, a circular swelling surrounding the base of the style. The stamens on these plants develop first on the inside and then farther out, unlike the perianth, which develops normally, that is from the outside inwards.

Perianth-segments and stamens are initially formed on the more or less flat base of the widened flower axis (Fig. 27). As a result of the tubular growth of a circular meristem (that is, cell-tissue capable of division indefinitely), situated between the youngest (innermost) perianth-segments and the youngest (outermost) stamens, the floral axis is turned into a beaker-shape, with the stamens inside and the perianth-segments outside, the latter following on from the leaf-scales of the flower axis. There can either be a sharp division between perianth-segments and leaf-scales of the axis (Pereskioideae and Opuntioideae) or they can intergrade gradually (Cactoideae). Additional longitudinal growth of the outer Zones causes the receptacle-tube to become even deeper.

There are usually a large number of perianth-segments; only the genera *Rhipsalis* and *Disocactus* have as few as 8–10. They are remarkable for their luminous colour (white, red, yellow, violet or in rare cases even green or brown) and often silky sheen. They are almost always free, being only rarely joined together in a true perianth-tube, as in *Disocactus* and *Schlumbergera*. In *Schlumbergera* the inner perianth-segments have grown together into a long tube with the tips turned outward from immediately above the pericarpel.

Cacti usually have regular flowers, but in derived groups so-called zygomorphic flowers also occur (Fig. 28). In the simplest examples the receptacle-tube has a simple or S-shaped curve, resulting at times in an oblique throat. A second possibility is uneven

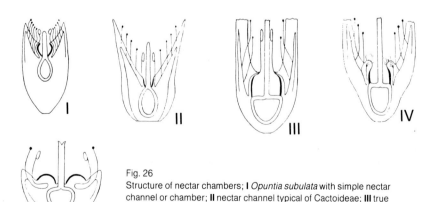

Fig. 26
Structure of nectar chambers; **I** *Opuntia subulata* with simple nectar channel or chamber; **II** nectar channel typical of Cactoideae; **III** true nectar chamber; **IV** nectar chamber with wool closure, *Denmoza* type; **V** disc-type found in *Rhipsalis*. (After Buxbaum.)

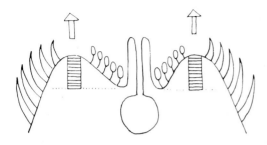

Fig. 27
Development of the receptacle-
tube. (Modified after Buxbaum.)

(anisophyllous) development of the perianth-segments, as found in extremely zygo-morphic flowers such as *Schlumbergera truncata*, where not only is the base of the perianth-tube curved upwards, but the upper perianth-segments are much enlarged and the throat of the perianth tube is extended on the upper side and markedly oblique. The zygomorphy of the Christmas Cactus *Schlumbergera x buckleyi*, on the other hand, is more apparent than real: the perianth-segments are completely similar in form but the lower ones recurve as the flowers open, while the others stay extended as a prolong-ation of the perianth-tube.

POSITION OF FLOWERS

Alone among cacti, the genus *Pereskia* produces genuine branched inflorescences. Most are terminal cymes, sometimes accompanied by more cymes in the axils of the upper leaves. In *Pereskia sacharosa* the solitary terminal flowers can develop into a whole inflorescence by repeated proliferation. Usually, however, cacti have solitary flowers arising from the areoles or, when the growing point is divided, from the axils. Exceptionally, some species of *Rhipsalis*, have multi-flowering areoles, especially the subgenus *Lepismium*, in which up to five flowers can grow from one areole.

When areoles are in the dormant state, it is practically impossible to tell the difference between the flower-producing (fertile) ones and the vegetative ones which can either remain permanently dormant or produce a side-shoot. There are, however, a number of

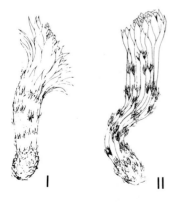

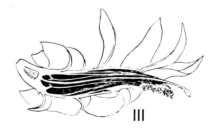

Fig. 28
Zygomorphic cactus flowers; **I** *Borzicactus samaipatanus*; **II** *Cleistocactus baumannii*; **III** *Schlumbergera truncata*; (**I** and **II** after Buxbaum, **III** after Schumann.)

Fig. 29
Mitrocereus fulviceps, longitudinal section through a flower. Bristles and woolly hair merely indicated. Cauline zone (*a*) later drops off with the flower. (After Buxbaum.)

Fig. 30
I Cross-section through a cephalium-bearing stem of *Espostoa sericata*; **II** and **III** *Myrtillocactus geometrizans*: **II** lateral inflorescence, and **III** old areole, *a¹–a¹* rudimentary buds; **IV** older lateral inflorescence of *Lophocereus schottii*, *b¹*, *b²* old spines, *c* young spines; **V** old flowering short-shoot of *Neoraimondia roseiflora*. (**I–IV** after Buxbaum, **V** after Rauh.) ▷

species in which the already macroscopic fertile areoles distinguish themselves from the vegetative ones by producing more bristles or, more frequently, longer woolly hair. In this case most of the hairiness comes not from the supporting areole but from the microscopic areoles of the cauline zone. From this it is understood that in the case of many, but not all cacti, the flower begins with numerous internodes and leaf-buds that will not become involved in the flower formation, but at the most remain short and stunted. Their tiny areoles nevertheless form bristles and hair, so that eventually the flower is totally surrounded by these hairy tufts (Fig. 29).

Whether this cauline zone falls off with the ripe fruit or remains on the stem depends on the position of the isolating tissue.

The fertile areoles can either occur haphazardly along the stem or cluster in a special, sharply defined, flowering zone called a cephalium. A distinction is made between two types of cephalium according to how they are formed:

1. In the first type, areoles which originated normally and are already differentiated and are some distance away from the growing tip, enlarge and develop copious long hair. The fertile areoles are distinguished from the vegetative simply by their increased production of bristles and/or wool. The number of ribs remains constant. A flowering stem can revert to vegetative growth.

2. In the second type, differentiation starts from the apical growing-point. Instead of ribs with vegetative areoles there appears the flowering zone — the cephalium. The vegetative and fertile zones are here sharply distinct, and as a rule there is no transition between them. Furthermore, the fertile zone usually cannot revert to vegetative growth.

These two contrasting types have been differentiated into pseudocephalia, in which the transformation into flowering areoles only happens later, and true cephalia, in which the flowering areoles originate at the growing-point. Another definition that has appeared in recent years seems more reasonable: according to this the term 'true cephalium' is only used when vegetative growth has finished by the time the cephalium starts to form; when, from that time, only flowers will be produced; and when the cephalium is distinct from the vegetative stem. Only two genera, *Melocactus* and *Discocactus* conform to these criteria and thus only they have true cephalia. All other types, regardless of how they occur, are classed together as pseudocephalia.

With *Melocactus*, then, and, less strikingly, *Discocactus*, vegetative growth is terminated when the flowering stage has been reached. Fertile areoles are then

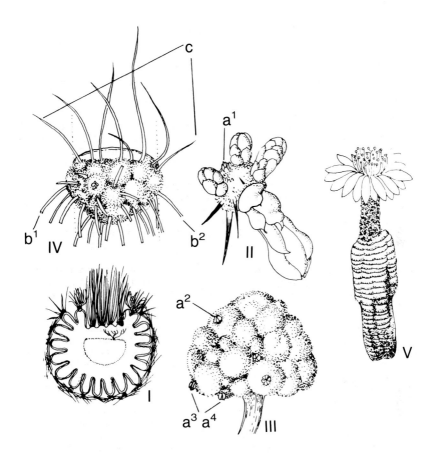

produced exclusively instead of vegetative areoles. Instead of spines they produce woolly hair and coarse bristles. The single areoles touch each other and run in spiro-stichies, in contrast to the vegetative areoles arranged along the ribs in orthostichies. At first a flat woolly cap appears, which in *Melocactus* takes on the form of an elongate woolly cylinder in the course of further growth. This cylinder can reach up to 100 cm or even longer. In *Discocactus*, on the other hand, the woolly cap remains quite small. Often a conspicuous ring-marking indicates a very definite interruption in growth and shows where an old cephalium has been.

The lateral inflorescence of *Neoraimondia* (Fig. 30, V) is almost identical in structure to the terminal cephalium of *Melocactus*. The areoles of younger, non-flowering plants produce stout spines up to 20 cm long. The plants subsequently go over to flower-production, and then the new areoles largely dispense with spines and produce a lot of wool, which makes them look considerably bigger. They produce flowering short-shoots, which to a great extent reflect the cephalium of *Melocactus* in structure. In their secondary axis, that of growth in girth, are areoles of the second type — the actual flowering areoles — compressed together in orthostichies. Their compact wool completely covers the axis. The flowering short-shoots can continue to grow for years,

31

reaching a length of up to 15 cm. The older flowering areoles soon become isolated from the other tissues by a thick, corky layer, and fall to the ground leaving a scar. This gives the whole inflorescence a cone-like appearance.

Something of a forerunner of the flowering short-shoots of *Neoraimondia*, can be seen in *Myrtillocactus*, especially the flowering short-shoots of *Myrtillocactus geometrizans*, and in *Lophocereus schottii* (Fig. 30, II–IV). In these examples, however, only balls of felt of varying size are produced, and the structure differs from the monopodial short-shoots of *Neoraimondia*.

In contrast to what happens in true cephalia, the formation of flowering areoles on pseudocephalia takes place without much affecting the organization and growth of the vegetative-apex. Usually only a small sector of the apex is given over to the production of flowering areoles, the rest remaining vegetative. So the shoot continues to grow, at the same time forming an uninterrupted flowering-zone — a lateral pseudocephalium — which grows in area as the shoot grows in length. When flower buds begin to form on lateral pseudocephalia, the leaf-primordium that subtends them, together with its areole, is still at the first stage of development, and the podaria remain small. They do not usually join up with the ribs and the areolar spines remain thin and weak. The result of this reduction of the podaria is that the whole pseudocephalium is more or less sunken relative to the vegetative ribs. Thus, it lies in a longitudinal furrow along the side of the stem (Fig. 30, I).

Lateral pseudocephalia grow in length for as long as the apex is capable of longitudinal growth. They can often become remarkably long, on *Espostoa* over 2 m. A plant's pseudocephalia are all on one side; for example, *Espostoa* carries them all facing west.

In a few cases the formation of flowering areoles is not limited to a small sector, but includes the whole vegetative apex, thus producing a terminal pseudocephalium. If the whole apex then continues to grow in height, it produces a pseudocephalium, like a military 'bearskin' that in the case of *Backebergia militaris* can easily grow up to 50 cm. Here, unlike *Melocactus*, the growth of the shoot continues unaltered, except that flower areoles appear in the place of vegetative areoles. Alternatively, the cephalium can terminate the growth of the shoot, and not grow any further, as for example in *Morawetzia*.

Finally, growth can continue through the terminal pseudocephalium after the formation of the flower buds. After fruiting, the apex of the shoot can revert to vegetative growth and form a new terminal pseudocephalium in the next flowering period. The number of bristle rings on a shoot corresponds to the number of flowering periods. This can be seen in *Cephalocereus apicicephalium*, *Stephanocereus leucostele* and *Arrojadoa*.

Pollination

Many cacti are self-compatible, that is they can form fruit with viable seeds by means of self-pollination. Often it does not even appear to be necessary for an insect or other pollinator to transfer the pollen. A number of species, such as those of the genus *Frailea*, have both fully opening flowers and so-called cleistogamous ones that never open but set seed all the same. Other species, however, are self-incompatible, which means that to fruit successfully they must be pollinated from another plant — but not one which has grown from a cutting of the one to be pollinated. Nothing is apparently known about the workings of the incompatibility mechanism.

Often, the natural consequence of obligatory cross-pollination is a remarkable variety in the resultant population. The variants within the genus *Lobivia* differ so much in stem size, spination and flower colour, that wittingly or unwittingly, whole series of so-called 'species' have been described from the extreme forms of a single, natural population.

Of particular interest is the way cactus flowers requiring cross-pollination have adapted to their pollinators. They can broadly be divided between day-blooming and night-blooming flowers. The day-blooming can the be subdivided into flowers dependent on: 1. Mixed range of visitors ('unselective'), 2. Bees and 3. Birds; while the night-blooming flowers are dependent on: 1. Night-flying moths, or 2. Bats.

Day-blooming flowers

These come into full bloom in the course of a day, and may then last several days or only a few hours. During the night some may close, while others may remain open. Their visual apparatus is highly developed, scent playing a comparatively minor rôle. Bird-pollinated flowers are nearly always scentless.

1. *'Unselective' flowers* include all those that because of their construction and size may be pollinated by a great variety of small to medium-sized insects. Insects with short prosbosces inevitably pollinate when collecting pollen or sipping nectar, or may do so simply by crawling around in the flower. The flowers in this group are of simple type, small to medium-sized, without exception rotate or with very short flower-tube, making the nectar easily available to insects with short prosbosces. They belong to ancestrally different species, both early and later evolved. Bees with short prosbosces are their main pollinators, next come flies, ground wasps and crevice wasps and even beetles.

2. *Bee-pollinated flowers* include all those types in which the nectar is hidden so deep inside a well-developed flower tube that only large, fat-bodied bees with a long proboscis can act as pollinators. According to the relative size of the insects to the flowers, they pollinate with their back while drinking nectar, or with their underside while flying in and out over the stigma. This flower-type includes the large-flowered species of all genera whose small-flowered species are 'unselective'.

3. *Bird-pollinated flowers* are a strongly represented group specially adapted to pollination by humming-birds. The birds drink the nectar while hovering steadily in front of the flower without settling — as do the day-flying humming-bird hawk-moths. As a rule the flowers are scentless; in colour the red range is predominant, principally brilliant red, alone or combined with yellow, then come yellow by itself, and sometimes also green. Finally in *Borzicacti*, biologically the most advanced form of cacti flowers, we find combinations of green with flame-red or yellow, known as parrot colours. The group can be divided into 4 types:
    1. Bell-shaped flowers (*Echinocereus*, *Lobivia*): the flowers have their sex organs in the centre, sometimes enclosed within the bell, sometimes exserted.
    2. Flag-type flowers (*Heliocereus*): this form resembles an amaryllis.
    3. Tubular flowers (*Cleistocactus*): the flower has a more or less narrow tube, straight or curved, which serves as part of the visual apparatus.
    4. Lipped or jawed flowers (*Aporocactus*, *Cleistocactus*): this type is a development of the tubular-flower type in which the mouth of the tube is oblique and the perianth-limb zygomorphic.

Night-blooming flowers

1. *Moth-pollinated flowers* have the highest level of adaptation among insect-pollinated flowers. The group is widespread and represented by numerous species. The main characteristics are: attraction over a distance by scent, which is usually pleasant to humans but can be less so in some varieties, or even actually unpleasant; the innermost perianth-segments round the entrance are light-coloured and visible even by dusk, while the outer perianth-segments are characterized by contrasting and often drab colours; the nectar is liberally secreted during the night and hidden in a long flower tube;

there is considerable surface exaggeration of the stigmatic rays.

Of all cacti it is the *Epiphyllum* species that has achieved the highest level of adaptation to night-flying moths, the best of all being *E. phyllanthus* with its slender, sparsely scaled flower-tubes that grow 16–22 cm long. Even the longest flower-tubes are still shorter than the longest proboscis of the tropical American moths, so that all species are capable of being exploited by these indigenous moths and thereby cross-pollinated.

2. Bat-pollinated flowers are, as a rule, medium-sized, campanulate-funnel shaped, tapering only slightly and gradually towards the base. Examples are found in *Carnegiea*, *Pachycereus*, *Stenocereus* and other arborescent cerei. The flower tube and the perianth-segments are thick and fleshy. This coarse, fleshy texture offers bats a good surface to hook on comfortably and firmly with both their thumb-claws when they come to the flowers. The perianth-segments around the flower entrance are characteristically short, and curve outwards and backwards when the flower is fully open. The numerous stamens, ranged close together, line the inner surface of the flower tube. As in moth-pollinated flowers, here too there is a marked contrast between the mostly drab-coloured outer perianth-segments and the light inner ones. However, in contrast to the generally pleasant scent of the night-moth pollinated flowers, the bat-pollinated ones are almost without exception unpleasant or downright repulsive. There are flowers that smell of cabbage, garlic, fish or rotten carrion. With these distinctive characteristics, the flowers are extraordinarily well-adapted for exploitation by the American flower-bats.

FRUIT AND SEED

When the fruit is formed, the axial tissue of the pericarpel surrounding the ovary is fundamentally involved, as well as the actual ovary (Fig. 31). Even in species of *Pereskia*, such as *P. aculeata*, that have a superior ovary, the swelling ovary is surrounded and eventually completely enclosed by the axial tissue lying below after the flower has faded. In these species, however, a distinct space remains between ovary and axial tissue.

Primitive forms such as *Pereskia*, and also many Opuntias, depending on the nature of the shoot, have fruit which can proliferate from the areoles to form more flowers and fruits, so that often entire chains of fruit can be produced (*O. bigelowii*).

The arrangement and corresponding position of the areoles on the pericarpel can be strongly modified by subsequent growth processes. In many cases they can develop prolific spines after flowering, and conversely, spiny areoles on the flower can fall off the ripe fruit, leaving it completely naked.

The receptacle-tube can be involved in fruit formation, for example in Opuntioideae, which usually have a very short receptacle-tube (Fig. 32). Only the upper layers of axial tissue plus the style, stamens and perianth will be cut off by a previously formed abscission layer. In the Cactoideae, if the receptacle-tube is stout, in many cases it is shed in its entirety, with or without the style, after flowering, above a flat abscission layer, as happens in the genus *Cereus*. Otherwise the receptacle-tube stays attached to the fruit in the form of more or less dry remains.

The fruit-wall (pericarp) of cactus fruits, which is formed from the ovary-wall and the pericarpel, can be juicy and fleshy, semi-fleshy, or dry, when the fruit is ripe. In juicy, fleshy fruits the numerous seeds are embedded in a pulp formed by the long deliquescent funicles (Fig. 33), which are thickly intertwined in a vitreous, juicy or creamy mass. In other instances the inner surfaces of the ovary, and especially the placentas and often the funicles too, are covered with hairs which make an only slightly juicy pulp. In the dry-fruited species the entire interior of the fruit can be filled with tough hairy felt.

The fruits open in various ways. Often they split open through tension in the fruit-wall or pressure exerted by the pulp. In some the top of the fruit with the floral remains springs off like a lid and then the valves split unevenly apart. Only *Espostoa blossfel-*

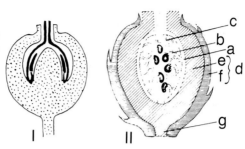

Fig. 31
I Longitudinal section through the fruit of *Pereskia aculeata*. Axial tissue dotted, ovary tissue and seeds black, space between them exaggerated; II diagrammatic longitudinal section through a cactus fruit. Carpel tissue *a* (white) with funicles *b* and hairs *c*, *d* pericarpel tissue. consisting of the actual axial tissue *e* and the coat tissue *f*, *g* pedicellate zone. (After Buxbaum.)

diorum has been observed to open regularly, that is, exactly between the placentas. The *Rebutia* fruit opens like a box along a crack running right round it. Very often the seeds are liberated when the fruit falls to the ground, the juicy fruits deliquescent (for example, *Notocactus*, subgenus *Malacocarpus*) and the dry ones weathering away. In many cases the seeds remain hidden in the apical wool, from where they are freed a considerable time later, still in a viable state (as in *Pelecyphora* and *Ariocarpus*).

Cactus seeds come in many shapes and sizes: flat, almost disc-shaped, rounded, pear-shaped or kidney-shaped. The large flat seeds of some Opuntias are up to 10 mm in diameter, while the smallest, like those of Parodias, are only 0.5 mm, and there is every size in between. The colour of the seeds ranges from dark brownish-black through all tones to light brown.

The construction of the seedcoat, the testa (Fig. 34) is important for classification. An enormous variety has emerged from Buxbaum's research with the light microscope and even more from Barthlott and Voit's work (1979) with the scanning electron microscope. The differences consist mainly in the varied construction of the individual testa cells. Besides their size and shape (isodiametric or elongate, with straight or variously indented anticlinal walls), the formation of the outer, periclinal cell-wall is crucial in deter-

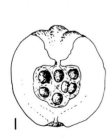

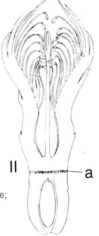

Fig. 32
I Fruit of *Opuntia inamoena* in longitudinal section; II longitudinal section through the flower of *Cereus repandus*, *a* isolating tissue; III fruit of *Mediocactus coccineus* with floral remains. (I and II after Buxbaum, III after Castellanos and Lelong.)

mining the character of the testa. It can be one of three different shapes:

1. Flat, usually very thickened (smooth, hard testa; when the wall thickening is completely reduced the testa is small-celled and soft).

2. Convex, whereby either the entire outer wall is weakly to pronouncedly uneven (verrucose testa), or only one part develops usually eccentric papillae or hair-like protrusions. (*Blossfeldia* is an extreme example).

3. Concave, as a result of the tendency to cohesion in the testa cells of the drying seed. This cohesive tendency affects a completely unthickened outer wall or one that is only so in a central area, causing it to curve inwards or even to split (pitted testa).

Fig. 33
Seeds of *Hamatocactus cachetianus* with fleshy funicle. (After Buxbaum.)

Fig. 34
Seedcoats (testa): **I** *Cephalocereus leucocephalus* with smooth glossy testa; **II** *Lemaireocereus dumortieri*, testa of a few large cells; **III** *Rebutia senilis*, more verrucose towards top; **IV** *Frailea grahliana* and **V** *Blossfeldia liliputana* with 'spiny' testa; **VI** *Escobaria vivipara* with pitted testa; **VII** *Mammillaria eshauzieri* with reticulate-pitted testa; **VIII** *Coryphantha salm-dyckiana* with small-celled, smooth testa. (After Buxbaum.)

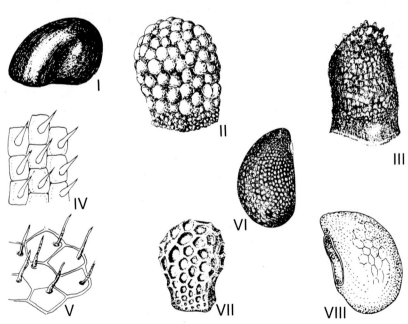

Further characteristics are depressed or elevated anticlinal walls and flat to crater-like depressions of the cell corners where three cells juxtapose (interstitial pits).

The testa is covered with a cuticle that often shows a complicated and specific pattern of convolutions. Occasionally the cuticle is raised and visible to the naked eye as a wrinkled, whitish skin, sometimes wrongly termed the aril-membrane.

A raphe (a ridge originating from the fusion of the funicle with the ovule) is only rarely distinguishable on cactus seeds. However, a hilum is always present; it is the scar that is left when the seed break away from the funicle. Since cactus ovules are campylo-tropous, the hilum lies very close to the micropyle, which in many cases can just about be seen as a small opening, but is often microscopic (Fig. 35). Hilum and micropyle can be separate (as in *Pereskia*), but usually form a single area known as the hilum-micropylar zone. Thickening of the funicle below the seed, coupled with a collar-like development, frequently leads to a crater-like hilum, sometimes so much so that the hilum area becomes larger than the seed itself. The whole seed is then finally cap-shaped (as in *Astrophytum, Frailea*). In some cases the hilum cavity fills up with a corky, spongy tissue, which occasionally grows into a large appendage, known as a strophiole, which is bigger than the actual seed (for example, in *Mammillaria pennispinosa*). Instead of a wall surrounding the point where the seed breaks from the funicle, the funicle itself can be widened at its point of attachment and partly mantle the ovule or the ripe seed. This phenomenon is known, in this case correctly, as an aril, particularly pronounced in the

Fig. 35
Seeds of **I** *Escobaria tuberculosa* showing hilum with raphe *a*; **II** *Echinocactus saltillensis* showing hilum; **III** *Hamatocactus setispinus* with crater-shaped hilum; **IV** *Astrophytum myriostigma*, hat-shaped seed; **V** *Mammillaria pennispinosa* with well-developed strophiole. (After Buxbaum.)

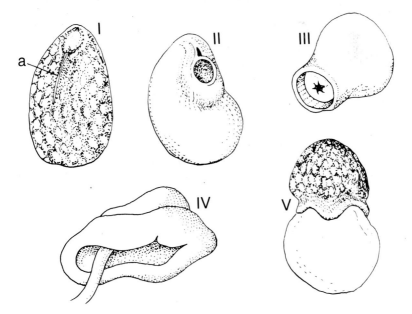

Opuntioideae, where the ovule is completely mantled by the widened funicle. When this occurs, the micropyle is never left open (Fig. 36). In the Opuntioideae the aril on the ripe seed is extraordinarily hard and engulfs it firmly but it is not fused with the brownish-black seedcoat underneath. If the funicle has hairs that become pulpy when the fruit forms, the aril coat is also hairy and becomes part of the pulp during ripening.

The endosperm, the seed's nutritive tissue formed after fertilization from a cell of the embryonic sac, is soon exhausted by the growing embryo. The most primitive cacti, the Pereskioideae and the Opuntioideae, have developed, instead of endosperm, a huge perisperm, (nutritive tissue produced from the ovular tissue) with the slender embryo lying round it as a ring. In the Cactoideae the storage function is now progressively passed over to the embryo, either to its embryonic leaves or cotyledons (as in the *Hylocereeae*) or to the hypocotyl, that is, the part between the cotyledons and the root or radicle. Simultaneously, the perisperm is reduced until it disappears totaly while the originally curved embryo continues to elongate.

GEOGRAPHICAL DISTRIBUTION

Cacti are confined almost exclusively to America. With the exception of the most northerly and southerly regions, they occur from Canada (latitude 56°N) to Patagonia (latitude 52°S). Their greatest diversity is centred in the region either side of the tropics, where they chiefly inhabit the prairies and arid wastelands. The low rainfall areas of Mexico and the neighbouring part of the United States afford the greatest number of species. Second are the dry areas of central and eastern Brazil. The South American Andes also host numerous species which live as high up as 4700 m, near the permanent snowline. As regards temperature requirements, the genus *Opuntia* is particularly adaptable and hardy, as demonstrated by *O. polycantha* in the north and *O. darwinii* and *O. australis* together with the genus *Maihuenia* in the far south. The high plains of the Andes at 4000–4700 m are dominated by Opuntias of the subgenus *Tephrocactus*. A few *Mammillaria* species are found in Mexico at altitudes of 3000–3500 m.

A large number of cacti are adapted to an exceptionally damp, warm, tropical climate and life in dense forest. These are the preponderantly epiphytic species of *Hylocereus* and *Rhipsalis*, whose main distribution is in Brazil and Central America, but they can occasionally also be found in drier locations. The only genus to have established an area

 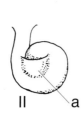  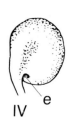

Fig. 36
Aril formation in *Opuntia*: I and II young ovules of *Opuntia vulgaris*, *a* wing-like outgrowth of the funicle, *b¹* and *b²* inner and outer integument, which in II are well curled-in and hidden; III longitudinal section through an older specimen, *c* chalaza, *d* micropyle; IV outside view of an ovule completely covered by the aril; *e* entrance. (I and II after Planchon, III and IV after Goebel.)

of natural distribution outside America is *Rhipsalis*, which is found in the tropical forests of Africa, Madagascar and Sri Lanka. It seems most likely that they were spread by birds, which would be possible since the sap of their berries is sticky, and the seeds could adhere to their feet. Another theory is that sailors brought branches of *Rhipsalis* back to Africa as Christmas decorations because the berries reminded them of mistletoe, but this is far less convincing since the similarity is too remote.

USEFUL CACTI

In their native lands cacti fill a significant rôle as useful plants. The fruit is by far the most used part and is eaten fresh, cooked or dried. Best-known are the fruits of some Opuntias, notably *O. ficus-indica*, which is cultivated for food. Fruits of other species are eaten too, both those with watery, colourless sap (including *O. streptacantha* and *O. leucotricha*) and those with strong red sap, which even colours the urine (including *O. engelmannii* and *O. lindheimeri*). Not all Opuntia fruits are edible, however; some are insipid or rather dry. The fist-sized fruit of some *Hylocereus* species are delicious, such as *H. guatemalensis*, *H. triangularis* and *H. undatus*, and they have been liberally planted. The fruits of many columnar cacti are also enjoyed, such as those of *Carnegiea gigantea* and *Myrtillocactus geometrizans*, the latter reminiscent of bilberries, while those of many *Echinocereus* species are regarded as delicacies, for example, *E. cinerascens* or the tiny berries of many Mammillarias. The fruits of *Pereskia portulacifolia* is marketed as Barbados gooseberries.

Aside from their fruits, fleshy cactus stems are valued in dry areas for their water content. The flesh of the giant *Ferocactus* species, such as *F. wislizeni*, has an aromatic, sweet—sour flavour and Mexicans eat it stewed or candied and made into sweets, earning it the name of 'candy cactus'. The stems of Opuntias and the young shoots of many columnar cactis are used as cattle fodder. Lastly the tough wood of *Cereus* species is used for fuel and building material in areas without trees.

Opuntias or, better still slender-bodied columnar cacti such as *Pachycereus marginatus* are planted as impenetrable hedges and enclosures.

Opuntia joints are cut lengthways and used as cooling covers, just as aloe leaves are in Europe.

Numerous cacti contain a variety of alkaloids. The most famous is *Lophophora williamsii*, with mescalin, which produces intoxication and hallucinations. Mescalin is also contained in many, but not all, *Trichocereus*. An effective heart stimulant is extracted from the stems of *Selenicereus grandiflorus* and used mainly in England and North America.

CACTUS CULTIVATION

SOIL

It is advisable to use a standard soil compost for most cacti, since it is practically impossible to re-create in cultivation all the extraordinarily different soils found in their natural habitats. The soil chosen should satisfy the following conditions:

1. It must contain light, porous material to provide good drainage.
2. It should not contain unpleasant, decomposing material that could cause rot.
3. It must contain plenty of nutrients without being over-rich.
4. It must be neutral or slightly acid, in other words not calcareous.

A suitable compost is obtained by mixing equal parts of leaf-mould, ordinary garden soil and coarse sand. Such a mixture will provide sufficient nourishment for most cacti to achieve normal growth. It will stay open without caking and, if treated correctly, will not go sour.

Many other mixtures can be just as successful. The individual ingredients are not crucial in themselves, provided the combination fulfils the above conditions. The larger the plant, the coarser the soil it requires. Some cactus growers add friable loam and use volcanic gravel or perlite as a lightener. A few cacti such as species of *Ariocarpus* and *Astrophytum*, grow on pure limestone, so in their case some lime should be added.

There are some ready-mixed cactus composts on the market, including so-called mineral soil, which deserves particular mention. Unlike the mixtures recommended above, this contains no humus or organic matter, and is specially recommended for sensitive varieties. Cacti can also successfully be grown in a 'soil-less' (peat-based) compost, if necessary with an appropriate addition of sand.

Most cacti may be grown in one of the above mixtures, but a few varieties make more specific demands on their soil. The tropical epiphytes and the so-called 'leaf-cacti' (*Phyllocactus*), the Christmas cacti (*Schlumbergera*) and species of *Rhipsalis*, require a largely humus mixture with a high nutrient content, since many of them grow very quickly. It is also important for them to have coarse material with good drainage, which may be provided by adding coarse grit, and so on.

PLANT CONTAINERS

Choose containers that give the cacti ample space but not too much. The soil should remain as uniformly moist as possible, and unnaturally rapid changes between wet and dry should be avoided. Miniature plant-pots, especially clay ones, are therefore unsuitable. Plants such as Rebutias, that remain small, can be grown successfully grouped together in a bowl. Larger plants are better grown in separate containers where they are more easily managed.

Plastic pots are better than clay ones as the soil cannot dry out through the side walls, leaching nutrients away from the centre. Consequently, the earth is evenly penetrated by the roots, instead of their forming a thick mat against the pot wall, as they would do in clay pots. Moisture is held more evenly and for much longer, so it is not necessary to water so often. The smooth pot-wall also makes it possible to knock out a plant for repotting with virtually no disturbance of the rootball. The soil must be kept aerated of course, so it must be correspondingly more open and porous when plastic pots are used. Obviously, all containers must have an adequate drainage hole in the bottom.

REPOTTING

Like all plants, cacti should only be repotted when a plant has grown too big for its pot and can no longer find sufficient nourishment, or when its growth is obviously disturbed — a possible indicator of disease, root disturbance or attack by insect pests. In general, it is unnecessary to repot all cacti methodically every year. Small, fast-growing seedlings will need potting-on more often, while older, established plants can stay where they are for two or three years. The new pot will usually be bigger than the old one, but the deciding factor must always be the state of root-development, since the root-network should soon fill the new pot properly.

Apart from emergencies, the best time for repotting is before the growth period has really begun, so that disturbance to the roots is minimal, and the new roots can then explore the fresh soil undisturbed. Exceptions to this are all early flowerers such as *Echinocereus*, *Echinopsis* and 'leaf-cacti', which should only be repotted after they have finished flowering.

It is important not to water any plants due for repotting for a few days previously so that the soil will tip out more easily.

Everything should be prepared for repotting so that the work can proceed without interruptions:

- Sufficient soil
- An adequate number of clean containers of different sizes (new clay-pots should be soaked for a few days)
- Crocks to cover the drainage holes
- Smaller crocks or fine gravel as further drainage
- Stakes and string for tying up larger plants
- A potting stick for backfilling and tamping down the soil
- A cloth or glove for handling these often painfully prickly plants safely and firmly.

Remove the plant from the old pot, protecting the roots by holding the plant firmly in one hand, turning the pot upside down and tapping its rim sharply a few times against a firm worktop to loosen the root-ball from the sides. Care must obviously be taken not to damage any part of the plant. If a very tangled root-ball is wedged in an old clay pot, it is often impossible to avoid breaking the pot.

All the old soil must be shaken off the root-ball, matted roots gently teased loose with a pointed stick, and dead or shrivelled roots cut back to the healthy part with a sharp knife. Healthy roots that have grown too long should also be pruned back to stimulate production of new roots. It is very important to watch out for the presence of mealy bugs (see Diseases and pests, pp. 304–5). These must be carefully and meticulously brushed or washed away before the plants are put into their new pots. Plants that have been washed must be allowed to dry off before planting.

Try new pots for size by holding their proposed occupant inside them. Cover the drainage hole with a curved crock, and then a layer of either smaller crocks or fine gravel, depending on the size of the pots, to assist drainage. Next, hold the plant inside in its final position and fill the fresh soil in around it, using a potting stick to make sure it goes well between all the roots. Still supporting the plant, give the pot a few sharp taps on the worktop and press the soil away from the rim by hand in order to leave sufficient watering space. The stem of the plant should just touch the soil. Only longer Cerei or Opuntias are planted slightly deeper to give them a better hold. It is also wise to stake them until they have firmly taken root again. Depending on the weather, the repotted cacti should not be watered for at least a week, so that any pruned or damaged roots may heal safely.

SITUATION AND CARE IN SUMMER

Conditions in a greenhouse or heated frame are ideal, but cacti also do very well on a window-sill, or even better in a glass terrarium in front of the window. If they are not kept in the same place all the year round, care must be taken to mitigate the effect of changing from dimly lit winter-quarters to well-lit summer ones. Plants should be shaded from direct sunlight for the first few weeks, and only when they show signs of new growth, should they be gradually accustomed to full sun and air.

Watering

When they are in their final position, the most essential care plants require is correct watering. This depends on so many factors that it is impossible to give precise instructions as to quantity and frequency. How much water plants need depends firstly on their growth and the temperature, and secondly on the speed at which the soil loses its moisture by evaporation which in turn depends on the type of soil and its porosity, and whether the containers are clay or plastic, standing alone or inside a jardinière.

When plants are brought out of their winter-quarters, they must be watered with great caution until they display the first signs of new growth. Once they are growing, they need ample humidity. When the plants become dry, they should be given a thorough soaking and then left to dry out in their own time before being watered again.

Some plants may temporarily suspend growth during the summer; this is an absolutely normal process for many species, and relates to conditions in their native habitat, so at ths time too they should be watered relatively sparingly.

After 'when' and 'how much', the next point is the quality of the water. Rainwater is ideal, but this is not always available to us in sufficient quantity. Tap water usually contains too much calcium for cacti, which as a rule prefer a weak acid reaction (pH 5–6). Water should therefore be tested with litmus paper, available from any pharmacy, and the reaction improved if necessary by adding acid. Nitric, sulphuric, phosphoric, citric or oxalic acid may be used, but it is best to alternate in order to avoid the build-up of any particular chemical in the soil. Oxalic acid is highly poisonous to humans and should be used with appropriate caution.

Fertilizers

Closely connected with watering is the subject of feeding. Like all other plants, cacti require mineral nutrients for their growth. These are originally contained in the soil, but as they are used up, the nutrients must be replaced by adding fertilizers according to the plant's stage of growth.

Newly planted cacti have adequate nutrients at first. Only when these nutrients have been largely exhausted, should fresh ones be watered in, depending on how the individual plants are growing. Fast-growing cacti, such as many Cerei, need more frequent doses of fertilizer than slow-growing ones, like many globose varieties. Resting cacti that show no sign of growth must on no account be given fertilizer. The actual type of fertilizer used is less important. Any compound fertilizers are suitable, since they also contain trace elements, but they should be low in nitrogen, as too much results in flabby growth.

Hardening off

During the growing period, everything possible should be done to promote the plants' development, but in the autumn they should be prepared for the winter by halting growth and hardening off. This is done by reducing their water and exposing them to as strong a light as possible, coupled with the full effect of night-time cooling, when the temperature should fall gently to freezing point. The result will be sound, hardy plants with splendid spines and, most important, greater willingness to flower. Housing them in their winter-quarters should be delayed as long as convenient, without excessively endangering them.

SITUATION AND CARE IN WINTER

With the exception of a few species that grow and bloom in winter, such as *Mammillaria plumosa*, and the epiphytes that live in a constant, damp, tropical forest climate, all cacti need their resting period in winter, and care must be taken not to interrupt this.

It is crucial that the plants should not be stimulated to grow at the wrong time. In poor winter light-conditions any growth results in many cacti like Opuntias and *Echinopsis* producing hideously misshapen, pitifully thin shoots, instead of normally formed, sturdy, well-spined ones. In others, the production of spines will, at the very least, be severely and irreversibly checked. Therefore warmth and moisture — the factors that principally favour growth — must be kept to a minimum.

Light plays a far less decisive role in cacti's winter rest. Surprisingly, it has been found that cacti are much less sensitive to light deprivation than might be expected from their characteristic demand for light during the summer growth period. Resting cacti can even spend months in complete darkness without coming to any harm.

In winter the following conditions are necessary inside a house (and of course the same applies to heated frames or greenhouses). It is most effective to put cacti in an unheated but frost-free place with an average temperature of 4–8°C and a reasonable amount of light. Care is then simple: a drop of water about every three or four weeks. It is even better to cut out watering altogether until the start of the growth season the following spring. If the cacti are wintering in a warm room, the greater evaporation at the higher temperature must be taken into account, and the plants watered accordingly to prevent the root-ball becoming dust-dry.

If there is no suitable wintering spot in the house, the last resort is to take the cacti out of their pots, pack them in a cardboard box and keep them in a cool place in complete darkness. Most species will withstand this sort of wintering without coming to any harm. Obviously the plants' condition should be checked occasionally and the spread of any rot or pest damage stopped.

CACTUS PROPAGATION

CUTTINGS

The simplest method of propagation is by cuttings. Many species produce numerous offsets, for example, *Echinopsis* or mat-forming Mammillarias. These 'pups' need only be severed with a sharp knife and the cutting is ready; they often break off spontaneously. The procedure is equally simple with the many-jointed Opuntias where, similarly, only a young shoot need be cut off; or with slender-stemmed Cerei such as the 'Queen of the Night', where just the end of a shoot is taken.

Leave the cuttings to dry for a week or more in fine weather, simply standing upright in an empty plant pot. When the cut surface has dried off and is covered with a firm skin, place the cutting on a porous, permeable material such as clean sand, compost and sand mixture, or pumice chippings until the roots emerge. Do not water them at this stage, or only very sparingly, from below. It is a good idea to cover them with a glass cloche as a protection against draughts, and to keep their base warm, which encourages root formation. The 'pups' of *Echinopsis*, many Mammillarias and some other species produce roots while still on the parent plant.

It is more difficult to obtain cuttings from unbranched globose or columnar cacti which only begin to produce side-shoots when the main growing tip is damaged. Either cut off the top of the plant and treat this as a cutting, or gouge out the growing point and thus stimulate the production of a side-shoot. Of course these drastic methods should generally only be used when a plant has become damaged or otherwise unsightly.

A particularly neat way of propagation is achieved with tubercles, which is naturally only possible with long-tubercled Mammillarias — for example, *M. wildii, M. plumosa, M. schiedeana, M. longimamma* or *Leuchtenbergia*. In this method the tubercles are detached from the parent plant and left to dry in the shade for one day. They are then treated as normal cuttings and provided with draught protection and a lightly moist bed, to avoid the danger of drying out. The new shoots appear not from the areole on the tip of the tubercle, but directly from its base.

GRAFTING

The second important method of propagation is by grafting, or attaching a cutting to a robust and vigorous stock. Astonishingly, cacti will readily graft to contrasting and not even near-related species, and with hardly any technical difficulty.

Grafting is essential with plants that are incapable of feeding themselves — perhaps the yellow, chlorophyll-free forms of *Lobivia (Chamaecereus) silvestrii* or the blood-red *Gymnocalycium mihanovichii* — and also the relatively few species that are considered difficult to cultivate and clearly have a very delicate root-system. It is unavoidable with the so-called 'cockscomb' forms (cristates), which keep appearing even in nature without recognizable cause. It is also appropriate for high grafts of trailing forms such as *Aporocactus flagelliformis, Schlumbergera truncata* or *Rhipsalidopsis x graeseri*. Finally, it is an indispensable resource either for saving an unhealthy plant that is too far gone to be handled as a cutting, or for propagating a rare species quickly.

As a stock, *Trichocereus* species have proved outstandingly useful. They have thick stems and not very prominent ribs, so they provide as large a surface as possible when they are cut across. These include *T. spachianus, T. macrogonus, T. pachanoi* and *T. schickendantzii*, which are all very vigorous and not sensitive to low winter temperatures. The rather slower-growing *Eriocereus jusbertii* is also very suitable, particularly for high grafts, because of its tall slender form. Grafts from *E. jusbertii* are also notable for their beautiful spines and free-flowering habit; however, this plant does like to be kept a little warmer in winter.

The grafting procedure is extremely simple. Use a sharp, smooth, stainless-steel knife and, with a slicing action (taking care not to crush), cut the top off the stock at the required height. The tissue at the cutting point must be fairly mature, but not so old that it has already become partly woody. Prepare the scion in the same way. Then trim off the epidermis, bevelling all round the edges of both stock and scion to ensure that they make contact properly. Place the scion on top of the stock in such a way that the vascular bundles, recognizable as a ring of dots, coincide as well as possible. The nutrient-conducting channels of the stock must have access to those of the scion in order to nourish the graft. To ensure that union takes place as evenly as possible over the entire cut surfaces, press the scion on the stock firmly but carefully, using cotton wool to protect the soft tip. It is also vital that pressure should remain constant even if the plant shrinks.

Alternatively, use the wedge-grafting method if you wish to achieve a weeping-tree effect by grafting the flat joints of the Christmas or Easter cacti on to a tall slender stock. The best stock to take for this is the slender *Eriocereus jusbertii*, which is exceptionally tough and able to supoort a large head later. First top the stock in the usual way and then make a vertical incision 2–3 cm deep in the middle of it. Trim the lower end of the scion into a wedge shape, insert this into the incision and stick a long cactus spine — not a metal needle — through both scion and stock to hold them together firmly in the required position.

SEED-SOWING

Undoubtedly the most fascinating method of propagation is from seed. Greenhouse-owners will find that sowing is possible virtually all the year round, but for anyone doing it indoors, the most favourable time is early spring when the sun is already climbing fairly high, and prolonged bad weather is unlikely.

When raising from seed, obviously cleanliness and great care are needed to eliminate from the outset all possible sources of danger for the tender young seedlings, and also to avoid confusing different species.

If seeds are sown in a single plant pot, this should be plunged in a compost-and-sand mixture in a larger container to maintain even soil humidity. Horticultural seed-trays of polystyrene, which come in a variety of sizes, can also be used. A mixture of two-thirds peat and one-third sand has proved very suitable as a potting base, but there are many other mixtures.

The containers should be filled and tapped firmly a few times, pressing the earth down lightly to about 1 cm below the rim of the tray or pot. Seed-trays should be divided into compartments with glass or plastic strips depending on the number of varieties to be sown, so that the different seeds cannot become mixed up.

Scatter the seeds evenly over the individual compartments or pots, which should then be clearly labelled to avoid confusion. Small seeds should be just lightly pressed down with a piece of board or cork mat so that they bed closely into the soil. Larger seeds, from Opuntias, for example, should be covered with soil to their own depth.

The containers should then be placed in water until the soil is fully soaked. Finally, it is advisable to spray the surface with chinosol or a similar fungicide, using a very fine over-head spray from a good height as a precaution against fungal attack. Cover the prepared containers with a sheet of glass and lay a sheet of tissue-paper on top to filter strong sunshine.

The primary conditions for speedy and even germination are thorough warmth and even humidity — damp, not wet. Most cacti enjoy temperatures rising to 25°–30°C by day and dropping to 18°–20°C at night. Under these conditions most will germinate in 8–14 days, but the hard-shelled Opuntias, for example, can lie for weeks or even months before germinating. To bring on earlier germination in this species, gently split the hard white aril with a sharp knife or a file to allow the embryo to take up water.

As long as the glass cover remains on the seed container, it must be regularly wiped dry so that no drops of condensation fall on to the seedlings. When germination is complete, expose the containers, still protected with tissue-paper, to full sunshine and ventilation, and proceed to normal watering, that is, allow them to dry out slowly and evenly before watering again. This way, growth will be perfectly synchronized with the alternation of day and night temperatures. When the seedlings show uninterrupted growth, remove the sheet of glass and handle them as grown plants, although with consideration for their limited reserves.

Opinions vary as to the best time to prick-out the seedlings into fresh soil. Slow-growing species, such as Parodias, should be left undisturbed for as long as possible, while fast-growing species may be pricked out within a relatively short time. Regardless of the stage the seedlings have reached, immediate pricking-out may be essential if there is an outbreak of damping-off or a carpet of algae forms on the surface of the seed-container.

To lift little seedlings out of the soil without hurting them, use a wooden plant-label cut into a two pronged fork and a dibber about the size of a pencil. This can also be used to make a good large hole in the solid damp soil, made up with the same mixture as for sowing. The young seedlings should then be set roots down, of course, and as a rule to the same depth as they were standing in the seed tray. Young cacti develop much better if they are close-set, practically shoulder to shoulder. As a rough guide to distance, place them their own thickness away from each other.

The newly pricked-out seedlings should be left for a few days without watering, in a warm, semi-shaded place, protected from direct sunlight and away from draughts, so that they can recover as quickly as possible and form new roots. Only then should they be slowly accustomed to air and sun again. When the seedlings are actually touching, perhaps even preventing further growth due to their over-crowded condition, they should be pricked out a second time, using the same technique as before, into individual pots.

At this early stage in the seedling's life, the correct amount of moisture is vital for strong, healthy growth. The soil should never become completely dried out, or damage will occur to the new roots, and it is best not to observe the resting season until the second year, when the plants are strong enough to benefit from it.

THE POSITION OF CACTI IN THE PLANT KINGDOM

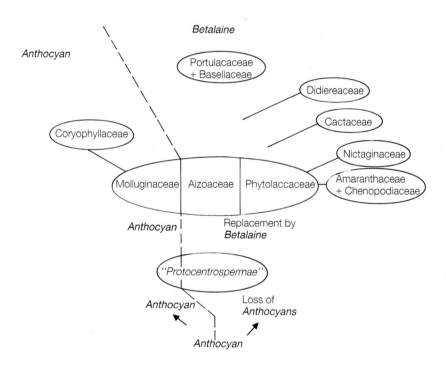

Cacti (*Cactaceae*, A.L. de Jussieu, Gen.Pl.310, 1789) belong to the *Centrospermae* (or *Caryophyllales*), with the following main characteristics:
- Ovules curved and usually centrally positioned. Seeds in the middle of the ripe fruit (= *Centrospermae*, Eichler 1878).
- Food tissue in the seeds mainly perisperm (originating from the nucleus, that is) and surrounded by the tightly rolled up or very crumpled embryo.
- In many families, nitrogen-containing Betacyan together with yellow Betaxanthin (= Betalaine) in place of the red or blue dye Anthocyan.
- Filter-element plastids with albumen contents (globular or polygonal, central crystalloid, with peripheral circular bundles of filaments, 'P-type' plastids).

Nearest to the common ancestors of all the *Centrospermae*, the *Protocentrospermae*, comes the group of the *Molluginaceae, Aizoaceae* (iceplants – sometimes known as *Ficoidaceae* or *Mesembryanthemaceae*) and *Phytolaccaceae* (red ink plants). These three families share numerous common characteristics. From this core the other families have evolved further.

The split into an Anthocyan branch and a Betalaine branch must already have happened within the *Protocentrospermae*. The important feature of the cactus families (*Cactaceae*), which are our principal concern here, is that close relationships exist with both the *Phytolaccaceae* (red ink plants), and the *Portulacaceae* (sun plants) and *Aizoaceae* (ice plants).

CACTUS IDENTIFICATION

Cacti are characterized by the following features:
- Xerophytes with usually succulent, columnar, spherical or flattened stems, very occasionally with flat green leaves.
- Leaves mostly rudimentary or modified into spines.
- Areoles – immature flattened short sections with felt, spines, bristles or hairs – in the leaf axils.
- Flower axis clearly developed, mostly consisting of internodes, divided into the pedicle area, a part surrounding the ovary (pericarp), and an elongated cylindrical part (receptaculum) situated above the ovary; set with areoles and long, leaflike scales, which often merge gradually into the sepals.
- Flowers bisexual, conspicuous, actinomorphic (radially symmetrical) or zygomorphic (bilaterally symmetrical), with a perianth (perigonium) usually consisting of numerous sepals; petals free, occasionally fused into a genuine tube.
- Stamens numerous. Pollen tricolpate, or with 6-12 round exit holes (pores). Outer layer of the pollen grain wall (exine) with net-structure, fine prickles and tiny holes. Pollen with triple nucleus.
- Ovaries with many simply-structured carpels; one style, very occasionally central with basal ovules, or else inferior with ± numerous ovules attached to the wall tissue of the ovary.
- Ovules curved, occasionally inverted, with mostly long funicles, often joined together in bundles.
- Fruit fleshy or dry, dehiscent or remaining closed.
- Basic chromosome count x = 11.

The family contains about 2000 species falling into 3 sub-families:
1. *Pereskioideae* with 2 genera.
2. *Opuntioideae* with 5 genera.
3. *Cactoideae* with 127 genera.

(Different systems vary in the broader or more limited number of genera they include, between 120 and 220.) The following scheme is based on Buxbaum's system, altered in a few places in conformity with those of Hunt and Barthlott.

PERESKIOIDEAE   K. Schumann

Flowers usually stalked, often proliferous. Ovary superior or inferior. Seeds with black seedcoat (testa). Trees or shrubs usually looking like normal deciduous trees, with broad flat leaves (*Pereskia*) or plants with jointed, very succulent shoots and subulate to cylindric leaves (*Maihuenia*). Two genera: *Pereskia* and *Maihuenia*.

OPUNTIOIDEAE   K. Schumann

Flowers sessile, frequently proliferous. Ovary inferior. Seeds with very hard light-coloured aril. Tree-like or low. Stems cylindric or globose or ± flattened, often jointed. Leaf-blades subulate or cylindric, usually deciduous, rarely (*Pereskiopsis*) broad and flat. With small, barbed, brittle spines (glochids). Five genera: *Quiabentia*, *Pereskiopsis*, *Tacinga*, *Pterocactus*, *Opuntia*.

CACTOIDEAE

Flowers sessile, without proliferous flower-axis. Ovary inferior. Seeds with thin, hard, black to light and soft seedcoat. Habit polymorphic. Leaf-blade nearly always completely reduced. The very varied and extremely polymorphic Cactoideae, with 127 genera, may be divided into the following 9 tribes:

I.   *Leptocereeae*
II.   *Browningieae*
III.   *Pachycereeae*
IV.   *Hylocereeae*
V.   *Cereeae*
VI.   *Trichocereeae*
VII.   *Notocacteae*
VIII. *Echinocereeae*
IX.   *Cacteae*

Tribe I Leptocereeae   F. Buxbaum

Pericarpel and receptacle-tube always very shoot-like, short; scales usually numerous, with spiny or woolly areoles. Stem columnar, branching from the base or laterally; branches numerous and thin. Six genera: *Leptocereus*, (very primitive), *Armatocereus*, *Neoraimondia*, *Neoabbottia*, *Samaipaticereus* and *Calymmanthium*.

Tribe II Browningieae   F. Buxbaum

Pericarpel and receptacle-tube thick-walled, densely covered with overlapping scales, sometimes with areolar wool in their axils, usually completely glabrous. Trees, ± freely branching from the base or more often higher up the trunk. Vegetative shoots densely spiny, on flowering branches spination weaker or absent. Related to the *Leptocereeae*. Three genera: *Rauhocereus*, *Castellanosia* and *Browningia*, with progressively less wool in the axils of the pericarpel scales.

Tribe III Pachycereeae   F. Buxbaum

Pericarpel and elongate receptacle-tube densely scaly, with spiny to woolly areoles, rarely absent. Trees, columnar, branching or solitary. Ribs present. The 13 genera can

be divided into 3 groups:
1. *Pterocereus, Escontria, Lemaireocereus, Pachycereus, Carnegiea.*
2. *Myrtillocactus, Lophocereus, Bergerocactus, Machaerocereus, Rathbunia.*
3. *Neobuxbaumia, Backebergia, Cephalocereus.*

Tribe IV Hylocereeae   F. Buxbaum

Flowers regular, seldom zygomorphic. Pericarpel scaly, frequently with spiny or hairy areoles, rarely without areoles or completely naked. Receptacle-tube short, strongly elongate or almost absent. True perigonum sometimes present. Habit polymorphic, some species epiphytic. Stems round in cross-section, with or without ribs, or 3–5-winged, flat leaf-like, often jointed. Flowers solitary or several together at lateral areoles or from composite areoles at the end of the joint. The 27 genera can be divided into 4 interrelated groups:
1. *Nyctocereus, Brachycereus, Peniocereus, Acanthocereus, Dendrocereus, Harrisia, Eriocereus.*
2. *Aporocactus, Heliocereus, Nopalxochia, Epiphyllum, Disocactus, Wittia, Pseudorhipsalis.*
3. *Weberocereus, Eccremocactus, Hylocereus, Wilmattea, Selenicereus, Mediocactus, Strophocactus, Cryptocereus.*
4. A rather isolated group with *Pfeiffera, Rhipsalis, Hatiora, Rhipsalidopsis, Schlumbergera.*

Tribe V Cereeae   F. Buxbaum

Flowers regular, seldom zygomorphic. Pericarpel and receptacle-tube scaly, without areoles. Shrubs, ascending or prostrate, or trees, columnar, branching or solitary. Ribs present. Flowers from normal areoles or a cephalium. The 10 genera may be divided into 3 groups:
1. *Jasminocereus, Stetsonia.*
2. *Praecereus, Monvillea, Cereus, Brasilicereus.*
3. *Pseudopilocereus, Stephanocereus, Coleocephalocereus, Buiningia.*

Tribe VI Trichocereeae   F. Buxbaum

Flowers regular, sometimes zygomorphic. Pericarpel and receptacle-tube scaly, with woolly or curly hair, pericarpel occasionally with spiny areoles, rarely areoles absent. Receptacle-tube (*Borzicactus*) petaloid; lower stamens occasionally reduced to hairs or scales. Branching or solitary, erect or decumbent, large or dwarf, columnar, rarely globose. Ribs clearly defined or ± divided into tubercles. Flowers from normal areoles, more rarely from a cephalium. The 23 genera divided into 4 somewhat artificial groups:
1. *Trichocereus, Weberbauerocereus, Haageocereus, Espostoa, Austrocephalocereus, Zehntnerella.*
2. *Borzicactus, Oreocereus, Morawetzia, Cleistocactus, Cephalocleistocactus, Denmoza, Arrojadoa, Micranthocereus, Matucana, Oroya.*
3. *Echinopsis, Lobivia, Rebutia, Sulcorebutia, Weingartia, Gymnocalycium, Mila.*
4. *Leocereus, Arthrocereus, Setiechinopsis.*

Tribe VII Notocacteae   F. Buxbaum

Flowers regular. Pericarpel and receptacle-tube scaly, with increasing coverage of areoles towards the top (acropetal), the upper part of the receptacle-tube with areoles with bristles or even spines. Occasionally areoles absent, very rarely scales are absent too, and then the receptacle-tube has a leafy crown (*Melocactus*). Sometimes the base of the inner perianth-segments grows into a short true perigonium. Stems globose or flattened to dwarf, rarely shortly columnar, branching from the base or solitary, ribbed or with ribs divided into tubercles. Flowers solitary or in clusters from normal areoles or a cephalium. The 18 genera are divided into 4 groups. It seems, however, questionable whether some genera (marked with a '?') really belong in *Notocacteae* at all.

1. *Corryocactus, Austrocactus, Eriosyce, Pyrrhocactus, Eulychnia*(?)
2. *Neoporteria, Islaya, Copiapoa.*
3. *Notocactus, Parodia, Blossfeldia, Frailea, Uebelmannia*(?) *Astrophytum*(?)
4. *Discocactus, Melocactus*(?)

Tribe VIII Echinocereeae (B. & R.) F. Buxbaum

Flowers regular. Pericarpel and usually also receptacle-tube scaly usually with spiny areoles. Stem short, columnar or globose, erect or decumbent, sometimes shrub-like, with thin branches, or large columnar and decumbent. Ribs present. Two closely related genera: *Wilcoxia* and *Echinocereus*, with strong links between *Wilcoxia* and *Peniocereus* in the *Hylocereeae.*

Tribe IX Cacteae

Flowers regular, rarely zygomorphic. Pericarpel usually scaly and with woolly or hairy areoles. Receptacle-tube without areoles, elongate, scaly or scales almost absent, or with a leafy crown, the pericarpel then naked. Stem short, columnar, globose or flattened, very large to dwarf, ribbed or tuberculate. Areoles monomorphic or dimorphic. Flowers arising from areoles or the upper part of a double areole (furrow, axil). This tribe includes 25 genera which can be divided into 3 groups:

1. *Echinocactus, Sclerocactus, Ancistrocactus, Hamatocactus, Echinomastus, Thelocactus, Normanbokea, Pediocactus, Neolloydia.*
2. *Coloradoa, Turbinicarpus, Strombocactus, Aztekium, Lophophora, Leuchtenbergia, Obregonia, Epithelantha, Pelecyphora, Ariocarpus.*
3. *Ferocactus, Stenocactus, Coryphantha, Escobaria, Ortegocactus, Mammillaria.*

CACTUS
IDENTIFICATION

Subfamily **PERESKIOIDEAE** K. Schumann

PERESKIA Mill. [incl. RHODOCACTUS (A. Berger) F.M. Knuth]

Trees, shrubs or climbers with slightly fleshy branches soon becoming woody and in age densely spiny. Leaves stalked, large ± deciduous during resting-period. Areoles without glochids. Flowers solitary or in panicles, mostly stalked, rotate, white, pink red or orange. Pericarpel naked or with leaf-like scales which are sometimes hairy and spiny. Ovary superior to inferior. Fruit globose or pear-shaped, fleshy, with or without spines. Seeds ± numerous, large; seedcoat shiny, black, brittle. Two groups are distinguishable according to flower-size: small-flowered (up to 1.5 cm Ø), mostly also small-leaved, shrubby species with brilliant red, orange, pink or white flowers. Large-flowered (up to 8 cm Ø), mostly also large-leaved species with brilliant carmine, orange, pink or white flowers. 20 species, from Florida to Brazil and from N Peru to E Bolivia.

Pereskia vargasii H. Johnson

Tree, 2–4 m tall, older branches often prostrate. Leaves almost sessile, ovate to broadly ovate and narrowing towards the tip, 1.5–2.5 cm long, fleshy. Areoles small with white felt and white hairs up to 1 cm long and 1–3 sharp spines up to 2.5 cm long, later grey with black tips. Flowers 3–5 crowded in the leaf-axils, small, up to 1.5 cm wide, white. Fruit a small, up to 6 mm across, ruby-red to almost black berry with white hairs. N Peru.

Pereskia bahiensis Gürke

Initially shrubby, later developing a trunk and becoming a tree up to 8 m tall; young shoots spineless, later the areoles with up to 40 spines, up to 9 cm long. Leaves lanceolate, up to 9 cm long. Flowers in small clusters, large, up to 8 cm Ø, carmine-red; floral axis with large leaves, up to 4 cm long, often proliferous. Brazil.

Pereskia aculeata Miller

Freely branching shrub with upright or prostrate, often climbing, terete stems up to 2 m long. Leaves elliptic to ovate, short-stalked, pointed, up to 10 cm long, somewhat fleshy, reddish underside. Areoles sparsely felted, with a pair of hooked spines and, after the leaves have fallen, up to 30 straight spines, up to 2 cm long, yellowish brown to black. Flowers in a many-flowered terminal panicle, up to 3 cm long and 5 cm wide, white, sometimes tinged yellow or pink. Fruit like a gooseberry in shape and size, almost completely smooth, yellow and translucent when ripe. Very variable species. Tropical America, West Indies and South America; naturalized in Mexico and Florida.

MAIHUENIA Philippi

Low, densely mat-forming dwarf shrubs with fleshy, jointed stems. Joints globular to cylindric. Leaves small, cylindric, deciduous or persistent. Areoles felted, without glochids. Spines needle-like, terete. Flowers solitary, from almost terminal areoles, stalked, rotate, medium sized, white, yellow or red. Pericarpel with leafy scales, glabrous or hairy. Fruit a soft berry; seeds numerous, lens-shaped; seedcoat glossy black, brittle. 5 species in the Andes of Chile and Argentina to Patagonia.

Maihuenia poeppigii (Otto) F.A.C. Weber

Forming mats up to 3 m wide. Joints cylindric, 6 cm long and 1.5 cm thick. Leaves cylindric, 4–7 mm long. Areoles sparsely white-felted with 1 central spine 1.5–2 cm long and 2 very short lateral spines. Flowers yellow. Fruit shortly obovoid, 4–5 cm long. Andes of S Chile.

Subfamily **OPUNTIOIDEAE** K. Schumann

QUIABENTIA Britton & Rose

Trees or shrubs with whorled, fleshy, terete branches and flat, fleshy leaves. Areoles white-felted, with numerous glochid-like spines. Flowers terminal, rotate, red. Pericarpel leafy. Fruit oblong, eventually smooth. Seeds large, round and flat with smooth whitish aril. About 4 species in Brazil and from E Bolivia to N Argentina.

Quiabentia zehntneri (B. & R.) B. & R.

Very spiny shrub with continuous main stem, 2–3 m high. Leaves ovate or almost orbicular, pointed, 2–4 cm long. Areoles with short, white wool and numerous fine whitish spines. Flowers 3–4 cm long and 7–8 cm wide, brilliant red. Brazil.

PERESKIOPSIS Britton & Rose

Trees, shrubs or climbers with irregularly branching, ± rod-shaped shoots and flat, fleshy leaves. Areoles with hair and true glochids, with or without spines. Flowers on shoots of previous season, rather large, rotate, yellow or red. Pericarpel mostly with leaves or scales. Fruit club-shaped, fleshy, red. Seeds few, almost round with narrow collar, white, felted-hairy. About 10 species in Mexico; also in Guatemala.

Pereskiopsis velutina Rose

Dense bushes, 1.2 m or more tall, of spreading, green, finely hairy shoots. Leaves ovate to lanceolate, 2–6 cm long and 1.5–2.5 cm wide, finely hairy. Areoles with a few short spines. Flowers yellow, green or reddish outside. Mexico.

TACINGA Britton & Rose

Erect, ± twiggy climber with rounded shoots. Leaves small, very reduced, cylindric. Areoles with very easily shed glochids. Flowers lateral around the shoot-tip, night-blooming, green or purple. Pericarpel and receptacle-tube united into a hollow axis, covered in tiny scales and areoles with numerous glochids. Stamens and style long-exserted from the flower in a tight bundle; perianth reflexed, a ring of long, curly hairs between outer stamens and perianth. Fruit oblong, formed from the whole hollow axis, green or reddish, evenly covered in areoles with glochids, very hard-fleshed. Seeds large, ovoid, the aril very hard, with sticky hairs that swell up and fill the fruit entirely. 2 species in Brazil, in the Caatinga (a semi-desert zone) of Bahia.

Tacinga funalis B. & R.

Shrub, initially erect, later bending and climbing. Stems sparsely branching, becoming rounded with age, 1–10 m long and 1–2 cm thick. Leaves small, up to 5 mm long, deciduous. Flowers green. Fruit 4–5 cm long. Brazil.

PTEROCACTUS K. Schumann

Dwarf shrubs, branching from the base with bulbous, tuberous root. Shoots club-shaped or thin and rather long, with tiny caducous leaves. Areoles with fine spines and small glochids. Flowers truly terminal, small, funnel-shaped, without tube; outer perianth-segments somewhat fleshy. Pericarpel slightly tuberculate, with numerous tufts of small spines. Fruit capsule-like, dry, woolly, with spines and glochids. Seeds flat, white. Aril broad and irregularly winged, hard. 6 species, Argentina, Patagonia to Straits of Magellan.

Pterocactus kuntzei K. Schumann

Shoots 3–4 cm long and 1 cm thick, brownish green, arising from a bulbous, tuberous root, up to 12 cm long and 8 cm thick. Areoles small, with tiny appressed spines. Flowers 2–3 cm long and 2–3 cm wide, yellow. Fruit dry. W Argentina.

OPUNTIA Miller [incl. CYLINDROPUNTIA (Engelm.) F.M. Knuth, AUSTRO-CYLINDROPUNTIA Backeb., CORYNOPUNTIA F.M. Knuth, MARENOPUNTIA Backeb., MICROPUNTIA Daston, TEPHROCACTUS Lemaire, NOPALEA Salm-Dyck, CONSOLEA Lemaire, BRASILIOPUNTIA (K. Schumann) A. Berger, GRUSONIA F. Reichenbach]

Shrubs or trees, usually freely branching; stems jointed, with cylindric club-shaped or flattened segments, rarely ribbed. Sometimes with strongly developed trunk. Leaves spindle-shaped or subulate. Areoles usually with wool, glochids and spines, these sometimes protected by a sheath ('sheathed-spines'). Flowers produced singly from areoles on the tips or edges of stem-joints, medium sized or conspicuous, rotate or funnel-shaped, without tube, yellow or reddish, rarely white. Pericarpel shoot-like, covered in scales with areoles which develop felt, glochids and sometimes also spines. Fruit pear-shaped or globose, fleshy or dry, with deep umbilicus. Seeds large, smooth, with hard, white, occasionally felted aril. About 250–300 species, often very difficult to distinguish from each other. Mainly Mexico, Peru and Chile, to a lesser degree in North America up to 50°N latitude, and in Central America, South America and Patagonia, from plains to mountains up to 4500 m. Introduced in other parts of the world (South Africa, Australia, Mediterranean region).

Within the genus *Opuntia* the following subgenera can be distinguished: *Cylindropuntia, Tephrocactus, Opuntia Nopalea, Consolea, Brasiliopuntia, Grusonia.*

Subgenus CYLINDROPUNTIA (Engelm.) F.M. Knuth [incl. AUSTROCYLINDROPUNTIA Backeb., CORYNOPUNTIA F.M. Knuth, MARENOPUNTIA Backeb., MICROPUNTIA Daston]

Stem segments elongate, terete, smooth or tuberculate or tessellate, but not ribbed. Spines often with papery sheath.

Opuntia clavarioides Pfeiffer

Bushy shrub, shoots finger-shaped or club-shaped, blunt; at times also spread into a cockscomb, light brown to deep reddish brown. Leaves reddish, 1–5 mm long, deciduous. Areoles tiny, with 4–10 fine white spines, starlike. Flowers rarely produced, 7.5 cm long and 5–6 cm wide, brownish green. Fruit ellipsoid, 1.5 cm long and 1 cm wide, with 1 woolly seed. Chile.

This species is only grown grafted, mainly on Platyopuntias.

Opuntia miquelii Monv.

Forming bushy colonies, up to 1 m high and 5 m wide. Shoots cylindric with many side-shoots, 3–6 cm thick and up to 20 cm long, green, later blue-green. Tubercles laterally compressed. Areoles large, white-felted, with brown glochids and eventually up to 12 stout, often somewhat downward-pointing spines up to 10 cm long, pale grey in age. Flowers 4–8 cm long, pink to almost white. Fruit ovoid or oblong, white. Chile (Atacama).

Opuntia subulata Engelm.

Tree up to 4 m tall, with a trunk thick as an arm and steeply ascending branches; younger shoots dark green with large tubercles, covered in upcurved, pencil-thick, almost terete leaves, up to 12 cm long and with a life-span of 3–4 years. Areoles with a few yellow spines. Flowers reddish to red. Fruit tuberculate, with leaves. S Peru.

Opuntia verschaffeltii F.A.C. Weber

Cylindric, tuberculate joints, finger-thick, 10–20 cm long, matt green. New shoots produce awl-shaped leaves 2–3 cm long. Areoles white-felted with yellowish glochids and 2–3 yellowish spines, up to 3 cm long. Flowers 3.5–4 cm long, fiery to orange-red. Bolivia, N Argentina.

Opuntia tunicata Link & Otto

■□
□□

Dense shrub, up to 60 cm high, with central trunk and whorled branches up to 15 cm long, profusely covered in shiny white sheathed-spines up to 5 cm long. Joints up to 4 cm thick, green to light blue-green, heavily tuberculate, easily snapped off. Areoles white-felted, with pale glochids and 6–10 reddish spines, 4–5 cm long, with shiny white papery sheaths. Flowers 5 cm long, greenish yellow. Mexico, Ecuador, Peru, N Chile.

Opuntia bigelowii Engelm.

□■
□□

Erect trunk, up to 1 m high, with numerous short, spreading branches, the upper crown-like, erect. Shoots club-shaped, up to 5 cm thick and 5 to 15 cm long, light green, tuberculate, unusually densely spined. Tubercles 4-angled, 1 cm long and wide. Areoles white-felted, with yellowish glochids, 6–10 radial spines and 6–10 central spines with straw-yellow sheaths. Flowers mostly at the shoot-tips, 4 cm long, purple. Fruit yellowish, mostly naked, heavily tuberculate. USA (Nevada, Arizona, California), Mexico (Baja California, Sonora).

Opuntia imbricata (Haw.) DC.

□□
■□

Shrub, 3–5 m high or tree with upright trunk and whorled branches, terminal joints 2–3 cm thick, strongly tuberculate, green to grey-green. Tubercles 2–2.5 cm long, laterally compressed. Leaves 8–24 mm long, terete. Spines 8–30, brown, 2–3 cm long, with white sheaths. Flowers mostly at the shoot-tips, 4–6 cm long and 8–9 cm wide, rose red to deep carmine. Fruit yellowish, heavily tuberculate, almost spineless. USA (Colorado to Texas and New Mexico), C Mexico.

This is the only hardy tree-Opuntia that has withstood temperatures down to −24°C for many years without damage, provided it has been adequately protected against damp.

Opuntia ramosissima Engelm.

□□
□■

Shrub up to 2 m high. Shoots slender, only slightly fleshy, up to 9 cm long, 6 mm thick, grey, often widely spreading, with slightly raised 4- or 6-sided areas. Areoles round, initially brown woolly, with pale glochids, spineless, or sometimes with 1 straight reddish spine up to 6 cm long, with yellowish sheath. Flowers 3–4 cm long, greenish-yellow, tinged with red. Fruit 2.5 cm long, almost ovoid, dry. USA (S Nevada, W Arizona, California), Mexico (Baja California, Sonora).

Opuntia inarmata Backeb.

Small plants with elongate-clavate to cylindric dark- later olive-green joints, 1.5 cm thick, tubercles only slightly raised. Leaves up to 15 mm long, upward-pointing. Areoles extended transversely, white-felted with tiny, hardly recognizable, glassy white glochids and (very occasionally) 1 porrect spine. Flowers large, 4 cm across, red, with slight orange tinge and wine-red stigma. Bolivia.

Opuntia marenae S.H. Parsons

Low, shrubby plants with thin cylindric shoots and tuberous roots. Areoles pale, initially with few spines, later with 8−9 or more of varying lengths, the outer ± appressed, 1−2 central of varying length pointing downwards, the longest at times horizontal. Flowers terminal, rather large, opening widely, cream. Ripe fruit in the swollen shoot-tip, splitting. Mexico (Sonora).

Subgenus TEPHROCACTUS Lemaire

Low shrubs or cushions, with globular or short-cylindric stem-segments. (Globular or jointed Opuntias). Spines often like paper or parchment. Fruit mostly dry, with glochids inside due to occlusion of the areoles.

Opuntia subterranea R.E. Fries

Unbranched or sparsely jointed stem, almost hidden in the ground, with stout root up to 12 cm long, and round joints 2−4 cm long. Flat, almost 4-sided tubercles, close-set with 1−7 short radial spines, recurved and appressed against the surface, whitish to brownish; no central spine. Flowers 2.5 cm across, brownish white, tinged with red, green outside. Fruit pear-shaped, up to 1.5 cm long. N Argentina.

Opuntia dimorpha C.F. Förster var. **pseudorauppiana** Backeb.

More or less compact cushions, 15−20 cm high and up to 30 cm wide, made up of globular-ovoid joints, 2.5 cm long and 2.5 cm wide, brownish green. Areoles fairly dense, brown-felted, with thick tufts of small white glochids, 7 brown spines 2 cm long, and 3 or 4 shorter whitish spines. Flowers light yellow. Chile (Coquimbo).

Opuntia floccosa Salm-Dyck ▪☐ ☐☐

Dense cushions, up to 2 m wide and 30 cm high, formed by acrotonous branching. Individual joints oblong, 5–10 cm long, 3 cm thick, heavily tuberculate, glossy green. Leaves small, thick, 5 mm long. Areoles with long, white, shining, woolly hairs and 1–3 thin yellow spines 1–3 cm long. Flowers 3 cm long, 3.5 cm across, yellow to orange. Fruit globose, 3 cm thick, tuberculate. Peru to C Bolivia, at altitudes of 4000–4500 m.

Opuntia articulata Pfeiffer ex Otto var. **papyracantha** (Phil.) Backeb. ☐▪ ☐☐

Loose cushions of elongate-globular, easily broken off, grey-green joints about 5 cm ∅. Areoles very large, with dense, brown glochids and 1–3 snow-white spines, 10 cm long and 7 mm wide, like paper or wood-shavings. Flowers 3–3.5 cm wide, white to pink, (seldom appearing in cultivation). Fruit 1–1.5 cm long, dry. W Argentina.

Opuntia rauhii (Backeb.) Rowley ☐☐ ▪☐

Dense clumps of short, cylindric joints, up to 25 cm long and 8 cm thick, densely covered with snow-white woolly hair standing rather on end, resembling a small *Oreocereus*. Areoles mostly with only 1 slender, yellow-tipped, white spine, 1.5 cm long. One of the most beautiful species. Peru, on the high grasslands at 3800–4500 m.

Opuntia crispicrinita (Rauh & Backeb.) Rowley ☐☐ ☐▪

Large, broad cushions of ± elongate, (only initially ± globular) joints, up to 4 cm long and 2 cm thick; tubercles fairly wide, oblong, with spreading, curly, white hairs and thin, slightly protruding, brown to horn-coloured spines. Flowers bright red. Peru.

Subgenus OPUNTIA (= PLATYOPUNTIA Engelm.)

Joints flattened, disc-shaped, covered in areoles. Leaves much reduced, caducous. Fruit fleshy, occasionally dry and not juicy.

Opuntia stenopetala Engelm.

Erect or prostrate and bushy with obovate joints, 10–20 cm long, grey-green or red tinged. Areoles fairly far apart with brown glochids and usually 2–4 spines, up to 5 cm long, reddish-brown to black, the larger ones flattened; lower areoles spineless. Flowers 5 cm long, fiery red. Fruit obovate, scarlet, spineless, or with few spines. Mexico.

Opuntia microdasys (Lem.) Pfeiffer

Shrubby, up to 60 cm high, with rather small, 10–15 cm long, elliptic, flat, softly hairy joints. Areoles fairly close-set, spineless but covered with very numerous, beautiful yellow glochids. Flowers 4–5 cm long, pale yellow. Fruit globose, deep red. Also var. *rufida* with reddish-brown glochids, and var. *albispina* with white. The var. *monstrosa* has small joints, closely covered in small, golden yellow areoles, almost touching each other. Mexico.

Opuntia pycnantha Engelm. var. margaritana Coulter

Low, bushy species with round to ovate joints, 10–20 cm long and up to 15 cm wide. Areoles close-set, brownish-felted, with conspicuous red glochids and up to 10 white or reddish spines, unequal, up to 1 cm, pointing obliquely downwards. Flowers 4 cm wide, sulphur-yellow, freely produced. Fruit 4 cm long, spiny. Mexico (Baja California, Isla Santa Margarita).

Opuntia scheerii F.A.C. Weber

Broad bushes about 1 m high with broadly elliptic shoots up to 30 cm long, bluish green. Areoles have short, brown glochids, up to 12 needle-thin yellow spines 1 cm long, and numerous yellow or white bristle-hairs clinging to the surface and pointing in all directions. Flowers large, 10 cm wide, pale yellow. Fruit globose, red. Seedlings with long white hairs. One of the most beautiful, but unfortunately rather large species. Mexico (Queretaro).

Opuntia rhodantha K. Schumann ■□ □□

Decumbent, freely branching, up to 30 cm high. Joints almost ovate, 7–12 cm long, 5–10 cm wide, quite thick, green to greyish-green. Areoles on brown tubercles with brown glochids and 2–4 protruding, white, yellow or brown spines up to 3 cm long; lower areoles without spines. Flowers large, 7–8 cm long and wide, purple to light pink, stigmas green. Fruit oblong, smooth, ±prickly. A particularly attractive species. USA (W Colorado, W Nebraska, Utah, Arizona, California) up to 2300 m altitude.

Opuntia macrocentra Engelm. □■ □□

Bush up to 90 cm high with ascending branches. Joints orbicular or ovate, up to 20 cm long, often bluish or purple. Spines absent, or at most 1–2 on the upper part of the joint, fine, upward-pointing, up to 7 cm long. Flowers yellow, often reddish when fading, 7.5 cm wide. Fruit up to 6 cm long, purple. USA (W Texas to E Arizona), N Mexico (Chihuahua).

Opuntia phaeacantha Engelm. □□ ■□

Prostrate or somewhat ascending, bushy plant with obovate joints 10–15 cm long, matt green or greyish-green, the lower part usually spineless. Areoles far apart with numerous yellow or brown glochids and 1–4 (–6) somewhat flattened spines, 1–6 cm long, brown at the base with pale to almost white tips, protruding (those at areoles along the edges of the joints pointing ±backwards). Flowers 5 cm wide, pretty yellow. Fruit pear-shaped, markedly narrowed towards the base, 3–3.5 cm long, red.

In habit, spine development and fruit shape, a very variable species. In temperate climate it is absolutely winter-hardy, even without protection. USA (Texas to Arizona), N Mexico (Chihuahua).

Opuntia erinacea Engelm. & Bigelow var. **ursina** (F.A.C. Weber) Parish □□ □■

Decumbent-spreading, with ± erect shoots. Joints elliptic or oblong-obovate, 6–12 cm long, 2.5–5 cm wide. Areoles 1 cm apart with yellow glochids and numerous spreading, somewhat flattened spines, often curving downwards, 5–10 cm long, very flexible, pale brown to white. Flowers 6 cm long and up to 7 cm wide, yellow or pink. Fruit ovoid or oblong, 2.5–3 cm long, with spines on the upper part. USA (California, Utah, Arizona, Nevada).

Subgenus NOPALEA Salm-Dyck

Shrubs or trees, with well-developed trunk and flat, oblong shoots. Leaves small, caducous. Areoles with yellow to brownish glochids and a few solitary spines. Flowers cylindric with erect perianth-segments, reddish; stamens and style well-exserted. Fruit fleshy, generally spineles, edible.

Opuntia auberi Pfeiffer ■□ □□

Up to 10 m high, with round trunk, often branching at right-angles. Joints narrow, stout, up to 30 cm long, blue- or grey-green. Areoles with brown glochids, either spineless or with 2–3 subulate spines, 2–3 cm long, white with brown tips. Flowers 9 cm long, rose-red. C and S Mexico.

Subgenus CONSOLEA Lemaire

Tree-like with somewhat flattened, unjointed trunk and ± cruciform crown of densely spiny shoots. Flowers with small perianth-segments, pericarpel ± flat, joint-like. Style abruptly swollen at base.

Opuntia moniliformis (L.) Haw. □■ □□

Tree up to 4 m high, the trunk somewhat flattened towards the top, the crown freely branching. Areoles at lower end of trunk with yellowish white wool 2 cm long and sharp, yellow or grey spines up to 12 cm long. Joints oblong often sickle-shaped, up to 30 cm long, reticulately tuberculate. Older areoles with 5–8 yellowish spines up to 8 mm long and brown glochids. Flowers 2.5 cm wide, yellow to orange, wide-opening. Fruit oblong-ovoid, 6 cm long. Hispaniola and the Island of Desecheo.

Subgenus BRASILIOPUNTIA (K. Schumann) Berger

Tree-like plants with continuous, rounded trunk and whorled crown; rounded side branches with almost leaf-like, easily shed, flat shoots. Flowers light yellow, with a wreath of hair between petals and stamens. Pericarpel laterally compressed, scales with short or longer spines. Fruit globose to club-shaped, yellow or red, with a very few large, round seeds covered with woolly felt. 3–4 species in Brazil, Paraguay, Peru, E Bolivia and Argentina.

Opuntia brasiliensis Haw. □□ ■■

Tree up to 4 m high with cylindric trunk and variously shaped crown. Branches flat or rounded, the higher side-shoots shaped completely like leaves, 15 cm long and up to 6 cm wide, bearing widely-spaced white areoles 3–6 cm long. Young plants fairly densely covered in yellow or red spines, 3 cm long. On older plants, small yellow flowers up to 5.5 cm long appear in great numbers along the edges of the leaf-like side-shoots. Fruit globose, 2.5–4 cm thick, yellow with short brown spines. S Brazil, Paraguay to Bolivia and N Argentina.

Subgenus GRUSONIA F. Reichenbach

Freely branching bushes up to 2 m high, with round, jointed and ribbed shoots. Leaves small, caducous. Areoles very spiny, only the flowering with glochids. Flowers at tips of shoots, rotate, yellow. Pericarpel woolly, with long spines and glochids. Fruit berry-like with deep umbilicus. 1 species in Mexico.

Opuntia bradtiana (J. Coulter) K. Brandegee (see colour plate on p. 71)

Of upright habit, up to 2 m high, forming large colonies with 8–10-ribbed branches 5–6 cm thick. Areoles on the ribs with 15–25 glassy spines up to 3 cm long, of which the central ones are reddish-brown when young; the longest spines point downwards. Buds reddish, flowers bright yellow, 3–4 cm wide. Mexico (Coahuila).

Opuntia bradtiana K. Brandegee (for text see page 68) ■□ □□

Subfamily **CACTOIDEAE** K. Schumann
Tribe I **Leptocereeae** F. Buxbaum
LEPTOCEREUS (A. Berger) B. & R.

Angularly branching shrubs, the stems with few wing-like ribs.Flowers small, shortly bell-shaped, with short perianth-segments and erect stamens. Pericarpel and receptacle-tube fleshy, densely spiny. Areoles on decurrent podaria. Fruit globose to ovoid, with spine clusters, deciduous when fruit is ripe. Seeds numerous, seedcoat black. 10 species, West Indies.

Leptocereus weingartianus (Hartmann) B. & R.

Decumbent or climbing, sometimes up to 10 m high, later round with woody trunk and thick tuberous roots. Terminal shoots 1—2 cm thick with 4—7 ribs. Areoles 1.5 cm apart, with 10—12 yellow to red-brown radial spines and up to 6 central spines up to 1.5 cm long. Flowers small, about 4 cm long. Hispaniola.

ARMATOCEREUS Backeb.

Either tall trees with thick trunk and ±densely branched crown, or shrubs branching from the base, with few to many erect columnar stems. Branches clearly jointed according to annual growth. Areoles occasionally elongate like cones. Flowers large, funnel-shaped, white or red. Pericarpel and receptacle-tube form a long, cylindric, thick-walled structure, the pericarpel densely covered in conspicuous podaria, the receptacle-tube more laxly so, the scales tiny, with bristly or needle-shaped spines in their axils. Fruit oblong-ovoid, with floral remains persistent, and dense spine clusters, deciduous when the pericarpel has dried. Seeds kidney-shaped, with basal hilum; seedcoat shiny black to brownish-black, verrucose and wrinkled. 11 species, Peru.

Armatocereus cartwrightianus (B. & R.) Backeb. □■ □□

Tree up to 5 m high with long, stout trunk and large crown of freely-branching, rather tangled, 7—8 ribbed stems 8—15 cm thick, young shoots densely covered with fine spines. Spines 16—20, dark brown or pale grey, at first up to 2 cm but reaching 12 cm or more with age. Flowers narrowly tubular, 7—9 cm long, white. Fruit globose or oblong, up to 9 cm long. S Ecuador to N Peru.

Armatocereus rauhii Backeb. □□ ■□

Tree 4—6 m high with short stout trunk and sparsely branching, stiffly erect, 10-ribbed side-shoots up to 20 cm thick, blue-grey or blue-green. Areoles with 7—10 ascending black spines 2—3 mm long, rarely a single central spine also present. Flowers 4 cm across, carmine red. Fruit globose, up to 5 cm thick, dark green. N Peru.

SAMAIPATICEREUS Cardenas

Tree-like, with few very compressed ribs, strongly cross-furrowed, especially when young. Flowers thick and stout-tubed. Pericarpel and receptacle-tube densely covered with imbricate scales with curly wool in their axils. Fruit globose, tuberculate, splitting lengthways. Seeds with broad hilum; seedcoat glossy, dark brown or blackish, finely pitted. 2 species in Bolivia.

Samaipaticereus corroanus Cardenas □□ □■

Tree up to 4 m high, with short trunk and numerous long, ascending branches 4 cm thick, dark green, with 4—6 narrow ribs. Areoles 1.5 cm apart, with about 5 very short, 2—3 mm long, brownish spines, later pale grey, and one downward-pointing spine up to 1 cm long. Flowers 4.5—5 cm long, white. Fruit globose, salmon-pink. Bolivia.

NEORAIMONDIA B. & R. (incl. Neocardenasia Backeb.)

Massive stems up to 10 m tall, branching from the base or higher up, with very large areoles with brown felt and long spines. Flowering areoles continuing to grow for a long period, producing cylindric flowering spurs up to 10 cm long. Flowers shortly funnel-shaped, white, pink or purplish red. Pericarpel and receptacle-tube very scaly with wool and few insignificant spines. Fruit globose to oblong, with cushions of brown felt and short spines on areoles, deciduous when the fruit is ripe. The genus divides into two subgenera: *Neoraimondia*: Shrub-like, branching from the base. Flowering spurs developing into cones up to 15 cm long. Pericarpel and receptacle-tube with short bristles. 1 species with several varieties in Peru. *Neocardenasia*: Tree-like with trunk 1–2 m tall. Flowering spurs not developing into cones. Pericarpel and receptacle-tube with long bristles. Seeds semi-elliptic with broad, basal hilum; seedcoat black, verrucose and wrinkled. 1 species in central Bolivia.

Neoraimondia arequipensis (Meyen) Backeb.

Massive stems up to 10 m tall and 40 cm thick, branching from the base like a candelabra, grey-green, 8-ribbed. Areoles very large with brown felt and variable numbers of flexible spines up to 25 cm long. Flowers greenish white to pink. Fruit 7 cm across, purple. Peru.

Neoraimondia arequipensis var. gigantea (Werderm. & Backeb.) Rauh

Distinguished by its very thick, ±parallel, tightly ascending stems, usually 4 (−5)-ribbed, and purplish red flowers. N Peru.

NEOABBOTTIA B. & R.

Tree-like, with long trunk and large crown of jointed branches. Flowers solitary from lateral areoles or out of cephalioid, terminal short-shoots, tubular with very short limb. Pericarpel and receptacle-tube covered with long, decurrent scales with felt and occasionally a small bristle in their axils. Fruit fairly large, ovoid, almost naked, with dried floral remains. Seeds small, with large, lateral, sunken hilum; seedcoat black, minutely tuberculate. 1 species in Hispaniola.

Neoabbottia paniculata (Lam.) B. & R.

Tree up to 10 m tall with long trunk and large crown, stems 4–6-ribbed. Areoles with 12–20 needle-like, up to 2 cm long, brownish or grey spines. Flowers at shoot-tips, up to 5 cm long, greenish white. Hispaniola (Dominican Republic and Haiti).

In the illustration, the pale green, jointed stems are *Neoabbotia*.

CALYMMANTHIUM Ritter

Freely branching shrubs or trees with 3–4-ribbed branches, the ribs crenate or tuberculate. Receptacle-tube forming a hollow tube like a sheath almost closed at the tip and enclosing the inner parts of the flower. Perianth-segments mainly formed from modified stamens growing together into a true perianth-tube, breaking free at anthesis by splitting the sheath. Pericarpel and receptacle-tube with small scales with woolly, spine-bearing areoles. Fruit 4–5-angled, cucumber-shaped, light green, with few or no areoles, deeply umbilicate after the floral remains fall off. Seeds few, obliquely ovoid with basal oval hilum; seedcoat matt dark grey, finely verrucose. 1 species in N Peru.

Calymmanthium substerile Ritt.

Freely branching shrub or tree up to 8 m tall, with 3–4-ribbed, light green, branches, the ribs thin, conspicuously crenate or tuberculate. Areoles with 3–8 radial spines up to 1 cm long and 1–6 central spines up to 5 cm long. Flowers night-blooming, fairly numerous near the shoot-tips, perianth-segments white to reddish, sometimes green-edged. N Peru.

72

Tribe II **Browningieae** F. Buxbaum
RAUHOCEREUS Backeb.

Mostly shrubby, columnar cerei, up to 4 m tall, usually branching from the base, erect, often forming impenetrable thickets. Ribs 5–6, divided into many-faceted tubercles. Areoles with wool and few stout spines. Flowers near the apex, large, bell-shaped, the limb spreading, white. Pericarpel densely covered with small scales and decurrent podaria of the receptacle-tube larger, their axils with curly brown woolly hair. Fruit ovoid, red and fleshy, with conspicuous floral remains. Seeds small, obliquely ovoid, with lateral hilum; seedcoat glossy black, shallowly verrucose with interstitial pits. 1 species in Peru.

Rauhocereus riosaniensis Backeb.

Stems up to 4 m tall and 8–15 cm thick, with 5–6 ribs divided into faceted tubercles 1.5 cm long. Areoles on upper edge of tubercle-tip, with a little felt with few (up to 4) subulate radial spines, and 2–4 central spines up to 5 cm, pale yellow with dark red points on young growth. Flowers 8–10 cm long and up to 5 cm across, white. N Peru.

CASTELLANOSIA Cardenas

Large shrubs up to 6 m tall, branching only from the base. Stems clearly jointed, only the lower joints being heavily spined, the upper, flowering ones having only tufts of bristly spines. Flowers medium-sized, elongate bell-shaped, perianth-segments rotate, red. Pericarpel and receptacle-tube densely covered with broadly ovate, imbricate, ciliate scales. Fruit globose, covered with broad scales woolly-felted in their axils, greenish yellow, dried floral remains persistent. Seeds very small, obliquely ovoid with lateral hilum; seedcoat reddish brown, almost smooth. 1 species in Bolivia.

Castellanosia caineana Cardenas

Grey-green, 9-ribbed stems, divided by deep constrictions into sections 30–40 cm long and 8–11 cm thick. Areoles of the lower 4–5 segments with 15–16 brown radial spines 8–40 mm long, and 3–4 central spines 4–7 cm long; areoles of the upper segments have tufts of about 25 white, grey or brown bristles 1–4 cm long. Flowers from the centre of these bristle tufts, 3–5 cm long, purplish red. Fruit 3 cm long, 2.5 cm across, greenish yellow. Bolivia.

BROWNINGIA B. & R. (incl. AZUREOCEREUS Akers & Johnson, GYMNOCEREUS Backeb.)

Columnar cerei several metres tall, ±freely branching near the ground from a short trunk, or higher up from a considerable trunk to form a candelabra-shaped crown or long, downward-curving branches. Vegetative areoles very strongly spined, but after the transition to flower production areoles thin-spined or completely spineless. Flowers conspicuous, night-blooming, stoutly tubular, with short rotate corolla. Pericarpel and receptacle-tube densely covered with imbricate, glabrous scales. Fruit juicy or dry, with dried floral remains persistent. Seeds slightly curved ovoid; seedcoat black or occasionally dark brown, verrucose or smooth. On the basis of fruit-structure, 2 subgenera can be distinguished: *Azureocereus*, with dry fruit, and *Browningia* with fleshy, juicy fruit. The subgenus *Browningia* is divided into the 2 series: *Acutisquamae* F. Buxb., with lanceolate to almost leaf-like scales on the flower (also smooth or coarsely verrucose seeds), and *Rotundisquamae* F. Buxb., with shortly obtuse scales on the flower (and seeds with smooth seedcoat). 8 species in Peru and Chile.

Browningia hertlingiana (Backeb.) F. Buxbaum

See text on p. 76.

Subgenus AZUREOCEREUS
Browningia hertlingiana (Backeb.) F. Buxbaum [= **Azureocereus hertlingianus** (Backeb.) Backeb.]
Pale blue-green columnar stems 5–8 m tall and up to 30 cm thick, which from about 1 m up produce equally thick, ascending, unbranched lateral branches with up to 18 or more ribs. Ribs tuberculately thickened at the areoles. Areoles on young, non-flowering shoots with 4 strong and up to 6 shorter radial spines, and 1–3 central spines up to 8 cm long; areoles on flowering portions with up to 30 flexible spines. Flowers 5 cm across, night-blooming, white. Fruit dry, 2.5 cm across. S Peru. (Illustration on p. 75.)

Subgenus BROWNINGIA
Browningia candelaris (Meyen) B. & R.
Tree up to 6 m tall with a solid, strongly spined, unbranched trunk up to 4 m tall and 50 cm thick, and a crown of thick, spineless side-branches, often curving downwards. Areoles of trunk with 20–50 straight, brownish spines 6–15 cm long; areoles of side-branches with dark woolly felt and few very thin, brownish black spines up to 13 mm long; areoles of flowering branches spineless or with bristly spines only. Flowers up to 12 cm long, white. Fruit 7 cm long and 4 cm across, yellow, fleshy, aromatic and edible. S Peru and N Chile.

Browningia microsperma (Werderm. & Backeb.) W.T. Marshall [= **Gymnocereus microspermus** (Werderm. & Backeb.) Backeb.]
Tree 4–6 m tall with a 30 cm thick trunk and numerous upright, branching side-axes. Ribs to 20 or more, not jointed. Areoles white-felted with up to 30 or more yellow-brown spines up to 1.2 cm long; many areoles also have a single stout spine and many longer ones pointing downwards. Flowers up to 6 cm long, white. Fruit 5-6 cm across, green. N Peru.

Browningia amstutziae (Rauh & Backeb.) Hutchinson ex Krainz [= **Gymnocereus amstutziae** Rauh & Backeb.]
Tree 5–7 m tall with thick trunk and sparsely branched crown of ascending, 11-ribbed, grey-green shoots, at first only 5–6 cm thick. Areoles with white or brown felt and up to 15 bristly, very flexible spines, at first brownish, later dark grey or blackish. Central spines 6, individually up to 4.5 cm long and pointing diagonally downwards. Flowers near the apex, broadly funnel-shaped, 4.5 cm long and wide, white. Pericarpel scales not ciliate, dark brown to black at the tip and lighter at the base. NC Peru.

Tribe III **Pachycereeae**
PTEROCEREUS MacDougall & Miranda
Unbranched or sparsely branched upright trunks with long, erect-ascending, 3–4 flat-ribbed branches. Flowers night-blooming, cylindric-funnelshaped, greenish white. Pericarpel and receptacle-tube covered with rather fleshy, imbricate scales recurved at the tip, with felt and a few very short spines in their axils. Fruit a globose, light-carmine berry with persistent dried floral remains. Seeds ovoid; seedcoat glossy black or brown. 2 species in Mexico.

Pterocereus foetidus MacDougall & Miranda
Unbranched or sparsely branching tree up to 8 m tall, with trunk up to 1.5 m tall and 14 cm thick. Branches perpendicular, with 3–4 flat, slightly crenate ribs 4–7 cm high and 3–5 mm thick. Areoles 2–2.5 cm apart, almost round, with white or grey felt and 10(–20) subulate, grey or reddish black spines up to 5 cm long, pointing in all directions. Flowers greenish white, evil-smelling, 8.5–9.5 cm long. Mexico (Chiapas).

76

ESCONTRIA Rose

Freely branching trees with short trunk and slender branches, or unbranched to sparsely branching stems with few ribs. Flowers tubular-companulate. Pericarpel and receptacle-tube densely covered with imbricate, parchment-like scales, glabrous or with few bristles. Fruit fleshy or ±dry with parchment-like scales and adherent floral remains. Seeds large, curved, with protruding hilum; seedcoat black or dark brown, rough and verrucose or glossy. 2 species in S Mexico and Guatemala.

Escontria chiotilla (F.A.C. Weber) Rose ■□ □□

Tree up to 7 m tall with short stout trunk up to 40 cm thick and densely branched, almost flat-topped crown. Areoles almost touching, with grey woolly felt and 10−15 straight, radial spines 5−10 mm long, and 1−4 strong central spines, the lowermost of which can be up to 7 cm long. Flowers 3−4 cm long and across, sulphur yellow. Fruit a globose, russet berry. Mexico. The illustration shows *Myrtillocactus geometrizans*, which resembles *E. chiotilla*. See also p. 84.

LEMAIREOCEREUS B. & R., [incl. STENOCEREUS (A. Berger) Riccobono, HERTRICHOCEREUS Backeb., ISOLATOCEREUS Backeb., HELIABRAVOA Backeb., POLASKIA Backeb., MARSHALLOCEREUS Backeb., RITTERO-CEREUS Backeb.]

Massive trees with short trunk and upright, columnar branches, or branching from the base, or single-stemmed, rarely shrubby. Flowers diurnal or nocturnal, tubular-funnel-shaped with short perianth. Pericarpel with small scales, receptacle-tube rather short. Areoles of the scales woolly with few spines. Fruit globose or ovoid, ±fleshy, with woolly and often spiny areoles that drop off when the fruit is ripe; floral remains deciduous. Seeds large, mostly flattened, ovoid or cap-shaped; seedcoat glossy black, smooth or verrucose. About 25 species in Central America, the West Indies to Venezuela and Colombia, the centre of distribution being SC Mexico.

Lemaireocereus beneckei (Ehrenb.) □■
[= Stenocereus beneckei (Ehrenb.) F. Buxbaum] □□

Unbranched or sparsely branching columnar stem up to 1.5 m tall and 6−9 cm thick, thickly covered with mealy white waxy powder that nevertheless easily falls off. Ribs 5−9, blunt, prominently divided into tubercles on new growth. Areoles at tubercle-tips,with 5−7 radial spines 10−15 mm long, and 1 sharp central spine 1−2 cm long, pointing obliquely downwards; spines bright red when young, later brown or grey. Flowers solitary from upper and lateral areoles, night-blooming, up to 7.5 cm long and 6 cm across, ivory white or yellowish. Fruit up to 2 cm across, strongly tuberculate, with spine-clusters in the areoles, fleshy at first, drying later. C Mexico.

Lemaireocereus chende (Roland-Goss) □□
[= Heliabravoa chende (Roland-Goss) Backeb.] ■□

Tree about 4 m tall, with short trunk 25−30 cm thick and freely branched crown of straight or slightly curving 7−8-ribbed branches. Ribs 2−3 cm high with rather sharp, somewhat wavy edges. Areoles 2 cm apart, circular, with reddish yellow wool and 5−6 subulate, brown, later grey radial spines 5−15(−30) mm long; rudimentary central spine occasionally present. Flowers solitary, from areoles near the apex, 4.5−5 cm long and 5−6 cm across, sweet-smelling, pale rose. Fruit globose, purplish-red. S Mexico (Puebla, Oaxaca).

Lemaireocereus chichipe (Roland-Goss) B. & R. □□
[= Polaskia chichipe (Roland-Goss) Backeb.] □■

Tree up to 5 m tall with short trunk up to 1 m thick, and freely branched, wide-spreading

crown of curving, columnar, 7–12-ribbed branches. Ribs divided by sharp furrows and thickened at the areoles. Young plants and young shoots have pure white markings like pointed arches on a dark green ground. Areoles close together, with 6–9 short radial spines 1 cm long, and 1 central spine. Flowers solitary, small, only 1 cm long, white, from areoles near the apex. Mexico (Puebla and Oaxaca).

Lemaireocereus stellatus (Pfeiffer) B. & R.
[= **Stenocereus stellatus** (Pfeiffer) Riccobono]
Erect, columnar, up to 4 m tall, branching from the base; branches ascending, 6–7 cm thick, light green when young, later dark green, with 8–10 (–15) sharply furrowed, blunt, somewhat crenate ribs. Areoles 1–1.5 cm apart, somewhat indented, white-felted, with 8–10 straight, spreading, white or brown radial spines up to 12 mm long, and 4–5 erect, brown central spines up to 2 cm long and bulbous at the base. Flowers near the apex, bell-shaped, 4–6 cm long, light rosy-red. Fruit globular, 3–4 cm across, red. C Mexico.

PACHYCEREUS (A. Berger) B. & R. (incl. MARGINATOCEREUS Backeb., PSEUDOMITROCEREUS Bravo & F. Buxbaum)
Gigantic columnar cacti, with mostly candelabra-like branching. Flowers tubular-campanulate with thick fleshy pericarpel and receptacle-tube, both clothed with numerous scales increasing in size towards the throat, and with wool, hairs and bristles in their axils. Fruit densely covered with large, felted areoles with long, stiff bristles, bursting open irregularly and drying out. Seeds very large, helmet-shaped; seedcoat smooth and glossy black. 5 species in Mexico.

Pachycereus pringlei (S. Watson) B. & R.
Massive tree up to 11 m tall, with short thick trunk and erect, usually 13-ribbed branches, occasionally even branching from near the base. Areoles large, oval, almost confluent, initially with thick woolly felt. Number and form of spines very variable: radial spines up to 12, subulate, up to 2 cm long; central spines up to 8, stouter and up to 3.5 cm long. Spines later deciduous, the flowering areoles often unarmed. On old plants the areoles are connected by a thin, felted groove. Flowers numerous, lateral, mostly near the apex but up to 2 m below, 6–8 cm long, white, flushed with green or red. Fruit globose, densely covered with bright yellow cushions of felt and yellowish bristles. Mexico (Sonora and Baja California).

Pachycereus marginatus (DC.) A. Berger
[= **Marginatocereus marginatus** (DC.) Backeb.]
Stems unbranched or branching from the base, 3–7 m tall, perpendicular, 8–15 cm thick, glossy dark green with 5–6 narrow-edged, later broadly rounded ribs and sharp furrows. Areoles close-set, usually confluent, with brown or grey felt and usually 7 very short, barely 2 mm long, subulate, radial, spines, later deciduous, and 1–2 similar, straight central spines, red when young. Flowers 1–2 at an areole, up to 5 cm long, stout, short cylindric, off-white, ±red or brown outside. Fruit globose, 4 cm thick, strongly tuberculate, with deciduous areoles. Mexico (Hidalgo, Querétaro, Guanajuato).

Pachycereus ruficeps (F.A.C. Weber) B. & R.
[= **Mitrocereus ruficeps** (F.A.C. Weber) Backeb.]
Freely branched tree up to 15 m tall, with trunk up to 60 cm thick and crown up to 5 m in diameter of fairly widely separated, vertical, grey-green branches up to 30 cm thick with 17–26 ribs. Areoles fairly close-set, with 8–12 thin, radial spines, and up to 3 stouter, rigid central spines up to 15 cm long; becoming thinner, longer towards the stem-apex and intermingled with dense yellow felt. Flowers solitary from woolly and fine-spined

areoles near the apex, night-blooming, 5 cm long, pinkish white, enveloped in dense fur. Mexico (Puebla). Species now usually considered to be same as *Neobuxbaumia macrocephala*.

CARNEGIEA B. & R.

Stout, many-ribbed stems up to 15 m tall, often producing up to 12 erect, candelabra-like side-branches halfway up. Flowers at the branch ends, fairly large, white, campanulate or funnel-shaped, opening from midnight to late afternoon. Receptacle-tube and pericarpel covered with decurrent podaria of the scales, with small tufts of felt in the scale axils. Fruit ovoid-oblong with small ovate scales and a few short spines or spineless, hard-fleshed, splitting lengthways from the top. Floral remains persisting when fruit is ripe. Seeds numerous, truncately curved ovoid, swollen above the hilum; seedcoat glossy black, smooth, finely sculptured. 1 species in the USA (Arizona and SE California), Mexico (Sonora).

Carnegiea gigantea (Engelm.) B. & R.

Stout, erect, many-ribbed stems, tapering gradually towards the top, up to 15 m tall, with 1–12 erect, candelabra-like, dark green branches, 30–65 cm thick, arising from the middle; 12–30 blunt ribs 1–3 cm high; areoles 2.5 cm apart, with 12–16 obliquely erect radial spines 1–2 cm long, and 6 stout central spines up to 7 cm long; the spines on flowering shoots paler and thinner. Flowers solitary at the areoles, 10–12 cm long and across, white. Fruit 5–6 cm long and 3.5–4.5 cm across, green, reddish or russet above. USA (Arizona, SE California), Mexico (Sonora).

LOPHOCEREUS (A. Berger) B. & R.

Large, dense bushes branching from the base into unbranched cerei, or occasionally tree-like with short trunk and sparsely branching crown. Lower areoles distinctly separate with short spines, upper, flowering, closely set, with numerous, long, bristly spines. Flowers numerous, small, sometimes several at an areole, mostly arising among the crests of bristles towards the stem-apex, broadly funnel-shaped, night-blooming, white to reddish, greenish or brownish outside. Receptacle-tube and pericarpel with several small, glabrous scales on prominent podaria. Fruit oval to oblong, almost spineless, dry floral remains persistent when ripe, splitting irregularly. Seeds curved ovoid; seedcoat glossy black, smooth, finely tessellate. 4 sometimes very variable species in NW Mexico and Baja California.

Lophocereus schottii (Engelm.) B. & R.

Large, dense bushes branched from the base, erect or ascending stems up to 7 m tall and up to 8 cm thick, light green with faint arching pruinose markings; 5–7(–9) ribs with deep furrows, flanks and crenate ridge. Areoles 5–10 mm apart, slightly felted, with 4–7 conical, bulbous-based, radial spines, 5–8 mm long, black, later becoming grey, and 1 similar central spine. Areoles on flowering shoots are larger, with 10–25 sturdy, flexible, grey-brown bristles up to 6 cm long. Flowers several at an areole, 3–4 cm long, white, night-blooming. Fruit globose, red. Mexico (Baja California, Sonora, Sinaloa). USA (S Arizona).

MYRTILLOCACTUS Console

Large trees with short trunk and much-branched crown of thick, usually 5–6-ribbed branches that have an attractive blue bloom when young. Flowers from lateral areoles that remain active for several years, relatively small, rotate, with very short tube, stamens exserted. Pericarpel almost globose with a few very small scales with tiny tufts of wool. Fruit almost globose, the dried floral remains persistent, and with violet-blue bloom (reminiscent of bilberries). Seeds small, almost spherical; seedcoat matt black and verrucose. 4 species from C Mexico to Baja California, and S Mexico to Guatemala.

82

Myrtillocactus geometrizans (Martius) Console ■□ □□

Tree up to 6 m tall with 50 cm thick trunk and flat, many-branched crown of 5–6-sided branches 6–10 cm thick. Areoles with some felt, 5 radial spines up to 2 cm long, and 1 flattened, downward-curving, sword-like central spine up to 6 cm long. All spines on new growth black with a white bloom, becoming greyish with age. Flowers 5–9 at lateral areoles, 2 cm long, 2.5 cm across, white. Fruit small, globose, dark wine-red, very sweet, edible. Mexico. Also illustrated on p. 79 (top left).

BERGEROCACTUS B. & R.

Freely branching bushes with sturdy, many-ribbed, very spiny branches. Flowers small, yellow with spreading limb. Pericarpel and short receptacle-tube with scales, woolly tufts and spines. Fruit globular, very spiny, dried floral remains persistent. Seeds obovate, sharply keeled; seedcoat glossy black, finely verrucose. 1 species, California.

Bergerocactus emoryi (Engelm.) B. & R. □■ □□

Freely branching bushes with decumbent or ascending shoots up to 60 cm long and 3–6 cm thick, with 20–25 low ribs. Areoles with 10–30 yellow radial spines and 1–4 sturdier central spines 3–4 cm long. Flowers lateral near the apex, 2 cm long and across, yellow. USA (SW California), Mexico (NW Baja California).

MACHAEROCEREUS B. & R.

Shrubby, the stout branches several metres long, erect or decumbent, and producing roots from the underside. Areoles hairy and very spiny. Flowers large, slender, funnel-shaped, opening widely, white or yellowish, open during the day. Receptacle-tube and pericarpel crowded with prominent podaria bearing very small scales and areoles with wool and spines that continue to grow as the fruit develops. Fruit globose, with dried floral remains, scarlet to dark red, very spiny all over, the spine bundles deciduous when the fruit is fully ripe. Seeds obliquely kidney-shaped with lateral hilum; seedcoat matt black, shallowly verrucose. 2 species in Baja California and neighbouring islands.

Machaerocereus eruca (Brandegee) B. & R. □□ ■□

Stem decumbent, sparsely branched, rooting from the underside, 1–3 m long and 4–8 cm thick, curving upwards at the tip. Ribs 12. Areoles large, 2 cm apart, with about 20 blue-green radial spines, and 1 very stout, dagger-like central spine up to 3 cm long and 3 mm thick, pointing obliquely backwards. Flowers 10–14 cm long and 4–6 cm across, white. Fruit 4 cm long, scarlet. Mexico.

RATHBUNIA B. & R.

Shrubby cacti 2–4 m tall, unbranched or branching bushily from the base with slender, erect shoots later arching and rooting when their tips touch the ground, thus forming thickets about 8 m across. Flowers scarlet, day-blooming, fairly large, tubular, somewhat curved, with oblique limb and very short, reflexed perianth-segments, stamens protruding like a paintbrush. Pericarpel closely covered with the podaria of the small scales; receptacle-tube with long decurrent podaria. Fruit globose or inverted pear-shaped, with floral remains, thin-skinned, red, glabrous or with tufts of fine spines. Seeds obliquely ovoid or almost globose; seedcoat glossy black, almost smooth, somewhat tessellate, with minute interstitial pits. 4 species on the W coast of Mexico.

Rathbunia alamosensis (J. Coulter) B. & R. □□ □■

Large shrubs, 2–almost 4 m tall, with arching green stems up to 8 cm thick. Areoles with 11–18 whitish, radial spines, and 1–4, much stouter, porrect, central spines up to 3.5 cm long. Flowers 4–10 cm long, scarlet. Mexico. Illustration shows *Rathbunia* in the foreground.

84

NEOBUXBAUMIA Backeb. (incl. ROOKSBYA Backeb.)

Large unbranched or branching stems with usually numerous low ribs and closely set areoles. Flowers small, cylindric-campanulate, night-blooming, often brownish red. Pericarpel and receptacle-tube with long, decurrent, fleshy scales with minute tufts of hair and a nectar-gland at the tip. Fruit rather angular ovoid with floral remains persistent; when ripe, a lid breaks off and the fruit opens like a star. Seeds obliquely kidney-shaped, with rather large, lateral hilum; seedcoat glossy dark or light brown, finely sculptured. 5 species in E and S Mexico.

Neobuxbaumia polylopha (DC.) Backeb.

Unbranched stems up to 13 m tall and up to 50 cm thick, light green when young, later leek-green, becoming grey with age, with 10–20(–30) narrow ribs, slightly sinuate, and separated by sharp furrows. Areoles 6–8 mm apart, very small, with yellowish-white, caducous woolly felt, 7–8 flexible, honey-coloured or brownish, later grey, radial spines 1–2 cm long, and 1, usually shorter central spine or none. In the flowering zone, from 2 m above ground to the apex, there are closely packed yellow spines 7 cm long, but no wool. Flowers near the apex, usually several together, 4–6 cm long and 3–3.5 cm across, dark red. Fruit violet-brown. E Mexico (Hidalgo).

Neobuxbaumia euphorbioides (Haw.) F. Buxbaum
[= Rooksbya euphorbioides (Haw.) Backeb.]

Nearly always unbranched, matt green stems 3–5 m tall and 10–11 cm thick, with 8–10 very prominent, sinuate ribs. Areoles 8–10 mm apart, with short white woolly felt, and usually 7–9 straight, pale grey, black-tipped radial spines 5–7 mm long, and 1 stouter, dark brown central spine 3 cm long; all spines at the apex are erect, elsewhere they stand out horizontally (thus resembling certain succulent euphorbias). Flowers towards the apex, numerous, 8 cm long, 7 cm across, dull pink. Mexico (Tamaulipas).

BACKEBERGIA H. Bravo

Arborescent, branching in candelabra fashion, the apex of non-flowering branches with a tuft of incurved spines and long white hairs. Flowers from the lateral areoles of a cephalium with spirally arranged areoles that carry abundant amber-coloured wool and long bristles. Flowers small, bell-shaped, reddish, night-blooming. Pericarpel and receptacle-tube with scales and abundant tufts of woolly hair and thin bristles. Fruit oblong, fleshy but soon becoming dry, with adherent floral remains later deciduous, scales with long tufts of woolly hair and numerous sharp bristles; long-persistent among the bristles of the cephalium: Seeds large, obliquely ovoid, somewhat flattened laterally and keeled; seedcoat glossy black, fragile. 1 species in W Mexico.

Backebergia militaris (Audot) H. Bravo
[= Backebergia chrysomalla (Lem.) H. Bravo]

Initially unbranched, later freely branching tree 12–18 m tall, with crowded, upright branches forming an almost solid mass up to 5 m in diameter. Ribs 11–14, areoles very close together, with short woolly felt and long white woolly hair; 10–12 flexible, bristly radial spines up to 1.5 cm long and 3–4 cm long towards the base, and 3–4 stouter, erect, yellow or brownish central spines, 1 of which can become over 10 cm long. Cephalia forming huge caps of yellowish brown wool almost 20 cm in diameter and 30 cm long. Flowers night-blooming, 5 cm long, 3.5–4 cm across. W Mexico.

CEPHALOCEREUS Pfeiffer (incl. PILOSOCEREUS Byles & in part Rowley, NEODAWSONIA Backeb., HASELTONIA Backeb.)

Large to gigantic, unbranched or sparsely branching many-ribbed columnar cacti, which when they reach flowering age produce a one-sided or overall cephalium, either

continuous, or in the case of *C. apicicephalium*, developed annually and grown through. Flowers campanulate or funnel-shaped. Within this genus the number of scales on the pericarpel and receptacle-tube is progressively reduced from species to species. Fruit sometimes with small tufts of hair, otherwise, according to how scaly the pericarpel is, ± textured or smooth and glabrous, fleshy, with persistent floral remains. Seeds numerous, obliquely pear-shaped, laterally compressed; seedcoat smooth, glossy black. About 12(?) species from Mexico to N South America.

Cephalocereus senilis (Haw.) Pfeiffer
Upright stems up to 15 m tall and 30 cm thick, branching only from the very base, not higher up except following damage, light green, later grey. Ribs 20–30, low, slightly crenate. Areoles crowded, initially felted, soon becoming glabrous. and with 20–30 or more white or grey, curly or twisting, bristly hairs 6–12 cm long, later growing up to 30 cm and clustering particularly thickly on the apex, also 3–5 stout, subulate, yellowish or grey spines 2–4 cm long. Only at a height of 6–8 cm does the cephalium form from brownish wool tufts and bristles, cloaking the top of the trunk first on one side, then entirely, like a shawl. Flowers 5 cm long, pink, night-blooming. Mexico.

Cephalocereus palmeri var. sartorianus (Rose) Krainz
[= Pilosocereus sartorianus (Rose) Byles & Rowley]
Tree 3–5 m or more tall, with erect, almost vertical branches 7–10 cm thick, blue-pruinose when young. Ribs 6–8 with narrow cross-furrows. Areoles white-felted, those near the apex with copious silky white hair, often curling sideways, and 7–8 straight radial spines up to 1 cm long, and 1 rather longer central spine; all spines straw-coloured, later grey. Flowering areoles with thick flocks of silky wool 4–6 cm long. Flowers 6–8 cm long, slender funnel-shaped or turbinate, 4 cm across, reddish-green outside; perianth-segments yellowish pink, darker outside. Fruit up to 4 cm across, dirty dark green with dark red flesh. E Mexico, between Veracruz and Jalapa.

Cephalocereus hoppenstedtii (F.A.C. Weber) K. Schumann
[= Haseltonia columna-trajani (Karw.) Backeb.]
Unbranched stems 6–10 m tall with 16 or more ribs almost divided into tubercles by cross-furrows. Areoles, soon glabrous, with 14–18 white radial spines up to 1 cm long, and 5–8 curved and ultimately downward-pointing central spines up to 8 cm long, yellowish, later white. Cephalium facing North, extending from 2–3 m up as far as the apex, narrow, with yellow tufts of woolly hair 4–6 cm long. Flowers 7 cm long and across, campanulate-funnelshaped, pale sulphur yellow. S Mexico.
The illustration shows a 'forest' of *C. hoppenstedtii* near Tehuacan. The plant nearest the camera, however, is *Neobuxbaumia tetezo*, which has more branches and fewer ribs than *C. hoppenstedtii* and does not develop a true cephalium. Immediately behind the plant of *N. tetezo* and largely hidden by it, apart from its apex (showing the cephalium down one side) and some of the lower part, is a trunk of *C. hoppenstedtii.*

Cephalocereus apicicephalium Dawson
[= Neodawsonia apicicephalium (Dawson) Backeb.]
Initially unbranched, then branching near the base into at most 10 shoots 1–3 m tall, 6.5–10 cm thick, dark blue-green, with 22–27 ribs and a white woolly cap covering as much as 4 cm down from the apex. Areoles below this cap completely glabrous, 6–10 mm apart, with 9–12 bristly, irregularly curved radial spines, initially straw-coloured but dark brown with age, up to 1 cm long at the upper end of the areole and 2–3 cm long below, also 2–6 almost straight, stiff, downward-pointing or protruding central spines 2–4 cm long. Flowers 5–6 cm long and up to 3 cm across, forming a ring in the woolly apical cap, yellowish pink. Mexico (Oaxaca).

Tribe IV **Hylocereae** F. Buxbaum

NYCTOCEREUS (A. Berger) B. & R.

Erect or prostrate-ascending stems, slender, branching, many-ribbed, with thick, tuberous roots. Flowers night-blooming, large, slender funnel-shaped. Pericarpel and receptacle-tube with spreading scales, very spiny and bristly. Fruit globose or ovoid, scaly, with spines or bristles. Seeds large; seedcoat glossy black. C America.

■□
□□

Nyctocereus serpentinus (Lagasca & Rodrigues) B. & R.

Initially a single stem, later branching from the base, up to 3 m long and 2–5 cm thick, with 10–12 ribs and areoles with 10–12 spines 1–3 cm long. Flowers at upper areoles, 25 cm long and up to 15 cm across, inner perianth-segments white, outside carmine-pink and reddish green. Mexico.

BRACHYCEREUS B. & R.

Low shrubby cacti, slender, cylindric, freely-branching from the base. Flowers narrowly funnel-shaped. pericarpel and receptacle-tube with small scales and large spiny areoles. Fruit ovoid, fleshy, at first very spiny. Seeds small, obovoid; seedcoat glossy brown, smooth. 1 species on the Galapagos Islands.

□■
□□

Brachycereus nesioticus (K. Schum.) Backeb.

The slender, 30–60 cm long stems form thick clumps of up to 300 stems. The 13–16 low ribs are almost divided into separate tubercles. Areoles carry more than 40 spines like horsehair, up to 3 cm long. Flowers 7 cm long, white. Galapagos Islands.

PENIOCEREUS (A. Berger) B. & R. (incl. NEOEVANSIA W.T. Marshall, CULLMANNIA C. Distefano)

Thin stemmed, shrubby cerei with tuberous root-system and semi-erect or prostrate branches usually 1–2 m tall, occasionally 3–4 m. A few species have both juvenile and adult forms. Flowers night-blooming or lasting till next morning, sometimes large and white, often streaked with greenish or reddish-brown, or red. The oblong pericarpel is densely covered, and the slender, tubular receptacle-tube less so, with decurrent podaria standing out like tubercles, the small scales on which are covered with hairs and bristles. Fruit juicy, red, oblong-ovoid, ± strongly beaked, with floral remains persistent and spiny areoles sooner or later deciduous, splitting lengthways. Seeds comparatively large, obliquely kidney-shaped with basal hilum; seedcoat glossy black, smooth or with fine cell structure. 2 subgenera: *Peniocereus:* Receptacle-tube relatively long and slender, cylindric, abruptly widening into a funnel towards the throat. Scales and areoles widely spaced on the receptacle-tube. 12 species in N Mexico and SW USA. *Cullmannia* (Dist.) F. Buxbaum: Lower part of receptacle-tube as far as the beginning of the lower stamens cylindric, above that only slightly campanulate-cylindric, not widening into a funnel, densely covered with short-spined areoles. 2 species in Mexico.

□□
■□

Peniocereus greggii (Engelm.) B. & R. (Subgenus **Peniocereus**)

From a gigantic tuberous root up to 60 cm in diameter and 60 kg in weight grow 3–6-angled stems up to 3 m long and 2–2.5 cm thick. Areoles with 6–9 conical radial spines and one 2 mm long central spine. Flowers 15–20 cm long, white. Fruit ovoid, beaked, up to 6.5 m long and 2–3.5 cm across, scarlet. N Mexico to USA (Arizona).

□□
□■

Peniocereus viperinus (F.A.C. Weber) Kreuzinger (Subgenus **Cullmannia**)

From a robust tuberous root grow fine silky-haired stems up to 8 mm thick and up to 3 m long, branching into a lax bushy form. Ribs 8–10, low. Areoles with about 8 small appressed spines. Flowers night-blooming, up to 8 cm long, red. Mexico.

ACANTHOCEREUS (A. Berger) B. & R.

Shrubby or tree-like, later arching or climbing, with few, usually thin ribs and stout spines. Flowers large, night-blooming, white, slender, long-tubed. Pericarpel and receptacle-tube with short scales and large, decurrent podaria. Areoles on the scales ± spiny. Fruit globose or ovoid, fleshy, dark red, scaly with spines in the axils, floral remains persistent. Seeds large; seedcoat glossy black. 8 species from Florida and Mexico to South America.

Acanthocereus colombianus B. & R.

Large, erect bushes up to 3 m high, with 3(−4)-winged branches up to 9 cm thick, with sharp, deeply sinuate margins. Areoles with 5−8 very short, sturdy radial spines, and 1−2 very strong central spines up to 5.5 cm long. Flowers large, white, brownish outside, up to 25 cm long. Fruit large, red, tough, spiny. Colombia.

DENDROCEREUS B. & R.

Tree-like with thick trunk and wide-spreading crown of numerous upright or arching freely-branching limbs with 3−5 winglike, crenate ribs. Flowers large, white, funnel-shaped, night-blooming. Pericarpel and receptacle-tube with few spiny scales deciduous after flowering. Fruit pear-shaped, green, naked, with hard, thick skin, not opening, initially with floral remains which later fall cleanly off. Seeds large, obliquely kidney-shaped with lateral hilum; seedcoat blackish russet prominently verrucose on the edge. The seeds are covered with a thin aril. 1 species in Cuba.

Dendrocereus nudiflorus (Engelm.) B. & R.

Tree up to 10 m tall with a massive trunk up to 60 cm in diameter, and a very large crown of erect or arching, much-branched limbs. Stems dark green, 3−5-winged, up to 12 cm thick. Areoles with 2−15 needle-like spines up to 4 cm long, later often absent. Flowers near branch-tips, 10−14 cm long, white. Cuba.

HARRISIA Britton

Erect trees up to 7 m tall with slender trunk and upright or arching branches; only 1 species (*H. earlii*) is decumbent. Trunk and branches cylindric. Flowers large, elongate funnel-shaped, night-blooming. Receptacle-tube very slender and thin-walled. Pericarpel and receptacle-tube densely covered with triangular or pointed scales and prominent podaria, with woolly hair in the scale-axils. Fruit globose or ovoid, when ripe almost smooth, thin-walled, without floral remains. Seeds sack-shaped cylindric, not keeled, with basal hilum, the hilum rim extended into a cylindric cavity; seedcoat glossy black, coarsely verrucose. About 12 species from the West Indies to Florida.

Harrisia gracilis (Miller) Britton

Much-branched tree up to 7 m tall, often with well-developed trunk and radiating crown of fairly slender, 9−11-ribbed branches. Areoles with 10−16 whitish, black-tipped spines 2−2.5 cm long. Flowers 20 cm long, night-blooming, white. Jamaica.

ERIOCEREUS Riccobono

Shrubby, ±freely-branching with slender, bending or decumbent, often climbing shoots with a few solid ribs and only sparse spines. Flowers large, white, funnel-shaped, night-blooming. Receptacle-tube thick with sometimes leaf-like scales and wool in the axils. Pericarpel densely covered with podaria bearing small scales with wool and sometimes solitary spines in their axils. Fruit strongly tuberculate, thick-walled, with floral remains that may drop off later, splitting lengthways when ripe. Seeds helmet-shaped with distinct, large-celled keel and basal hilum; seedcoat satiny black, finely verrucose. 7 species in C South America.

92

Eriocereus tortuosus (Forbes) Riccobono ■□ □□

Shrubby, with branches up to 1 m long and 2–4 cm thick, dark green, mostly 7-ribbed, erect only initially, later arching or prostrate and often tortuous. Areoles 2 cm apart, with 6–10 spreading spines up to 2 cm long, and 1–3 stouter central spines 3–4 cm long, red at first but later almost black. Flowers 16 cm long, white. Argentina.

Eriocereus pomanensis (F.A.C. Weber) A. Berger □■ □□

Fairly erect, blue-green or grey-green, almost round stems, 2–4 cm thick when young, with 4–6 blunt ribs, not tuberculate. Areoles 1.5–2 cm apart, with 6–8 subulate, radial spines, 1 cm long, red or white at first, later grey with black tips, and 1 similar central spine 1–2 cm long. Flowers 15 cm long, white. Fruit globose, slightly tuberculate and scaly, without spines, red. NW Argentina.

APOROCACTUS Lemaire

Slender pendent or ascending ±rounded stems, freely branching from the base, with low ribs and close-set, fine-spined areoles, often with aerial roots. Flowers large, with S-shaped curved tube. Pericarpel and receptacle-tube with small scales and bristly hair; scales on the upper part of the receptacle-tube are glabrous. Stamens in 2 series, in a tight bundle like a paintbrush, protruding far out of the flower with the style. Fruit berry-like, small, globose, bristly, red. Seeds few, obovoid; seedcoat red-brown. 5 species in Mexico.

Aporocactus flagelliformis (L.) Lem. □□ ■□

Slender, rounded stems up to 1 m long and finger-thick, with 8–13 ribs and of pendent habit. Areoles 3–7 mm apart, with 15–20 fine spines, reddish at first, then brown. Flowers up to 10 cm long, purplish pink. Mexico.

Aporocactus martianus (Zucc.) B. & R. □□ □■

Fairly stout, somewhat branched stems up to 1 m or more long and up to 2 cm thick, with 8 low, blunt ribs, pendent or clambering with roots. Areoles 6–10 mm apart, with 6–10 needle-like radial spines 5–7 mm long, honey-coloured with a brownish base, and 3–4 stronger, darker central spines. Flowers 10–12 cm long, almost straight, scarlet, narrowly violet-edged. Mexico (Oaxaca).

HELIOCEREUS (A. Berger) B. & R.

Ungainly shrubs with few-angled, soft-fleshed, sparsely-spined stems. Flowers large, wide-opening, lasting several days, usually red. Pericarpel and receptacle-tube with small scales with spines or bristles. Fruit globose or ovoid, fleshy, tuberculate, with dried scales and spines. Seeds ovoid to kidney-shaped; seedcoat black with fine cell-structure. 3 species (with several varieties) in Mexico.

Heliocereus speciosus (Cav.) B. & R.

Freely-branching shrub with erect, leaning or pendent stems up to 1 m long or more, 4-angled, often reddish tinged, with strongly serrate ribs. Areoles on the rib-notches with 5–8, later 25 or more nearly erect, very pointed, yellow or brownish spines 1–1.5 cm long. Flowers opening to a wide funnel-shape, magnificent carmine-red tinged with blue lustre blending into green base. Because of its unique flower-colour it is much used for hybridization. Mexico.

Heliocereus speciosus var. amecamensis (Heese) Weingart.

Distinguished from the species by light green 3–5-angled stems and large, pure white flowers with greenish shine at the base. A magnificent mutant collected once only near Amecameca on the volcanic mountain Ixtaccihuatl.

NOPALXOCHIA B. & R. (incl. LOBEIRA Alexander)

Erect or pendent stems, narrowed like a stalk at base, flattened and leaf-like above with crenate, sinuate or bluntly serrate edge. Flowers very large, campanulate-funnel-shaped, day blooming. Pericarpel and short receptacle-tube slender, covered with spreading scales, without bristles. Fruit ovoid, fleshy, somewhat angular and scaly. Seeds large and black. 3 species in Mexico.

Nopalxochia ackermannii (Haw.) F.M. Knuth

Stems about 30 cm long, wavy-edged with a stalk-like base, dark green, in outline sometimes rather like an oak-leaf. Flowers large, about 14 cm long, scarlet with greenish throat. Seldom true to type. Mexico.

Nopalxochia phyllanthoides (DC.) B. & R.

Freely-branching shrub growing barely 1 metre tall, with lanceolate, pointed, bluntly serrate, light green, often red-tinged, flat stems, narrowed like a stalk at the base, with distinctly prominent mid-rib and lateral veins. Flowers 10 cm long, campanulate-funnel-shaped, pink. Mexico.

EPIPHYLLUM Haworth (incl. MARNIERA Backeb.)

Epiphytic shrubs, freely-branching, erect or pendent or climbing with aerial roots. Crenate or strongly-serrate, flat-offsets arise from a terete or angular base, or less usually short, lateral flat-offsets arise from long, terete long-offsets climbing with roots. Areoles in the notches with some wool or, less usually, bristles. Flowers night-blooming, often staying open the following day, funnel- to salver-shaped with very long, narrow tube. Pericarpel scaly, with long decurrent podaria; scales glabrous or with a few fine bristles. Receptacle-tube with only a few scales of the same sort. Fruit fairly large, berry-like, ovoid, slightly angular, drying and decaying, dried floral-remains usually deciduous. Seeds numerous, ovoid to kidney-shaped; seedcoat dark brown, smooth or pitted with shallow depressions. About 20 species in the tropical rainforests of C America, in N South America and in Mexico.

Epiphyllum anguliger (Lem.) G.Don
■□
□□

Freely-branching, with lanceolate, fairly fleshy, fresh green offsets widening from a terete base, with pronounced mid-rib vein and deep, wide-toothed margins, lobes ±protruding at right angles, indentations ±deep and pointed. Areoles sometimes with 1–2 small white bristles. Flowers 15–16 cm long with 8 cm long tube, sweet-smelling, outer perianth-segments yellowish flesh-coloured, inner pure white. Mexico.

Epiphyllum chrysocardium Alexander
□■
[= **Marniera chrysocardium** Alex.) Backeb.]
□□

Epiphytic, with very stout stems up to 30 cm thick, with very broad-lobed, serrate edges, lobes up to 15 cm long and 4 cm wide, ending in a ±canoe-shaped point. Areoles small, sometimes with 2–3 bristles. Flowers 32 cm long with 16 cm long tube, outer perianth-segments dull mauve, inner white. Mexico (Chiapas).

DISOCACTUS Lindley (incl. BONIFAZIA Standley & Steyermark, CHIAPASIA B. & R.)

Small, terete stems with flattened side-joints or branching from the base. Shoots erect or pendent, broadening out from a stalk-like base, with pronounced mid-rib and crenate, serrate edges. Flowers usually solitary, lateral, sessile, tubular, narrowly campanulate or salver-shaped. Pericarpel and receptacle-tube with a few appressed scales. Perianth-segments few, erect, spreading or reflexed. Fruit a globose or ovoid berry, floral remains falling away cleanly, with small scales or ±naked. Seeds ovoid or weakly kidney-shaped; seedcoat black, finely wrinkled or with interstitial pits. 5 species in tropical and sub-tropical America and the West Indies.

Disocactus nelsonii (B. & R.) Lindinger
□□
[= **Chiapasia nelsonii** (B. & R.) B. & R.]
■□

Freely-branching, slender long-shoots, flat and thin above, up to 1.2 m long, with curved, crenate side-shoots 10–25 cm long and 3–4 cm wide. Flowers lateral, near shoot-tips, 7–8 cm long, carmine flushed with violet. Mexico (Chiapas).

Disocactus quezaltecus (Standley & Steyermark) Kimnach
□□
[= **Bonifazia quezalteca** Standley & Steyermark]
□■

Bushily-branching, with terete long-shoots flattened at the end, and flattened side-shoots with widely-spaced, slight notches and tapering or somewhat rounded tips. Flowers 8.5–9 cm long, narrow-tubed, curving sharply upwards at the base, pale purple, stamens and stigma long-exserted. Fruit a globose, 18 mm, red and yellow berry. Guatemala.

Disocactus ramulosus (Salm-Dyck) Kimnach ■☐
[= **Rhipsalis ramulosa** (Salm-Dyck) Pfeiffer] ☐☐
Shrub, freely branching from the base, with terete long-shoots up to 1.5 m long, and numerous fresh-green short-shoots 10–25 cm long and 2 cm wide, tapering at the base into a stalk 1–6 cm long, and with slightly serrate edges. Areoles initially often with bristles, later glabrous. Flowers lateral, solitary, rotate, small, whitish green. Pericarpel with 2–3 small scales. Fruit pea-sized, green at first, later whitish. Mexico to Bolivia, Peru.

WITTIA K. Schumann
Epiphytic shrubs with very thin, oblong, leaf-like, crenate-edged, erect, later pendent stems. Areoles without spines. Flowers small, tubular-funnelshaped, perianth-segments connivent to about mid-way forming a tube. Pericarpel smooth or tuberculate, with small scales but no hair or bristles. Fruit a pear-shaped, blunt-angled berry, floral remains persistent or deciduous. Seeds pear-shaped; seedcoat dark brown with shallow, convex, polyhedral cells, but no interstitial pits. 1 species in Panama, Colombia and N Peru.

Wittia amazonica K. Schumann ☐■
☐☐
Freely-branching, shrub-like, with erect, later pendent, lanceolate, ±strongly crenate, leaf-green shoots, 15–40 cm long and 5–9 cm wide, with stalk-like base and pronounced mid-rib. Flowers small, 3–4 cm long, outer perianth-segments bright carmine with purplish-blue recurved tips, inner perianth-segments erect and white. Fruit up to 1.5 cm long, off-white. Costa Rica, Panama, Venezuela, Ecuador to NE Peru.

PSEUDORHIPSALIS B. & R.
Shrub-like, arching, with long, leaf-shaped stems rounded at the base, with crenate edges and no spines. Flowers small, with short, distinct tube and spreading perianth-segments. Pericarpel with few, small scales. Fruit a globose-ovoid berry. Seeds ovoid; seedcoat dark brown, smooth, with small, sporadic interstitial pits. 3 species in Mexico, Costa Rica and Jamaica.

Pseudorhipsalis macrantha Alexander ☐☐
■☐
Bushily branching, with arching stems, rounded at the base. Shoots leaf-like, light green, up to 90 cm long and 4.5 cm thick, tapering towards the tip, with notches 2–3 cm apart. Areoles tiny, grey-felted. Flowers solitary, 3 cm across, with recurving perianth-segments, creamy white, golden-yellow when drooping, outer perianth-segments brownish, reddish outside. Fruit a globose, 7–8 mm, red berry. S Mexico.

Pseudorhipsalis himantoclada (Roland-Gosselin) B. & R. ☐☐
☐■
Large, pendent bushes 1 m or more long with thin, flat, 4–5 cm wide, glossy, vivid green shoots, red-tipped when young, with crenate edges and very pronounced mid-rib; lateral shoots hardly longer than 20 cm, with stalks only 2–3 cm. Areoles sparsely felted, with small, long-lasting, reddish scales. Flowers solitary, 2.6 cm long, perianth-segments somewhat spreading, white inside, brownish or reddish outside. Costa Rica.

WEBEROCEREUS B. & R. (incl. WERCKLEOCEREUS B. & R.)

Slender, rounded, 3–4-angled or even flat shoots with crenate-serrate edges, climbing with aerial roots or arching. Areoles small, only weakly spiny. Flowers medium to large, shortly funnel-shaped, night-blooming. Areoles on pericarpel and receptacle-tube with woolly felt and spines or bristly hairs. Fruit globose, tuberculate, with spiny areoles or hairy, with dried floral remains. Seeds — as far as known — ovoid; seedcoat black with fine cell structure. 5 species in Costa Rica, Panama and Guatemala.

Weberocereus biolleyi (F.A.C. Weber) B. & R.

■□
□□

Shoots very long and slender, pendent, 7–15 mm thick, rounded or bluntly angular, brownish red. Areoles small, wide apart, mostly spineless, only occasionally with 1–3 short, weak, yellow spines. Flowers 3–5 cm long, bell-shaped, perianth-segments fleshy, yellowish green to reddish brown. Pericarpel with white spines. Costa Rica.

Weberocereus trichophorus Johnson & Kimnach

□■
□□

Climbing, rounded or faintly 6–7-angled, strong green shoots 8–12 mm thick. Areoles with 10, in age up to 20 stiff, moderately strong, yellow spines 3–12 mm long, and 30–40 ±curly hairs 5–20 mm long. Flowers campanulate-funnelshaped, up to 6 cm long and 3.5 cm across, flesh-pink, purple outside. Pericarpel densely covered with fine tubercles with fairly long, loose hairs. Fruit oblong, 3 cm long, 2.5 cm across, purplish-red. Costa Rica.

ECCREMOCACTUS B. & R.

Epiphytes with flat and stout, pendent shoots with flat, crenate edges. Flowers medium-sized, funnel-shaped, night-blooming, only opening slightly. Pericarpel with thick scales and short hair in the axils, angled owing to the elongate podaria. Short receptacle-tube with small, somewhat spreading, spineless scales. Fruit oblong, juicy, with a few spineless areoles, red, without floral remains. Seeds small, oblong to cap-shaped, with basal hilum; seedcoat black, verrucose with interstitial pits. 1 species in Costa Rica.

Eccremocactus bradei B. & R.

□□
■□

Erect, later pendent, small shrub, with jointed, crenate, flat and stout shoots 15–30 cm long, 5–10 cm thick, light matt green, with central axis somewhat prominent on both sides. Areoles small, with 1–3 dark brown spines up to 6 mm long. Flowers night-blooming, 5–7 cm long, somewhat asymmetric, outer perianth-segments thick, bright pink, next ones thinner, pale pink to fawn, inner ones white. Costa Rica.

HYLOCEREUS (A. Berger) B. & R.

Freely-branching shrub, climbing with aerial roots, with very long (up to 10 m) 3-angled or -winged shoots. Ribs often crenate. Areoles with short felt and a few short spines or bristles. Flowers very large, funnel-shaped, night-blooming. Pericarpel and receptacle-tube with broad, leaf-life scales, but no woolly hair or spines. Fruit large, extensively scaly, usually red, opening irregularly. Floral remains persistent or deciduous. Seeds numerous, elongate-ovoid to kidney-shaped; seedcoat glossy black, smooth or delicately textured with fine interstitial pits. About 20 species from Mexico and the West Indies as far as N South America.

Hylocereus undatus (Haw.) B. & R.

□□
□■

Very strong, dark green shoots up to 7 cm thick, with 3 thin wings and wavy, sinuate edges, horny when old. Areoles in the notches with 1–3 conical spines 2–4 mm long. Flowers up to 30 cm long, outer perianth-segments greenish yellow, inner white, broad, bristle-tipped. Fruit oblong, 10–12 cm thick, red, with broad scales and white flesh. Original habitat unknown. Cultivated as an ornamental plant and for its edible fruit.

WILMATTEA B. & R.

Slender, triangular shoots, climbing with aerial roots. Areoles with a few short spines. Flowers small, very short-tubed, night-blooming. Short pericarpel and very short receptacle-tube with broad triangular scales with some wool and a few spines. Fruit scaly. Seeds unknown. 1 species in Guatemala and Honduras.

Wilmattea minutiflora (B. & R.) B. & R. ■☐ ☐☐

Shoots with almost straight edges. Areoles with 1–2 tiny brownish spines. Flowers 5 cm long, sweet-smelling, reddish outside, white inside. Guatemala, Honduras.

SELENICEREUS (A. Berger) B. & R. (incl. DEAMIA B. & R.)

Slender-limbed shrub, climbing with aerial roots, with 5–7-angled or -ribbed stems (*Selenicereus*) or offsets with 3–5–8 thin, wing-like ribs (*Deamia*). Short-haired areoles with mostly fine spines. Flowers large to enormous, night-blooming. Pericarpel and receptacle-tube with numerous tiny scales and large, prominent podaria; areoles with ±long, woolly hair or fine bristles. Fruit large, ovoid, tuberculate owing to podaria, the hairy areoles with bristles or sharp spines. Pericarp thick-fleshed, reddish, floral remains mostly deciduous. Seeds pear-shaped; seedcoat matt black, coarsely verrucose, with indistinct interstitial pits. About 20 species from Texas through Mexico and the West Indies to Argentina.

Selenicereus grandiflorus (L.) B. & R. (Subgenus **Selenicereus**) ☐■ ☐☐

Stems up to 5 m long, 2.5 cm thick, 5–8-ribbed, with 1 tuft of brownish wool on tip. Areoles white-felted with 7–11 yellowish, later grey, spines 4–6 mm long. Flowers up to 30 cm long, outer perianth-segments brownish orange-yellow, inner pure white. Jamaica, Cuba, Haiti, Mexico. (Illustration turned through 90° clockwise).

Selenicereus inermis (Otto) B. & R. ☐☐ ■☐

Slender, 1–2.5 cm thick, glossy, light green stems with 3–5 sharp, straight or slightly crenate edges. Areoles up to 6 cm apart with no spines and only a few bristles when young. Flowers 15 cm long, pericarpel and receptacle-tube with scales and occasional spines, hairless, outer perianth-segments yellowish green, inner white, both reddish at base. Style thick, stigma yellowish green. Venezuela, Colombia.

Selenicereus testudo (Karw.) F. Buxbaum
[= **Deamia testudo** (Karw.) B. & R.] (Subgenus **Deamia**) ☐☐ ☐■

Freely-branching epiphyte, climbing over trees or rocks, or also pendent. Stems up to 25 cm long and of varying form, 5–8-ribbed, mostly with 3 or more broad wings, decumbent close to its support, with very broad side-wings, those on underside much smaller, roots growing out of furrows. Flowers to 25 cm long, white. S Mexico to Colombia.

MEDIOCACTUS B. & R.

Epiphytes with long, arching, mostly triangular-winged, thin stems. Areoles with short spines and bristles. Flowers very large, funnel-shaped. Pericarpel and receptacle-tube with small scales, a little felt and short spines, pericarpel tuberculate. Fruit ovoid, red, with persistent floral remains. Areoles felted and spiny. Seeds obovoid; seedcoat black, pitted with fine depressions. About 4 species from Brazil to Argentina.

Mediocactus coccineus (Salm-Dyck) B. & R.

Usually triangular-winged, up to 2 cm wide, light green, arching stems with slightly curved edges. Areoles raised, with 2–4 conical, reddish, later brownish, spines 1–3 mm long, and 8–10 appressed white bristles. Flowers 25 cm long, white, yellowish at base, green outside. Brazil to Argentina.

STROPHOCACTUS B. & R.

Thin, broad, flattened shoots, edges not crenate, clinging closely to the support with aerial roots from the middle of the shoot. Areoles with woolly hair, bristles and numerous short spines. Flowers night-blooming, with very long slender tube. Pericarpel and receptacle-tube with a few oblong scales with hair, bristles and spines in the axils. Fruit ovoid with bristly spines. Seeds auriculate; seedcoat black. 1 species in Brazil.

Strophocactus wittii (K. Schumann) B. & R.

Epiphytic, high-climbing, freely-branching and jointed shrub, with leaf-like, occasionally triangular stems. Stems elliptic to lanceolate, up to 10 cm wide and 3–4 times as long, clinging closely to the support, crenate. Areoles with white woolly felt and numerous strong, sharp spines up to 12 mm long. Flowers up to 25 cm long, flesh-pink outside, snow-white inside. Brazil.

CRYPTOCEREUS Alexander

Climbing with aerial roots, at intervals branching bushily, with deeply notched flat-shoots. Areoles small with 3 short spines. Flowers large, night-blooming. Pericarpel and receptacle-tube with small scales with wool and bristles in the axils, also strong spines on pericarpel. Fruit oblong-globose, with floral remains and areoles with felt and long spines. Seeds oblong to clavate; seedcoat glossy black, smooth. 1 species in Mexico.

Cryptocereus anthonyanus Alex.

Climbing stem, up to 1 m or more long and 7–15 cm wide, with glossy green branches. Branches flat and rather stout, with alternately projecting wings 2.5–4.5 cm long, rounded and slightly narrowing towards the tip. Flowers 12 cm long, outer perianth-segments red, recurved, inner creamy and erect. Mexico (Chiapas).

PFEIFFERA Salm-Dyck

Small, freely-branching shrubs with upright or pendent shoots, 4-ribbed, 3-winged, or flattened, out of a rounded base, with crenate edges and no aerial roots. Areoles with hairy felt, short bristles or bristly spines. Flowers small, lateral, narrowly bell-shaped, receptacle-tube absent or at most, very short. Pericarpel thick-walled, angular, with scales with wool and bristles in the axils, occasionally 1 spine. Fruit a globose or ovoid, sharply angular berry with woolly and bristly-spined areoles and small, dried floral remains. Seeds elongate-cylindric or ovoid; seedcoat glossy black, shallowly verrucose or with interstitial pits. About 6 species in Argentina and Bolivia.

Pfeiffera ianthothele (Monv.) F.A.C. Weber

Shrub-like, moderately branched, epiphytic or growing on the ground. Stems 1.5–2 cm thick and several decimetres long, 4-angled or occasionally triangular, without aerial roots. Edges sinuate, areoles with 6–7 thin, bristly spines 4–5 mm long. Flowers lateral, occasionally terminal, small, 2–2.4 cm long, white or yellowish, flushed with pink outside. Fruit round, violet-pink. Argentina.

RHIPSALIS Gaertner (incl. ACANTHORHIPSALIS (K. Schumann) B. & R., ERYTHRORHIPSALIS A. Berger, LEPISMIUM Pfeiffer)

Mostly epiphytic, erect, later arching shrubs, freely-branching towards the tips, with offsets of very many forms, with or without aerial roots. Areoles small or tiny, with 1 minute scale, on the surface or ±immersed in the cortex. Areoles with a little short felt, single hairs or short bristles, rarely spiny. A few species have a composite terminal areole, from which arise the continuation of the shoot and flowers. Flowers solitary or in

[Rhipsalis monacantha Grisebach (see text overleaf)]

106

clusters of up to 5 through the formation of subsidiary buds. Flowers tiny to conspicuous, regular, white, pale yellow to reddish with few perianth-segments. Pericarpel somewhat angular, turbinate-cylindric, with very thick walls. Receptacle-tube absent. Fruit a pea-sized, juicy, white, pink or deep purple berry with dried floral remains attached. Seeds oblong, oval to spindle-shaped, mostly slightly curved; seedcoat black or dark or light brown, faintly reticulated or shallowly verrucose. About 50 species in warm South America, principally Brazil, and transported to Florida, Mexico, Central America and the West Indies, also to the old world: East and West Africa, Madagascar and Ceylon.

According to the vegetative structure of the shoots, the genus may be divided into 6 subgenera: *Acanthorhipsalis* K. Schumann: segments flat or 3-angled, with spiny areoles. *Goniorhipsalis* K. Schumann: segments distinctly 3- or more angled, ribbed or wing-ribbed, stout. *Phyllorhipsalis* K. Schumann: segments leaf-life and 2-edged, continuing to grow from the tip, even when the shoot divides into narrower and wider segments; narrower segments sometimes as thin as a stalk. *Phyllarthrorhipsalis* F. Buxbaum: stem segments leaf-like with acrotonous branching exclusively from the areoles. *Rhipsalis* Gärtner: stem segments rounded or at most with rib-like folds, very different in appearance. *Lepismium* Pfeiffer: segments leaf-like or 3–4-angled, elongate. Pericarpel sunken in shoot axis.

Rhipsalis monacantha Grisebach (Illustration on p. 107)
[= **Acanthorhipsalis monacantha** (Grisebach) B. & R.]
Freely branching, erect, later pendent shrub with flat, leaf-like or triangular, serrate shoots 2–3 cm wide and up to 45 cm long, narrowing at the base into a winged stalk. Areoles with yellowish, woolly felt and 1–2 stout, erect, very sharp, blackish spines 6–10 mm long. Flowers laterally at areoles of upper joints, up to 15 mm long, pale orange. Fruit globose, orange or pale pink. Argentina.

Rhipsalis pentaptera Pfeiffer
Freely-branching shrub. Branches in 1s, 2s or 3s, 7–12 cm long, 6–15 mm thick, 5- or (rarely) 6-angled, ribbed or almost winged, vivid dark green. Areoles in small cross-furrows. Flowers from upper part of segments, usually 2–3 blooming in succession from 1 areole, 7–8 mm long, white. Fruit white, pale rosy red on top. S Brazil and Uruguay.

Rhipsalis cereoides Backeb. & Voll
Sharply triangular, very occasionally rectangular, strong green segments 4–10 cm long and up to 17 mm thick, often twisted round where they join, so that the angles alternate with the ones below, with aerial roots in the joints. Areoles small, with some felt and 2–4 very short bristles. Flowers up to 3–4 at the same time, 2 cm across, white. Fruit translucent pale pink. Brazil (Rio de Janeiro).

Rhipsalis houlletiana Lem.
Pendent shrub up to 2 m or more long, offsets rounded at base, thin and flattened, leaf-like above; lanceolate part up to 40 cm long, 3–5 cm wide, pointed on both sides, deeply serrated, vivid green, sometimes red-rimmed, serrations 2–3 cm long, up to 1 cm wide. Areoles with hardly perceptible felt and no bristles. Flowers 2 cm long, funnel-shaped, not opening wide, pendent, creamy white. Fruit a pea-sized, carmine red berry. E Brazil.

Rhipsalis robusta Lem.
Erect shrub, with elliptic or ovate segments, rounded above, tapering at the base, sometimes 3-faced, relatively deeply crenate (1 cm or more), 20 cm long, 10 cm wide, up to 4 mm thick, dark green. Areoles with sparse woolly felt and 1 or several bristles. Flowers up to 6 from 1 areole, 1.2–1.4 cm long, 1.5–1.8 cm across, wide-opening, pale yellow. Brazil (Rio de Janeiro).

Rhipsalis platycarpa (Zucc.) Pfeiffer

Freely-branching, erect shrub, up to 80 cm tall and higher, resembling *Epiphyllum phyllanthus*. Joints leaf-like, 8–30 cm long and 4–5 cm wide, strongly crenate, with pronounced mid-rib, dark green, sometimes red-rimmed. Areoles with sparse woolly felt, no bristles. Flowers lateral, solitary, about 2 cm long, off-white, barely opening. Fruit a semi-globose, greenish white berry. Brazil (Organ Mountains).

Rhipsalis hadrosoma G.A. Lindb.

Freely-branching shrub, pendent or decumbent over rocks, stems 10 cm long and 1.5–2 cm thick, blunt ended, matt light green; areoles small, red edged, with few bristles. Flowers numerous, wide-opening, up to 2 cm across, white. Fruit a large, up to 10 mm across, deep purple berry. Brazil (São Paulo).

Rhipsalis fasciculata (Willd.) Haw.

Bushy, freely-branching, with pendent, cylindric, low-ribbed shoots, 4–5 mm thick. Areoles numerous, 1 cm apart, with 1 tuft of whitish hair 3–4 mm long. Flowers numerous, very small, 6–8 mm long, 5 mm across, whitish green. Fruit globose, 6 mm across, white. Brazil and Madagascar.

Rhipsalis cereuscula Haw.

Freely-branching bush with mostly pendent, 20–30 (–60) cm long, 3–4 mm thick, dark green, long-shoots, and numerous crowded, 4–5-angled, 1–3 cm long, light green, shortly cylindric short-shoots in spiral or whorls. Areoles wide-set on long-shoots, close-set on short-shoots, with very sparse woolly-felt and 2–4 short white bristles. Fruit an obconic white berry. Uruguay to C Brazil.

Rhipsalis mesembryanthemoides Haw.

■□
□□

Freely-branching, initially erect, later pendent, dense, globose bush, up to 40 cm long, with terete, woody, small stems. Long-shoots terete, up to 20 cm long and 2 mm thick, with aerial roots; on these in a close spiral are spindle-shaped, 7–15 mm long and 2–4 mm thick, light green short-shoots. Areoles on long-shoots scattered, with sparse woolly felt and 1–2 small bristles, on short-shoots with more abundant woolly felt and 3–4 bristles. Flowers solitary, normally on the short-shoots only, 8 mm long, 15 mm across, white. (The illustration shows a very unusual form in which most of the flowers are on the long shoots.) Fruit globose, white or reddish tinged. Because of its leaf-like short-shoots the plant is reminiscent of a *Mesembryanthemum*. E Brazil (Rio de Janeiro).

Rhipsalis capilliformis F.A.C. Weber

□■
□□

Exceptionally freely-branching, densely tussocky, pendent shrub, with thread-like long-shoots, 10–15 cm long and 2–3 mm thick, and spiralling or whorled, slender, pendent, often bluntly 4-angled short-shoots, 2–3 cm long and 1–1.5 mm thick. These with a few small areoles with barely visible woolly hair, no bristles, and 1 tuft of white flocky wool on the tip. Flowers numerous, mostly terminal, 6–7 mm long, whitish. Fruit a globose, white berry. The whole plant somewhat resembles a wig. E Brazil.

Rhipsalis epiphyllanthoides Backeb.

□□
■□

Terete or weakly-angled shoots, 2–4 cm long, standing compactly one on top of the other. Areoles on slightly reddish projections, white-felted, initially with 12, appressed towards the top, 4 mm long, fine white bristles. Flowers up to 3 cm across, pale yellow, darker-tipped. Brazil.

Rhipsalis pilocarpa Loefgren
[= Erythrorhipsalis pilocarpa (Loefgren) Berg.]

□□
□■

Small, epiphytic shrub with terete, jointed, pendent stems, 5–12 cm long and 3–6 mm thick, branching in whorls. Areoles close-set, with some wool and 3–10 grey hair-spines. Flowers several at a time at terminal areoles, 2.5 cm across, white. E Brazil.

Rhipsalis megalantha Loefgren

Pendent shrub, freely-branching in whorls, with cylindric stems up to 35 cm long and 1 cm thick, vivid green, flushed with reddish brown when young, and terminal segments 8–15 cm long. Areoles with very small scales and little wool. Flowers lateral, numerous, very large, rotate, up to 3.5 cm wide, yellowish white, sunken in shoot axis. Fruit a bright red berry, 13 mm across, surrounded with white bristles at the base, leaving a cavity when it falls. Brazil (São Paulo).

Rhipsalis cruciformis (Vell.) Cast.
[= Lepismium cruciforme (Vell.) Miquel]

Moderately-branching, climbing or pendent shrub, with 10–30 cm long and 1–2.5 cm thick, 3-angled or flat stems, sap-green or grey-green, often flushed with red, and with aerial roots. Areoles with 1 paintbrush-like tuft of whitish wool and bristles. Flowers numerous, companulate-rotate, 10 mm long, white. Fruit globose, 7 mm across, violet, surrounded with wool at the base, leaving a cavity when it falls (subgenus *Lepismium*). Rather variable species. Brazil to Paraguay.

HATIORA B. & R. (incl. PSEUDOZYGOCACTUS Backeb.)

Freely-branching, erect, later spreading and arching shrubs, in age consisting of uniform shoot segments 2–5 cm long, clavate to bottle-shaped or completely cylindric, in 1 case (*H. epiphylloides*) flat and 2-edged. Areoles tiny, combined in 1, usually depressed, compound areole on the stem-segment apex, laterally very few or none. New shoots and flowers only from terminal areoles. Flowers campanulate-funnel-shaped, yellow or bluish-violet to deep violet, with no receptacle-tube as such, but stamens and perianth-segments fused together at the base to form a very short tube. Pericarpel shortly turbinate, with decurrent scales on the upper edge, making it slightly angular. Fruit a translucent, turbinate berry without adherent floral remains. Seeds obliquely ovoid, laterally very flattened; seedcoat dark reddish-brown, glossy, verrucose. About 3 very variable species in Brazil.

Hatiora salicornioides (Haw.) B. & R.

Extremely freely-branching, initially erect, then spreading and finally arching shrub, up to or over 1 m long; stem-segments 2–3 cm long, swelling to a club-shape from a thin, terete base, standing in pairs or more numerous whorls. Areoles tiny with short bristles. Flowers yellow. Fruit white. Species very variable in growth. Brazil (Rio de Janeiro, Minas Gerais).

Hatiora herminiae (Campos-Porto & Cast.) Backeb.

Erect and arching shrub, up to 30 cm, dichotomous or branching in whorls, with cylindric stems, not thickened to a club-shape, matt dark green, with fine grey felt on tips. A few small, lateral areoles with small scales and 1–2 tiny bristles each. Flowers solitary, only rarely in pairs, at felted, terminal areoles, large, 2 cm long and 2.5 cm across, violet-blue. Fruit an olive green berry 8 mm across, with grey, membranous lid. Brazil.

RHIPSALIDOPSIS B. & R. (incl. EPIPHYLLOPSIS Backeb. & F.M. Knuth)

Freely-branching small or dwarf epiphytes, with 3–4(–2)-angled stem-segments with tiny, bristly, marginal areoles, or flattened, 2-angled segments. Branches and flowers arising exclusively from a compound areole at the segment-tip. Flowers relatively large, shortly funnel-shaped, opening rotately, without receptacle-tube (but lower perianth-segments and outer stamens fuse together to form a short tube). Pericarpel 4–5-angled. Fruit a 4–5-angled berry, with floral remains, later easily snapped off. Seeds elongate, obliquely ovoid, rather flattened laterally; seedcoat smooth, reddish brown. 2 species in S Brazil.

Rhipsalidopsis rosea (Lag.) B. & R.　　　　　　　　■□
　　　　　　　　　　　　　　　　　　　　　　　　　□□
Dense, bushy, dwarf shrub up to 25 cm high, with erect or spreading to arching stems, joints 2–4 cm long and 3–5-angled or flat, often cereiform low down, flat and spathulate higher up, rounded at the top, gradually tapering to the bottom, 2–3 mm thick, with 2–3 notches on the edge. Areoles with short woolly felt and a few deciduous bristles. Flowers terminal, 3–4 cm across, pink. S Brazil (Paraná).

Rhipsalidopsis gaertneri (Regel) Lindinger　　　　　□■
[= **Epiphyllopsis gaertneri** (Regel) Backeb. & F.M. Knuth　□□
Vigorously branching shrub with arching, jointed branches. Lower stems 3–6-sided, ovoid or ellipsoid, rounded, 1–2 cm long. Areoles with some woolly felt and 6–20 fairly soft bristles. Upper stems leaf-like, wide and straight or obovate, 3–6 cm long and 1.5–3.5 cm wide, crenate, with 3–6 notches on each edge. Areoles with 3–12 short bristles, terminal composite areole with bristly spines up to 1.5 cm long. Flowers solitary or several together on tips of youngest joints, 4–7.5 cm long, brilliant scarlet. Fruit obovoid, sharply 5-angled, red, fleshy, later dry and hard. S Brazil (Santa Catarina, Minas Gerais).

SCHLUMBERGERA Lemaire (incl. ZYGOCACTUS K. Schumann, EPIPHYLLANTHUS A. Berger)

Small epiphytic shrubs, upright, later arching, with dichotomous branches of stem-segments of equal length, flat and leaf-like, with crenate or strongly serrate edges and marginal areoles, or else rounded to flattened with lateral areoles. At the apex of the stem-segment is a group of areoles, or one oblong, immersed, composite areole, from which flowers and new shoots arise; the base of the stem-segment often with aerial roots. Flowers regular or strongly zygomorphic. Pericarpel smooth, turbinate, rounded or angled. Receptacle-tube very short, extended into a straight or strongly curved perigonium. In zygomorphic flowers the throat strongly oblique, perianth-segments straight or variously recurved, forming a prominent upper lip and receding lower lip. Stamens are in bundles, either enclosed or extruding from below upper lip. Fruit pear-shaped, angled or rounded, red or lime green, frequently with adherent floral remains. Seeds kidney-shaped or semi-ovoid; seedcoat dark brown or black, glossy, with interstitial pits. About 6 species in Brazil.

Schlumbergera opuntioides (Loefgren & Dusen) D.R. Hunt　□□
[= **Epiphyllanthus obovatus** (Engelm.) B. & R.]　　　　　■□
Erect or arching small shrub with obovoid, 5–6 cm long, up to 2-3 cm wide and 6 mm thick, dark green stem-segments. Areoles lateral and on the flat surfaces of joints, whitish-felted, with up to 30 spreading spines 5 mm long. Flowers zygomorphic, up to 6 cm long, 4.5 cm wide, deep pink. Fruit a blunt-angled, lime-green berry. Stem-segments vary considerably in size, shape and spination according to age and environmental conditions. Brazil (Serra da Mantiqueira).

　　　　　　　　　　　　　　　　　　　　　　　　　□□
Schlumbergera orssichiana Barthlott & McMillan　　　□■
Freely-branching shrub with semi-upright or arching, jointed offsets, and flattened, leaf-like, up to 5 cm long stem-segments, long-toothed and somewhat wavy-edged. Flowers zygomorphic, very large, 9 cm long and across. Perianth-segments white with deep pink edges, not recurved. Fruit a blunt-angled, pale lime-green berry. Brazil (Serra do Mar).

Tribe V **Cereeae** F. Buxbaum
JASMINOCEREUS B. & R.
Tree-like, with stout trunk and crown of thick, columnar, jointed, erect branches. Flowers large, funnel-shaped, chocolate brown. Pericarpel thick, receptacle-tube with broad-oval, spreading scales with woolly hair in the axils. Fruit ovoid, smooth, with tiny, membranous scales. Fruit-wall thin, very hard, floral remains usually attached. Seeds small, curved-ovoid; seedcoat shiny black, strongly verrucose. 1 very variable species on the Galapagos Islands.

Jasminocereus thouarsii (F.A.C. Weber) Backeb.
Tree up to 8 m tall with 30 cm thick trunk and branches dense and spreading or less numerous and vertical. Branches divided by deep constrictions into slender 15-ribbed or thicker 18-ribbed stem-segments. Areoles with short woolly felt and up to 10 or more spines about 4.5 cm long. Flowers very variable in size, 5–10 cm long, chocolate brown with yellow streaks. Fruit plum-like, reddish-purple, 7 cm long, 3 cm thick. Galapagos Islands.

STETSONIA B. & R.
Massive trees with short, thick trunks and freely branching crown of long, thick, upright branches. Flowers large, funnel-shaped, wide opening, white. Pericarpel densely covered with broad, ciliate scales, receptacle-tube with broader, more widely-spaced scales. Fruit stout ovoid, light lime-green, similarly covered with scales, floral remains deciduous leaving brown scar. Seeds obliquely elongate-ovoid, with broad, lateral hilum; seedcoat black, coarsely verrucose. 1 species in NW Argentina and Bolivia.

Stetsonia coryne (Salm-Dyck) B. & R.
Tree 5–8 m tall with short trunk up to 40 cm thick, with up to 100 and more, 8–9-ribbed branches, up to 60 cm long and 9–10 cm thick. Areoles with 7–9 subulate, spreading radial spines 3 cm long and 1 central spine 5 cm long. Flowers 15 cm long, white. NW Argentina, Bolivia.

PRAECEREUS F. Buxbaum
Mostly ±freely-branching cerei with slender, erect or arching stems several metres tall. Flowers night-blooming, sturdily campanulate-funnelshaped, sometimes rather curved. Pericarpel and thick-walled receptacle-tube with several broadly rounded, fleshy, glabrous scales with long decurrent podaria. Fruit fleshy, shortly ovoid, red, splitting along one side only, initially with dried floral remains. Seeds elongate-ovoid, rather flattened laterally; seedcoat black, verrucose. About 7 species in Venezuela, Ecuador, Peru, Bolivia and S Brazil.

Praecereus smithianus (B. & R.) F. Buxbaum
[= Monvillea smithiana (B. & R.) Backeb.]
Shrubby, with leaning, up to 8 cm thick stems, tapering at the tip, with (8–)9–11 strongly crenate ribs. Areoles felted, with up to 13 dark grey, later pale grey spines 3–4 cm long. Flowers 6–8 cm long, white. Fruit ovoid, 3–4 cm across, red. Venezuela.

Praecereus diffusus (B. & R.) F. Buxbaum
[= Monvillea diffusa B. & R.]
At first erect, then bending over, up to 2 m long and 4–5 cm thick, and often forming dense thickets, slender stems, usually with 8, high, fine ribs. Areoles with 6–10 radial spines of varying thickness and length between 6–12 mm, and 1–3 subulate, pale grey, black-tipped central spines 2–3 cm long. Flowers 7.5 cm long, white. Fruit shortly-ovoid to pear-shaped. S Ecuador and N Peru. (Illustration turned through 90°).

118

Praecereus maritimus (B. & R.) F. Buxbaum   ■□
[= **Monvillea maritima** B. & R.]   □□

At first erect, up to 4–5 m tall and 5–8 cm thick, often climbing high among trees and shrubs, with a single stem or a few rather weak ones. Stems with 4–6, somewhat wavy-edged ribs. Areoles sunken, 2–3 cm apart, with 8, unequal, grey, black-tipped, radial spines, and 1–2 stouter central spines 5–6 cm long. Flowers 6 cm long, white. Fruit oblong, rather angular. S Ecuador and N Peru.

MONVILLEA B. & R.

Mostly freely-branching shrubs with slender, semi-erect to prostrate or climbing stems. Areoles with weak, needle-like spines. Flowers conspicuous, slenderly funnel-shaped, wide-opening, night-blooming. Pericarpel and receptacle-tube with only a few small to tiny, glabrous scales. Tube not deciduous; after blooming the flowers remain attached. Fruit oblong-pearshaped or rounded, red, with dried floral remains. Seeds obliquely-ovoid; seedcoat shiny black, finely verrucose to almost smooth with interstitial pits. About 12 species in N and C South America (Paraguay, S Brazil and the Brazilian islands, NE Argentina and NE Bolivia).

Monvillea calliantha Fuaux & Backeb.   □■
   □□

Sturdy, erect, 4–5 cm thick, green stems, with 8–9, 8 mm high ribs. Areoles 1.5 cm apart with 6–9 stiff, sharp radial spines round the top, 3–4 bristly ones round the bottom, and usually 3 central spines, the upper ones of both being 3.5–4 cm long, porrect or pointing downwards, the lower ones 1.5 cm long and curved downwards. Flowers 7 cm long, 9 cm wide, pale yellow to cream. Original distribution unknown.

Monvillea rhodoleucantha (K. Schumann) A. Berger   □□
   ■□

At first erect, later prostrate, decumbent or climbing stems, 1–2 m long and 2–4 cm thick, with 7–9, weakly crenate ribs. Areoles 5–15 mm apart, with 6–7, later up to 12, subulate, radial spines, 7–10 mm long, yellowish brown at first, then white with black tips, and 1–3 similar, up to 2 cm long central spines. Flowers 13 cm long, 5–6 cm wide, white, reddish outside. Fruit ellipsoid, up to 7 cm long, red. N Paraguay.

Monvillea spegazzinii (F.A.C. Weber) B. & R.   □□
   □■

At first erect, later leaning or decumbent stems up to 2 m long and 1.5–2 cm thick, 4-sided, tuberculate, blue-green with white marbling. Areoles on the tubercles, 2.5 cm apart, on young shoots with 3 blackish spines, thick at the base and 4 mm long, on older branches with 5 radial spines 1.5 cm long, and 1 central spine. Flowers 11–12 cm long, white, reddish outside. Fruit a clavate-ellipsoid, almost stalked berry. Paraguay.

Monvillea haageana Backeb.   ■□ □□

Erect or climbing, vigorously branching stems, up to more than 3 m long, 2–3 cm thick, tapering at the top, bluish green, with 5, weakly tuberculate ribs. Areoles up to 3 cm apart, with 5–8 slender, dark brown spines up to 2 mm long. Flowers up to 12 cm long, ivory, blue-green outside. Paraguay.

CEREUS Miller

Mostly large trees with candelabra-like branching, erect, with short trunk and dense crown, or shrubs a few metres high branching from the base, or prostrate to ascending, low bushes. Branches usually with a few thick ribs. Areoles woolly with a few stout spines. Flowers large to very large, funnel-shaped, night-blooming, white or pink. Pericarpel and receptacle-tube on the more primitive species with small to very reduced scales; more advanced species with tiny scales on a decurrent podarium. Receptacle-tube deciduous, without, or sometimes with the style after flowering. Fruit smooth, fleshy, red or yellow, splitting longitudinally, or plum-like and not splitting. Seeds numerous, large, curved-ovoid; seedcoat glossy black, unevenly verrucose. About 40 species in South America: N Argentina, Paraguay, Uruguay, E and S Brazil.

Cereus jamacaru DC.   □■ □□

Tree up to 10 m tall with 60 cm thick trunk and large, dense crown of ascending branches, or branching from the base. Young branches bluish-green, jointed, up to 15 cm thick, with 4–6 compressed, slightly crenate ribs up to 3.5 cm high and divided by sharp furrows. Areoles in the notches directly above the protrusions, 2–4 cm apart, grey felted, with 5–7 subulate, pale yellow or brownish, later black, radial spines up to 15 mm long, and 2–4 spreading central spines 8–20 cm long. Flowers lateral, night-blooming, 20–30 cm long, oblique, white, light green outside. Fruit up to 12 cm long, 8 cm across, bright red. Brazil.

Cereus peruvianus (L.) Miller var. **monstrosus** DC.   □□ ■□

Several metres high, branching shrub-like, side-branches often not properly developed and frequently growing into one another; new growth pale green with a bluish tinge. Ribs about 12, distinctly separate, 3.5 cm high, often curved, and very soon divided into round or oblong tubercles by deep grooves between the areoles. Areoles 1–4 cm apart, with 5 radial spines and 1(–3) central spines, all spines dark brown with light tips, usually finely needle-shaped, 8–14 mm long or on older stem-segments up to 2 cm or more. Flowers 13–15 cm long, white. Fruit depressed globose, 4.5–5.5 cm thick, yellow with a light-spotted fine bluish bloom. Its odd appearance has made it popular for cultivation, particularly dwarf varieties which branch even more freely and look quite bizarre. Original habitat unknown. Similar forms known in *C. jamacaru* DC. and other species.

BRASILICEREUS Backeb.

Upright-leaning, bright green stems, 1–4 m high and no more than 2.5 cm thick. Flowers shortly bell-shaped, upcurved, yellowish-green. Very short pericarpel and thick-walled receptacle-tube with relatively few scales, occasionally with 1–2 long bristles. Fruit pear-shaped, tumid, with a few scales remaining, very deeply umbilicate under the floral remains. Seeds not described. 2 species in Brazil.

Brasilicereus markgrafii Backeb. & Voll   □□ □■

Usually unbranched, up to 1.5 m tall and at most 2.5 cm thick stems, grey-green, with about 13 ribs. Areoles 5–10 mm apart, grey-felted, with 12–18 radial spines 6–10 mm long, obliquely protruding, and usually 1(–4) central spines up to 4 cm long; all spines needle-fine and brittle, initially pale bone colour, later dark grey-brown. Flowers 6 cm long, 5 cm wide, campanulate-funnelshaped, pale greenish. Pericarpel curved. Brazil.

PSEUDOPILOCEREUS F. Buxbaum

Tree-forming and tree-like or branching near the base, rarely unbranched stems, remaining low or up to 10 m tall. Branches with 4–12 ribs. Flower-bearing areoles usually ±very woolly. Flowers from discrete areoles or from the cephalium. Flowers tubular to bell-shaped, mostly regular, sometimes curved to zygomorphic, night-blooming. Pericarpel and lower part of receptable-tube usually completely naked and smooth, upper part of receptacle-tube with several rows of large, broadly rounded, fleshy scales, the short outer perianth-segments spreading or recurved. In *P. nobilis* the lower perianth-segments protrude. Fruit depressed globose, fleshy, smooth, with firmly attached floral remains, opening irregularly. Seeds very variable, elongate, curved-ovate with lateral hilum, to squat with subbasal hilum; seedcoat shiny black, shallowly verrucose with interstitial pits. About 24 species in the arid region of E Brazil (*P. nobilis* in the West Indies).

Pseudopilocereus glaucochrous (Werderm.) F. Buxbaum
[= **Pilocereus glaucochrous** (Werderm.) Byles & Rowley]

Columnar stem, sparsely branching, up to 4 m tall and 5–7 cm thick, erect or weakly curving, 9-ribbed, with a beautiful light blue bloom, later grey-green. Areoles 1 cm apart, with dense, yellowish-white woolly felt, 9–12 spreading, straw-yellow, later greying radial spines 15–20 mm long, and 3–4 nearly erect, central spines 2–3(–5) cm long. Apex tipped with straw-yellow spines and wool up to 4 cm long. Flowers slender tubular, 4.5–5.5 cm long, whitish, crimson outside, often in vertical rows. Fruit depressed globose, 3–5 cm thick, greenish or slightly reddish, bloomed. Brazil (Bahia).

Pseudopilocereus salvadorensis (Werderm.) F. Buxbaum
[= **Pilosocereus salvadorensis** (Werderm.) Byles & Rowley]

When free-standing, a tree up to 4 m tall, with short trunk and many-branched crown, when among bushes trunk longer and more sparsely branched, with greenish grey, 7–9 ribbed shoots up to 10 cm thick. Areoles with greyish white, woolly felt, 10–11, appressed, radial spines up to 1 cm long, at first yellowish, then grey-brown, and 4 very sharp up to 2.5 cm long central spines in cross-formation; apex with white-grey wool and tipped with yellowish spines. Flowers often several, below the apex, campanulate-funnelshaped, 6.5–7 cm long, white. Fruit slightly depressed globose, 3.5–5 cm thick, dark blue, with bluish waxy bloom. Brazil (Bahia).

Pseudopilocereus fulvilanatus Buining & Bred.

Up to 3 m tall, branching, tree-like stems 10–11 cm thick with 5–6 ribs, green with a blue bloom near the top. Areoles densely close-set with short grey hairy felt, about 11, strong, spreading radial spines 10–25 mm long, and 1 upward-pointing central spine up to 45 mm long. Flower-bearing areoles with dense clumps of golden brown or brown wool. Flowers bell-shaped, 5 cm long, 3 cm wide, white, green outside. Fruit flattened spherical, 3 cm high, 4.5 cm thick, very wrinkled and furrowed, dark brown with violet bloom. Brazil (Minas Gerais).

Pseudopilocereus azureus Buining & Bred.

Erect, branching tree-like, 6–7 m tall, 11–12 cm thick stems, green below and sky-blue at the top, with 7–8 narrow ribs, rounded above and somewhat elevated between the areoles. Areoles round, at first white, later light brown woolly-felted, with, below ±bunched, white to pale cream, 2 cm long, vertical, hair tufts, and numerous needle-shaped yellow spines 1.5–2.5 cm long and 1 central one 3 cm long, pointing upwards. Flowers wide funnel-shaped, 6 cm long, 4 cm wide, greenish white. Receptacle-tube and pericarpel blue-green. Fruit flattened spherical, 3 cm high, 5.5 cm wide, glabrous, ±furrowed, red. Brazil.

124

STEPHANOCEREUS A. Berger

Solitary, seldom branching, 2–5 m high stems, jointed by rings of bristles. Flowers tubular-campanulate, white, night-blooming, from apical cephalium which is later grown-through to form the bristle-collar. Long hair and bristles on lower zone of flowers. Pericarpel and receptacle-tube with only a few tiny scales. Perianth-segments curved outwards. Fruit oblong, green with a blue bloom, with blackish floral remains. Seeds large, ovoid or pear-shaped; seedcoat matt black, verrucose. 1 species, Brazil.

Stephanocereus leucostele (Guerke) A. Berger

■ ☐
☐ ☐

Mostly solitary, seldom branching, 2–5 m tall and 4–8 cm thick stems, with unequal joints, with bristle-collars at joint ends, and 13–18 low ribs. Areoles with 1–1.5 cm long white woolly hair almost masking the stem, and up to 20 white radial spines 0.5–1.5 cm long and 1–2 stiff, white to golden, central spines 3–4 cm long. Flowers from apical cephalium or an older one, 6–7 cm long, white. Brazil (S Bahia).

COLEOCEPHALOCEREUS Backeb.

Erect, unbranched, up to 5 m tall stems, or prostrate or ascending, up to 2 m long, shooting from the base to form groups. Flowers from a one-sided ±depressed cephalium with long hair and long, thin, curved bristles or from the bottleneck-shaped, narrowed, flower-producing section with low, narrow ribs. Flowers conspicuous, slender funnel-shaped to campanulate funnelshaped, night-blooming. Pericarpel naked, receptacle-tube striate. Fruit ovoid, smooth and glabrous, with dried floral remains, deliquescent. Seeds globose to elongate campanulate-pearshaped, with a broad basal hilum; seedcoat black, very coarsely verrucose. About 6 (?) species in Brazil.

Coleocephalocereus fluminensis (Miquel) Backeb.

☐ ■
☐ ☐

Up to 2 m long and 10 cm across, semi-prostrate and upcurved stems, branching at the base, dark green, with 10–17 ribs. Areoles close-set, with white woolly felt, 4–7 radial spines and 1 central spine; flower-producing stems with 2–10 stout spines and 2–4 small, erect ones; all spines pale to greyish yellow, up to 3 cm long, flexible. Cephalium with copious white wool and short and long bristles, up to 5 cm wide and often extending 1 m downwards. Flowers up to 7 cm long, whitish pink. Fruit slender, turbinate, 2–3 cm long, shiny violet. Brazil.

Coleocephalocereus luetzelburgii (Vaupel) F. Buxbaum
[= Pilosocereus luetzelburgii (Vaupel) Byles & Rowley]

☐ ☐
■ ☐

Usually unbranched, sometimes sprouting from the base, 1(–1.5) m tall, globose when young, then elongate-ovoid; when 15–20 cm high becoming bottle-shaped and elongating into a thin neck 60–80 cm long with 13–16 ribs. Areoles on the stout part with whitish woolly felt, 15–18 needle-shaped, yellowish to grey radial spines up to 1.5 cm long, and about 4 stouter central spines up to 3 cm long. Flower-bearing part slender, with woolly apex and areoles with 1–2 cm long, sparse white woolly hair. Flowers mostly close together below the apex, 4.5–5 cm long, campanulate-funnelshaped, white to pink. Fruit depressed globose, 2.5–3.5 cm across, light green, bluish bloom. Brazil.

Coleocephalocereus pluricostatus Buining & Bred.

☐ ☐
☐ ■

Erect, up to 3.5 m high and up to 9 cm thick stems, sprouting from the base, with 20–25 ribs, and in the cephalium of older plants up to 34. Areoles grey-felted, later glabrous, with 5 slender, needle-shaped, yellowish radial spines up to 11 mm long, and 1 central spine 6 mm long. Cephalium up to 1.3 m long and up to 6 cm across, comprising about 7 ribs, with dense, silky wool and yellow, brown to brownish-black matted bristles. Flowers campanulate-funnelshaped, about 26 mm long and 15 mm wide, white, reddish outside. Fruit inverted top-shaped, 17 mm long, 15 mm across, reddish. Brazil.

Coleocephalocereus aureispinus Buining & Bred.

■□
□□

Stems 1–2 m tall and 5–6 cm thick, sprouting from the base, green, with about 22 ribs notched above the areoles. Areoles with creamy white, later light grey woolly felt, finally glabrous, with about 50 needle-shaped, 7–16 mm long, golden to pale yellow, radiating spines; on underside of areoles a few greyish-white hairs about 1 cm long. Flower-bearing areoles cushioned with pale orange-yellow wool and light brown to golden yellow bristles, 2.5–3.5 cm long and irregularly curved. Flowers 34 mm long and 22 mm across, white, pale golden-pink outside. Fruit globose, 38 mm long, 25 mm across, dull blue. Brazil (Bahia).

[Some experts would place this species in the genus *Pseudopilocereus* (see p. 124).]

BUININGIA F. Buxbaum

Slender, up to 90 cm long, ascending stems, freely sprouting from the base, or for the first few years hemispherical to spherical; after cephalium begins to develop, becoming a stout, conically tapering stem with additional spherical offsets at the base. Flowers from a lateral cephalium with dense wool and long, thin bristles. Flowers medium-sized, narrowly tubular, all one colour. Pericarpel naked, receptacle-tube with a few small, slightly grooved scales. Outer perianth-segments spreading into a trumpet, inner ones connivent in a narrow, straight tube. Fruit a turbinate to ovoid, red berry with floral remains persistent until the fruit falls. Seeds variable, obliquely-ovoid to pouch-shaped, with basal hilum; seedcoat shiny black, verrucose. 3 (?) species in Brazil.

Buiningia aurea (Ritter) F. Buxbaum

□■
□□

Freely sprouting from the base, 20–40 cm tall and 6–7 cm thick shoots, green, with 10–16 slightly tuberculate ribs. Areoles in the grooves, white-felted, with 10–15 golden, needle-shaped, radial spines 5–15 mm long, and 1–4 thick, needle-shaped, porrect central spines, 2–5 cm long. Cephalium beginning at a height of 15–20 cm, very wide, on the side receiving the strongest sunlight, with thick balls of 1–2 cm long wool, and numerous 2–3 cm long, needle-fine, curved, golden bristles. Flowers 30–37 mm long, 15–20 mm wide, lime-green. Fruit 16–22 mm long, 12–15 mm thick, scarlet. Brazil (Minas Gerais).

Buiningia brevicylindrica Buining

□□
■□

At first spherical, later short cylindric, up to 30 cm tall and 17 cm thick, sprouting from the base, fresh green, with ±conical head and up to 18 vertical ribs, swollen above the areoles. Areoles with short whitish-yellow wool, later glabrous, and 7 radial spines 2–3 cm long and 4 cruciform central spines up to 6 cm long. All spines significantly shorter after formation of cephalium. Cephalium already on apex when plant 8 cm tall and still spherical, up to 7 cm wide and 20 cm long, with white wool and golden yellow, mostly straight spines. Flowers tubular, up to 32 mm long and 15 mm wide, creamy white. Fruit globose, 17 mm across, shiny red. Brazil (NE Minas Gerais).

Buiningia purpurea Buining & Bred.

□□
□■

Stems up to 90 cm long and 10 cm thick, sprouting from the base, green or dark green, 13-ribbed. Areoles with 12 spreading, needle-shaped, often somewhat curved, golden yellow to red, later grey radial spines 12–25 mm long, and 4 central spines, one 70 mm long, the others 30–35 mm. Cephalium facing south-west, up to 50 cm long, with grey wool and bristles coloured like the spines. Flowers tubular, 30 mm long, up to 12 mm wide, purple. Fruit globose to oval, 17–25 mm long, 17 mm thick, shiny red. Brazil (NE Minas Gerais).

Tribe VI **Trichocereeae** F. Buxbaum

TRICHOCEREUS (A. Berger) Riccobono (incl. HELIANTHOCEREUS Backeb. p.p., LEUCOSTELE Backeb.)

Unbranched, or branching candelabra-form from the base, up to 1 m tall, many-ribbed stem, erect, rarely prostrate-decumbent. Ribs often with cross-furrows between the stout-spined areoles. Flowers from upper part of offsets, campanulate-funnelshaped or short funnel-shaped, large, white, red or yellow, some day-blooming, some night-blooming. Pericarpel and receptacle-tube with narrow scales with profuse curly hair in the axils. Fruit half-dry, dehiscent, with or without floral remains, brownish to greenish, hairy, but no bristles or spines. Seeds large, ovoid; seedcoat black, verrucose. About 50 species in the South American Andes, especially Argentina and Bolivia, besides Peru, Chile and Ecuador.

Trichocereus candicans (Gillies) B. & R.

Branching from the base and often forming extensive colonies; stems 0.35–1 m tall, 6–8–12–15 cm thick, bright pale-green, later darker, with white woolly felt and bright yellow spines at apex. Ribs 9–11, blunt. Areoles 1.5–2 cm apart, large, white-felted, with 10–14 honey-coloured to white, 2–4 cm long, spreading radial spines, and 1–4 stronger, darker-tipped, up to 10 cm long central spines. Flowers at apex, up to 25 cm long, sweet-smelling like lilies, usually white, outer segments reddish. Fruit ellipsoid-globose. This species is very variable and intergrades with related species. The orange flowers of the specimen illustrated are not typical. NW Argentina.

Trichocereus thelegonus (F.A.C. Weber) B. & R.

Prostrate or ascending, with few branches, up to 2 m long and 7–8 cm thick stem, new growth light green, later darkening, with 12–13 ribs, divided by furrows into hexagonal tubercles. Areoles are 8–10 mm apart, with yellowish-white woolly felt, later glabrous, 6–8 spreading, needle-shaped, 1–2 cm long, honey-coloured, later brown to blackish, radial spines, and 1 straight, 2–4 cm long central spine. Older plants have more spines. Flowers lateral, 20 cm long, wide opening, white, greenish outside. Fruit ovoid, 5 cm long, yellowish to red, densely hairy. Argentina. (Illustration turned anticlockwise through 90°).

Trichocereus macrogonus (Salm-Dyck) Riccobono

Tree with few branches, up to 6 m tall (in cultivation up to 2 m and 7 cm thick), with erect, columnar, blue-green, usually 7-ribbed stems. Areoles 1–1.5 cm apart, grey-felted, with 6–9, up to 2 cm long, horn-coloured, later black, radial spines, and 1–3 stronger, downward-pointing, 2.5 cm long central spines. Flowers night-blooming, 2–4 on apex, up to 17 cm long and 7 cm wide, white. Fruit depressed globose, up to 3 cm long, 4.5–5 cm thick. Not known in the wild.

Trichocereus spachianus (Lem.) Riccobono

■□
□□

Upright, branching from the base, up to over 2 m tall and 6–8 cm thick stems, with 10–15 ribs, glossy green. Areoles 6–10 mm apart, with golden yellow, later white wool, 8–10 thin, needle-shaped, amber to brown radial spines 6–10 mm long, and 1 stouter and longer central spine. Flowers several at the apex, 20 cm long, night-blooming, wide-opening, white, green outside, with black hairs. Fruit green with black hairs. W Argentina.

Trichocereus huascha (F.A.C. Weber) B. & R. var. grandiflorus (B. & R.)
Rausch [= Helianthocereus grandiflorus (B. & R.) Backeb.]

□■
□□

Stems branching from the base, 20(–30) cm tall and up to 6 cm thick, forming small groups, rich green, with 14 ribs. Areoles 6 mm apart, yellow-felted, with 8–9(–12) thin, whitish yellow, brown-tipped radial spines up to 1 cm long, and usually 1, 1 cm long central spine (later another 3–4 more weaker ones). Flowers usually solitary at the apex, day-blooming, 8–10 cm long, blood red. Stem and spines are deceptively similar to a small *Trichocereus spachianus*. Argentina.

Trichocereus chilensis (Colla) B. & R.

□□
■□

Shrubby or tree-like, branching upright from the base with numerous ascending, velvety, dull-green shoots up to 3 m or more high and 10–12 cm thick, with 10–17 ribs, notched above the areoles and almost divided into angular tubercles. Areoles 2–2.5 cm apart, felted, with 8–12 strong, initially amber, later grey, radial spines 1–2 cm or occasionally up to 4 cm long, and 1–4 central spines, 4–7(–12) cm long. Flowers lateral towards the apex, 14 cm long, pure white, brownish white outside. Fruit globose. Host plant for the parasitic mistletoe *Phrygilanthus aphyllus*. Very variable in growth, particularly in spination. Chile.

WEBERBAUEROCEREUS Backeb.

Shrub-like, occasionally tree-like columnar cacti, in age sometimes with stout spines. Flowers large, regular or zygomorphic, whitish, brownish or reddish. Pericarpel and receptacle-tube densely covered with scales and hairs. Fruit globose, yellowish-orange to reddish, dried floral remains falling off like a lid. Seeds small; seedcoat black, smooth. About 6 species in Peru.

Weberbauerocereus weberbaueri (K. Schumann) Backeb.

□□
□■

Up to 4 m tall shrub, with upright or curving stems, 6–10 cm thick, with 25 sharply cross-furrowed ribs. Areoles with thick grey felt, and with 6–8, flexible, central spines up to 6 cm long, reddish at first, then brownish yellow, and about 20 weaker and shorter radial spines. Flowers near apex, up to 11 cm long, slightly curved, inner perianth-segments white, outer green to chocolate brown. Fruit up to 4 cm across, yellowish orange with green scales. Rather variable species. S Peru.

HAAGEOCEREUS Backeb. (incl. BINGHAMIA B. & R., NEOBINGHAMIA Backeb., PERUVOCEREUS Akers)

Medium-sized stems, solitary or branching upright from the base, or low, semi-upright, or prostrate and rooting from the underside. Ribs numerous, very densely spiny. Flowers mostly near apex, open from late afternoon until next morning or noon, campanulate-funnelshaped, opening to flatly rotate, white, pink to red, occasionally greenish. Pericarpel and receptacle-tube with numerous small scales and distinct decurrent podaria, usually with very small tufts of hair in the axils. Fruit ovoid to elongate globose, fleshy, drawn together under dried floral remains, usually muddy greenish-red, otherwise grass-green, yellow or carmine pink. Podaria no longer evident. Seeds somewhat curved or obliquely ovoid; seedcoat glossy black with rather irregularly placed interstitial pits. About 50 sometimes very variable species from Peru, of which a large number are worthy at best, of varietal rank. (The plants described under the name *Neobinghamia* Backeb. are natural hybrids between *Espostoa* and *Haageocereus*.)

Haageocereus chosicensis (Werderm. & Backeb.) Backeb.

Slender, 19-ribbed stems up to 1.5 m tall and up to 6 cm thick, branching from the base, the apex with dense woolly felt, with reddish-yellow to brownish or whitish bristly hairs or spines intermingled. Areoles 1 cm apart, with thick yellowish-white felt, with 30–50 bristly, cream or yellow, darker tipped radial spines, and 3–4 amber-coloured, then greyish yellow, darker-tipped central spines up to 2 cm long. Flowers just below apex, narrowly funnel-shaped, 6–7 cm long, 2.5–3 cm wide, lilac red. Fruit globose, up to 4 cm across, green to pink, finally wine-red. Peru.

Haageocereus divaricatispinus Rauh & Backeb.

Groups of upright, 18–19-ribbed stems up to 1.2 m tall and 10–15 cm thick, freely branching from the base. Areoles with some white felt, with numerous, but not enveloping, white, hairy bristles 2.5–3 cm long, and porrect radial spines of various colours, yellow to purple, and usually 1, initially erect, later downward-pointing, strong needle-like, pale brown central spine up to 4 cm long, in addition to 3–6 shorter, greyish yellow, brownish-tipped spines. Flowers 10 cm long, dark purple. Fruit ovoid, up to 6 cm long and 4 cm thick, pale wine-red. Peru.

Haageocereus versicolor (Werderm. & Backeb.) Backeb.

Groups of upright or sometimes decumbent, 16–22-ribbed stems up to 1.5 m tall and 8 cm thick. Areoles somewhat felted, with 20–30 fine radial spines 5 mm long, and 1–2 upward- or downward-pointing central spines 1–4 cm long; all spines yellow to dark chestnut, in ±separate zones. Flowers near apex, slender-tubed, 8–10 cm long, 6.5 cm across, white, green outside. Fruit roundish, 3 cm across, yellow. N Peru.

Haageocereus zonatus Rauh & Backeb.

Shrubs up to 1.5 m tall, branching near base, with upright 13–14-ribbed stems 7–13 cm thick. Areoles close-set, golden-brown felted, with 15–25(–40) similar, spreading, thin, pale yellow radial spines up to 5 mm long, and 1–2(–4) tough, horizontal or downward-pointing, brown central spines 2–2.5 cm long. Flowering areoles producing much wool, tufts of wool in zones and persistent. Flowers 7 cm long, white. NC Peru.

Haageocereus acranthus (Vaupel) Backeb. ■□ □□

Upcurving or upright, sparsely branching stems, up to 2 m tall and up to 8 cm thick, with 12–14 ribs with many tubercles at apex. Areoles close-set, with yellow to dark-brown felt and 20–30 yellow radial spines 1 cm long, and 1 (or several) stronger, downward-pointing central spines up to 4 cm long. Flowers 6–8 cm long, greenish white. Fruit broadly round, green at first. Peru.

Haageocereus repens Rauh & Backeb. □■ □□

Decumbent stems often half-buried in the sand, up to 2 m long and 5–8 cm thick, rooting from the underside, with 19, very narrow ribs constricted between the tubercles, with usually slightly upturned tips. Areoles small, ochre yellow, later grey, with numerous, about 40, thin, almost bristle-shaped, amber-yellow, later grey, radial spines, and 1–2(–4) amber-yellow central spines up to 2 cm long and obliquely downward-pointing. Flowers 6–7 cm long, 3.5 cm across, wide-opening, pure white, muddy purple outside. Fruit red. N Peru.

Haageocereus decumbens (Vaupel) Backeb. □□ ■□

Decumbent, curving, not upturned, often jointed stems, 0.5–1 m long and 5 cm thick, branching from the base and rooting from the underside, with 15–20 ribs. Areoles close-set, with short woolly felt, 20–30 horizontally pointing, thin, up to 5 mm long radial spines, white to yellowish at base, with brown or red tip, and 5 stouter, dark red, black-tipped central spines 2–5 cm long. Flowers near apex, 6–8 cm long, 5–6 cm across, white, chocolate brown outside. Fruit oblong, 2.5 cm long, 1.5 cm thick, dark chestnut. S Peru.
(Illustration turned anticlockwise through 90°).

Loxanthocereus hoffmannii Ritter □□ □■

When first collected, this plant was misidentified as *Haageocereus setosus*. The different flowers show that it is allied to *Borzicactus* (see pp. 142-145).
Stem decumbent, 1 m or more tall, 6 cm thick, branching from base, with 15–20 low, crenate ribs; areoles close-set, with yellowish wool and long white hairs. Radial spines 20–50, about 8 mm long, bristly, clear brown, usually 3 central spines, 1 of them suberect, up to 3.5 cm long. Flowers at apex, surrounded by hairs up to 7 cm long, 7.5 cm long and 2.5 cm across when fully open, tubular with slightly oblique limb, the tube scarlet with small scales hairy in their axils, the inner perianth-segments crimson; stamens shorter than the limb; stigmas green. Fruit globose, 3 cm across, light green, sparsely hairy; seeds matt black. C Peru.

Neobinghamia climaxantha (Werderm.) Backeb. ■□ □□
[= Espostoa melanostele × Haageocereus chosicensis]

Over 1 m tall and 6–8 cm thick stems, branching from the base, ±thickly enveloped in white wool, with 19–27 ribs. Areoles close-set, with numerous white woolly hairs up to 1 cm long, 50–70 honey-coloured, radial spines 5–8 mm long, and 1–3 sharp, honey-coloured central spines 1.5–2 cm long. Flowers from very spiny and woolly areoles, in regular zones that usually cover a third to a half of the stem circumference. Flowers 5.5–6.5 cm long, deep rose pink. Peru, in the area where both parental species occur.

ESPOSTOA B. & R. (incl. PSEUDOESPOSTOA Backeb., FACHEIROA B. & R., VATRICANIA Backeb., THRIXANTHOCEREUS Backeb.)

Columnar cacti up to 4 m tall, ±freely branching from the base or higher, with erect branches. Areoles with numerous spines and sometimes long hairs forming a web-like covering on the stem. Flowers from a lateral cephalium with thick wool intermingled with bristles. Flowers medium-sized, campanulate-tubular, reddish to white. Pericarpel and receptacle-tube densely covered with long scales and hairs. Fruit globose to ovoid, juicy, greenish or carmine red, ±scaly, with dried floral remains. Seeds mostly curved ovoid with truncate base; seedcoat black, verrucose or almost smooth. Two species with cap-shaped seeds with extra-large hilum and dull brown seedcoat, shallowly verrucose. According to their vegetative structure 2 subgenera may be distinguished: *Espostoa*: areoles spiny and very long-haired, cephalium chiefly with soft wool and only sparse bristles. *Facheiroa* (B. & R.) F. Buxbaum: areoles with spines only, no long hairs, cephalium woolly or bristly, sometimes also with needle-shaped spines. About 12 sometimes very variable species mainly in Peru, also in Brazil and Bolivia.

Espostoa melanostele (Vaupel) Borg □■
[= Pseudoespostoa melanostele (Vaupel) Backeb.] (subgenus *Espostoa*) □□

Shrub 1–2 m tall, branching from the base with 10–15 cm thick stems, white hairy-felted, with 18–20 ribs. Areoles very close-set, with dense white or brownish wool up to 1 cm long, enveloping the stem; very numerous (40–50), amber-yellow, later blackish radial spines 5–10 mm long, and 1–3 amber-yellow central spines 4–10 cm long, mostly pointing obliquely upwards. Cephalium 50–70 cm long, up to 10 cm wide (covering 8 ribs), with a compact mass of wool, whitish at first, later intense yellowish brown. (Occasionally a double cephalium forms from 2 adjacent ones.) Flowers 5–6 cm long, 5 cm wide, night-blooming, white. Fruit rounded to pear-shaped, up to 5 cm long, whitish yellow to reddish. N to C Peru.

Espostoa lanata (Kunth) B. & R. (subgenus *Espostoa*) □□ ■□

Tree up to 4 m tall, with trunk up to 20 cm thick, and dense, candelabra-form crown of 20–30-ribbed branches up to 15 cm thick. Areoles close-set, with long white woolly hair enveloping stem, numerous needle-shaped, yellowish red-tipped radial spines, 4–7 cm long, and usually 2 very stout, porrect, several centimetres long, central spines, yellowish with reddish-brown tips. Cephalium becoming several metres long. Flowers 6 cm long, whitish. Fruit strawberry-like, carmine red. N Peru.

Espostoa guentheri (Kupper) F. Buxbaum □□
[= Vatricania guentheri (Kupper) Backeb.] (subgenus *Facheiroa*) □■

Up to 2 m tall and 10 cm thick stems, branching from the base, with 27, weakly tuberculate ribs. Areoles 1 cm apart, with short, yellowish-white felt and about 15 dark honey-coloured spines 5–22 mm long. Cephalium up to 50 cm long, reddish-brown to whitish, with yellowish-white wool and numerous spines 4–6 cm long. Flowers 8 cm long, 2.5–3 cm wide, campanulate-tubular, yellowish-white, night-blooming. Fruit ±scaly. Bolivia.

Espostoa blossfeldiorum (Werderm.) F. Buxbaum [= **Thrixanthocereus** ■□
blossfeldiorum (Werderm) Backeb.] (subgenus *Facheiroa*) □□
Unbranched stems, only rarely branching from the base, 3–4 m tall, up to 10 cm thick, with 18–25 ribs. Areoles close-set, 5 mm apart, with 20–25 thin, needle-shaped, glassy radial spines 6–8 mm long, and 1–4 brownish or blackish central spines up to 3 cm long. Cephalium facing south-west, about 1 m long, 3–4 cm (4–8 ribs) wide, with dense, yellowish-white wool and numerous close-set thin, strong, glassy bristles 4–5 cm long, dark brown. Flowers up to 6 cm long, 5 cm wide, slender funnel-shaped, cream, greenish white, smelling of carrion, night-blooming. Fruit cherry-sized. N Peru.

AUSTROCEPHALOCEREUS Backeb.

Upright, 1–5 m tall stems, branching from the base, with areoles producing abundant hair. Flowers from a lateral cephalium, small to medium-sized, wide tubular-campanulate or ovoid-campanulate, night-blooming. Lower half of very short pericarpel and thick-walled receptacle-tube with no scales or only very few rudimentary ones, upper half covered with somewhat spreading scales. Perianth very short, rotate, half-opening. Fruit fleshy, broadly ovoid or depressed globose, smooth and shiny, with dried floral-remains. Seeds elongate-curved or ovoid; seedcoat matt black, finely verrucose, or rather shiny, shallowly verrucose, with interstitial pits. The genus subdivides into 2 subgenera, the considerably more primitive *Espostoopsis* (F. Buxbaum) F. Buxbaum (flowers conspicuous, campanulate-funnelshaped) and the more highly evolved *Austrocephalocereus* Backeb. (flowers small, highly reduced, almost ovoid-campanulate, with very short perianth). 3 species in Brazil.

Austrocephalocereus dybowskii (Roland-Goss) Backeb. □■
□□
Numerous, rarely branching stems, ascending from base up to 4 m high, 8–10 cm thick, with over 20 ribs and completely cocooned in white, later pale grey hairs. Areoles close-set, with numerous short, hairy, yellow radial spines, and 2–3 needle-like, yellowish to brownish central spines up to 3 cm long. Cephalium up to 60 cm long, from a dense mass of white woolly tufts, without bristles. Flowers tubular-campanulate, 4 cm long, white. Fruit globose, up to 2.5 cm across, pink. Brazil (Bahia).

Austrocephalocereus purpureus (Guerke) Backeb. □□
■□
Upright, up to 5 m tall and up to 12 cm thick, only exceptionally branching stems, with 25 ribs, notched above the areoles. Areoles close-set in flowering zone, otherwise further apart, with 15–20 or more radial spines up to 15 mm long, and 4–6 yellowish or dark-brown central spines up to 5 cm long. Cephalium up to 1 m long and 12 cm wide, of compact, pale grey wool intermingled with reddish-brown or blackish bristles. Flowers 3.5 cm long, pale pink. Fruit narrowly turbinate, 2 cm long, violet-purple. Brazil.

ZEHNTNERELLA B. & R.

Stems up to 4 m high and up to 7 cm thick, usually branching from near the base into a mass of slender, very spiny branches. Flowers small, with almost cylindric tube, white. Pericarpel and receptacle-tube with small scales with white hair in the axils. Inside the tube at the base is a ring of long white hairs. Fruit small, globose, with dried floral remains. Seeds very small, curved ovoid; seedcoat brown or black, distinctly verrucose. 1 species in NE Brazil.

Zehntnerella squamulosa B. & R. □□
□■
Columnar cactus up to 4 m tall, freely-branching from the base up, with 20 cm thick stem and a mass of upright, slender, 17–20-ribbed branches up to 7 cm thick. Areoles with 10–15 needle-like, nut-brown spines up to 3 cm long. Flowers 3 cm long, white. Fruit globose, 2 cm across. NE Brazil.

BORZICACTUS Riccobono (incl. AKERSIA Buining, BOLIVICEREUS Cardenas, CLISTANTHOCEREUS Backeb., LOXANTHOCEREUS Backeb., MARITIMOCEREUS Akers, SETICEREUS Backeb., HILDEWINTERA Ritter)
Slender columnar cacti, unbranched or sprouting from the base, upright or decumbent or ascending, up to 1.5 m tall, or initially broad, depressed-globose, later very short, thick. Ribs sometimes with cross-furrows between the areoles. Spines very diverse. Flowers tubular to funnel-shaped, slightly or strongly zygomorphic. Tube sometimes curved into an S-shape. Receptacle-tube vivid orange to scarlet or light red. Pericarpel and receptacle-tube covered with triangular or pointed scales with dense, long, curly hair in the axils. At the base of the tube (closing the nectar chamber) is, in some cases, a ring of true hairs (not staminodes). Fruit globose, with dried floral-remains, remaining fleshy or later drying out, with numerous scales, hairs and bristles or ±naked. Seeds mostly obliquely ovoid, or elongate-curved, very rarely cap-shaped with inflated holum; seedcoat shiny black or brownish black, strongly, finely or shallowly verrucose, with interstitial pits. 30–40 species in Ecuador, Bolivia and Peru.
[Another species of Borzicactus (Loxanthocereus hoffmannii Ritter) is illustrated on p. 137.]

Borzicactus sepium (Kunth) B. & R.　　　　　　　　　　　　■□ □□
Unbranched or moderately branching from the base, up to 1.5 m tall and 4 cm thick stems, with up to 9 ribs, somewhat jointed by narrow cross-furrows above the areoles. Areoles 1.5–2 cm apart, initially with yellowish-white woolly felt and 8–11, obliquely outward-pointing, radial spines up to 1 cm long, red at first, later brown and grey, and 1 stouter central spine up to nearly 3 cm long. Flowers up to 7.5 cm long, pink, red outside. Fruit globose, 1.5–2 cm across, edible. Used as a hedge-plant on account of its erect habit of growth. Ecuador.

Borzicactus sepium var. **morleyanus** (B. & R.) Krainz　　　　□■
[= **Borzicactus morleyanus** B. & R.]　　　　　　　　　　　　□□
Usually upright, bushy stems, 4–6 cm thick, leaning or prostrate with age, with 11–16 ribs divided into tubercles by V-shaped notches above the areoles. Areoles about 1 cm apart, white-felted, with 15–20 needle-shaped, brown spines, later grey or white, unequal, 5–10 cm long. Flowers 5–7.5 cm long, dark carmine-red. Fruit globose, 1.5–2 cm thick. Ecuador.

Borzicactus samaipatanus (Cardenas) Kimnach　　　　　　□□
[= **Bolivicereus samaipatanus** Card.]　　　　　　　　　　　■□
Upright stems up to 1.5 m tall and 3.5–4 cm thick, sprouting from the base, with 14–16 low, slightly crenate ribs. Areoles 3–4 mm apart, with light brown felt and up to 20 fine, needle-shaped, yellowish-brown spines, unequal, 4–10–30 mm long. Flowers 3.5 cm long, S-shaped, brilliant red, with purple stamens and violet anthers. Fruit globose, 9–11 mm long, 7–9 mm thick, with dense white and brown wool. Bolivia (Santa Cruz).

Borzicactus roezlii (F. Haage) W.T. Marshall　　　　　　　□□
[= **Seticereus roezlii** (F. Haage) Backeb.]　　　　　　　　□■
Broad, laxly branching shrub, up to 2 m tall, with grey-green, 9-ribbed stems up to 7 cm thick. Areoles up to 2 cm apart, separated by cross-furrows, initially with yellow felt, with 9–12, light brown, subulate radial spines up to 1 cm long, and 1 horizontal or downward-pointing central spine 1–4 cm long. Flowers numerous, round the apex, dark carmine-red, 6–7 cm long, usually zygomorphic with straight or curved receptacle-tube, oblique limb and somewhat recurved perianth-segments. Fruit 2–4 cm long, 2.5–4 cm across, yellow to reddish orange. N Peru.

142

Borzicactus acanthurus (Vaupel) B. & R.　　　　■□
[= **Loxanthocereus acanthurus** (Vaupel) Backeb.]　　□□
Decumbent stems, sometimes ascending or arching over rocks, up to 30 cm long and
2–5 cm thick, with 15–18, rounded ribs, cross-furrowed, with sharp notches. Areoles
with up to 20 short, thin, yellowish radial spines, and 2–5 very similar central spines up to
1.5 cm long. Flowers 4–5 cm long, narrow-tubed, scarlet. Fruit globose, 2–2.5 cm
thick. C Peru.

Borzicactus aureispinus (Ritter) Hutchison & Kimnach　　□■
[= **Hildewintera aureispina** (Ritter) Backeb.]　　□□
Stems up to 1.5 m long and 2–2.5 cm thick, with 16–17 ribs, freely-branching mainly
from below, and dangling from overhanging rocks. Areoles 3–5 mm apart, with light
brown felt and about 30 fine, spreading, golden yellow not greying, radial spines 4–
10 mm long, and about 20 rather stouter central spines 5–10 mm long. Spines on older
flowering stems often longer. Flowers lateral on stems, 4–6 cm long and 5 cm across,
outer perianth-segments orange-yellow with vermilion or blood-red central streak,
inner perianth-segments white to pale pink. Fruit globose, 7–10 mm across, green to
reddish green. Bolivia.

Borzicactus icosagonus (Kunth) B. & R.　　□□
[= **Seticereus icosagonus** (Kunth) Backeb.　　■□
Decumbent to ascending stems, up to 60 cm long and 6 cm thick, with 18–20 ribs,
forming large, low colonies. Ribs ±strongly tuberculate. Areoles with about 30 golden-
yellow, bristle-shaped spines up to 1.5(–2) cm long, and flowering areoles with
hair-fine, golden-yellow bristles 2–3 cm long. Flowers 7–8 cm long, vermilion to scarlet
or orange. Fruit large, yellow, with whitish to brownish hair. S Ecuador to N Peru.

Another species referable to *Borzicactus* is *Loxanthocereus hoffmannii* (see pp. 136,
137).

OREOCEREUS (A. Berger) Riccobono (incl. AREQUIPA B. & R.)
Usually low, upright to ascending columnar stems, branching from the base, more rarely
taller, sparsely branching, up to 2–3 m tall, some species remaining globose (and
flowering) for a long time, only later becoming columnar. Ribs notched between the
areoles, or areoles on tubercles, densely spiny, usually with very long hairs enveloping
the stem. Flowers mostly near apex, tubular, straight or ±strongly zygomorphic and
somewhat compressed laterally in the curved zone, whole flower vivid red. Pericarpel
and receptacle-tube evenly covered with pointed scales with hairy tufts in the axils,
podaria long-decurrent. Fruit pear-shaped or rounded, with scale-remains and tufts of
hair, or almost smooth, with dried floral-remains, dry-fleshed, opening with a hole at the
base. Seeds very variable, ±drop-shaped; seedcoat matt black, occasionally shiny
black, shallowly verrucose with large interstitial pits. 12 species, sometimes very
variable, in Bolivia, S Peru, N Chile, Argentinian Andes at altitudes above 3000 m.
　　□□
Oreocereus celsianus (Lem.) Riccobono　　□■
Upright or ascending stems, up to 1 m tall and 8–12 cm thick, branching bushily from the
base, dark green, with 10–17 blunt, tuberculate ribs. Areoles 10–18 mm apart, with
yellowish woolly felt, with white woolly hair up to 5 cm long, 9, stiff, yellow, later darker,
radial spines, up to 2 cm long, and 1–4 stouter central spines up to 8 cm long. Flowers
lateral, near the apex, 7–9 cm long and 3 cm wide, dull pink. Fruit globose. Bolivia,
S Peru, N Chile.

Oreocereus hendriksenianus Backeb.

■□
□□

Dense, broad colonies of ±upcurved stems, 1–1.4 m tall, branching from the base, with 10 broad ribs with shallow cross-furrows. Areoles yellow-felted at first, later dark grey, with abundant wispy, dangling, black to brown, later white, woolly hair, 8–9 radial spines 1.5 cm long, and 1–4 horn-yellow, gently curved, central spines up to 7 cm long. Flowers near the apex, up to 8 cm long, carmine red. Fruit globose or oblong, up to 5 cm across, reddish-yellow to yellowish-green, hairy. The hairs and spination of this species very variable. S and C Peru.

Oreocereus trollii (Kupper) Backeb.

□■
□□

Small groups of upright stems, sprouting from the base, up to 50 cm tall and 10 cm thick, with 15–25 low, strongly tuberculate ribs enveloped in dense wool. Areoles 3 cm apart with white woolly hairs up to 7 cm long, 10–15 bristle-shaped radial spines and 1 (to several) strong, yellow, reddish or brown central spines. Flowers 4 cm long, pink to carmine. N Argentina, Bolivia.

Oreocereus rettigii (Quehl) F. Buxbaum
[= **Arequipa rettigii** (Quehl) Oehme]

□□
■□

Initially globose and unbranched, later stout cylindric, up to 60 cm long and up to 15 cm thick, sometimes decumbent and branching from the base. Ribs 16–20, straight or gently spiralling, divided into low tubercles. Areoles 5 mm apart, pale yellow- later grey-felted and glabrescent, with about 30 spreading, very thin, glassy white, often interlacing radial spines, unequal, 10–15 mm long, and 3–5(–10) white, sometimes brown-tipped, almost black when old, central spines up to 5 cm long. Apex with light wool and erect, brownish spines. Flowers near apex, zygomorphic, up to 7 cm long, bright carmine-red. Fruit up to 2.5 cm long, yellow to carmine red, with floral remains. S Peru.

MORAWETZIA Backeb.

Upright or prostrate-stemmed shrubs, freely branching from the base, up to 1 m tall. Areoles with spines and occasional to absent bristly hairs. At the flowering stage, stems become club-shaped and produce a terminal cephalium with a mop of bristles and hairs, only rarely grown through. Flowers large, somewhat zygomorphic, slender-tubed, bluish carmine-red. Pericarpel and receptacle-tube with small triangular scales and long decurrent podaria, with long curly hair in the axils. Primary stamens modified into short, pointed-triangular staminodes. Fruit obovoid to pear-shaped, with dried floral-remains, upper part somewhat sculptured, lower part almost smooth. Seeds elongate helmet-shaped; seedcoat shiny black, small-celled, verrucose. Differing from *Oreocereus* in its terminal cephalium and staminodal scales. 1 species in C Peru.

Morawetzia doelziana Backeb.

□□
□■

Bushes, freely branching from the base into stems 1 m tall and 6–8 cm thick, with 10–11 ribs, somewhat constricted between areoles. Areoles 1.5 cm apart, grey-felted with about 20 pointed spines up to 3 cm long, later 4 stouter, cruciform, yellow to dark brown central spines up to 4 cm long. Numerous long, white, woolly hairs towards the end of the shoot. At the start of the flowering stage shoots become club-shaped at the tip and twice as thick as at the base. Cephalium of long white woolly hairs and whitish-yellow bristles up to 5 cm long. Flowers 10 cm long, bluish carmine-red. C Peru.

CLEISTOCACTUS Lemaire

Stems slender, erect or decumbent, up to more than 2 m tall, branching from the base, with numerous transversely furrowed ribs. Areoles close-set with numerous thin, prickly spines. Flowers abundant, slender-tubular, straight or curved, with straight or obliquely truncate limb, whole flower brightly coloured, perianth-segments very small, scarcely opening. Pericarpel and receptacle-tube densely covered with narrow-lanceolate scales often with long woolly hairs in the axils. Fruit small, globose, glabrescent, with persistent floral-remains. Seeds small, obliquely ovoid; seedcoat shiny black with rows of fine, interstitial pits.

2 subgenera can be differentiated according to flower-structure.: *Annemarnieria* F. Buxbaum: Flowers straight or slightly curved, ±radially symmetrical, with straight or only slightly oblique throat. The protrusion of the receptacle-tube which covers the nectar chamber carries the lowermost stamens. *Cleistocactus*: Flowers S-shaped, curved, zygomorphic, with strongly oblique limb. No stamens on the diaphragm above the nectar chamber. About 30 species from S Peru across Bolivia to Argentina, Paraguay and Uruguay.

Cleistocactus wendlandiorum Backeb.

Unbranched, 3 cm thick, light green stem, with about 22 ribs. Areoles with about 40 very thin, 1 cm long, dense, upright, whitish to cream spines and a few more, yellowish, central ones. Flowers 5 cm long, orange to vermilion, emerging horizontally but bent upwards through a right-angle above the pericarpel, somewhat swollen close to the base and curving gently outwards. Bolivia.

Cleistocactus candelilla Card.

Erect or decumbent stems, up to 1 m high and 3 cm thick, branching from the base, with 11—12 cross-furrowed ribs. Areoles brown-felted with 13—15 radial spines up to 5 mm long, yellowish brown at the top, whitish below, and 3—4 slightly flattened central spines. Flowers straight or somewhat curved, 3.5 cm long, outer perianth-segments yellow; brown tips, inner ones purple; white edges. Fruit 1 cm across, pale salmon. Bolivia.

Cleistocactus straussii (Heese) Backeb.

Erect, up to 3 m tall and 8 cm thick stem, branching from the base, with up to 30 ribs. Areoles with 30—40 white bristles up to 17 mm long, and 4 downward-pointing, pale yellow spines up to 2 cm long. Flowers lateral, on upper stem, 8—9 cm long, dark red. Fruit pear-shaped, top umbilicate, 2 cm thick, with brown wool, red. N Argentina and Bolivia.

Cleistocactus smaragdiflorus (F.A.C. Weber) B. & R.

Decumbent to nearly erect stems, up to 1 m long and 3 cm thick, with 12—14 ribs. Areoles with light brown woolly felt and 10—14, pale yellow, radial spines 1 cm long, and 4—6 rigid, pale yellow, central spines 15—20 or 30—35 mm long. Flowers 5 cm long with light red tube and emerald green perianth-segments. Fruit globose, 1.5 cm thick, light red. Argentina.

CEPHALOCLEISTOCACTUS Ritter

Shrub up to 5 m high, with branches 1—3 cm thick arising from the base and above, ribs with transverse furrows above the areoles. Flowers from a lateral cephalium with long, bristle-shaped spines. Flowers thick-tubed, narrowing to spindle-shaped towards the opening. Perianth-segments very short. Pericarpel and receptacle-tube densely covered with small, pointed scales, with bristly hair and wool in the axils. Nectar chamber not closed off with a diaphragm. Fruit globose with scales and hairs, juicy, greenish carmine, dehiscent, with firmly attached floral-remains. Seeds small, obliquely ovoid, laterally compressed; seedcoat shiny black, almost smooth, with very small interstitial pits. 1 species in Bolivia.

Cephalocleistocactus chrysocephalus Ritter ■□ □□

Shrub 2–5 m high, sprouting from the base and above, with somewhat pointed branches 3–5 cm thick, with 11–14 ribs. Branches with cephalia usually arching bow-shaped. Areoles with yellowish-brown, later white felt, with 15 glassy radial spines and 6 central spines 2–3 cm long. Cephalium up to 1 m long, 3–4 cm (4–7 ribs) wide, with areoles with yellow to brownish felt and up to 30 brownish, weak, bristly spines 3–4 cm long. Flowers 4.5–5 cm long, carmine red. Fruit 2.5–3 cm thick and 1.7–2 cm long, pale greenish to carmine red. Bolivia.

DENMOZA B. & R.,

Solitary, up to 1 m tall and 30 cm thick stems, with numerous, densely spiny ribs. Flowers mostly near the apex, medium-sized, tubular, with almost closed throat, straight or curved in an S-shape. Stamens and style extruding from the throat in a bunch. Pericarpel and receptacle-tube densely covered with red scales, finely hairy in the axils. Fruit globose, semi-dry and leathery, with deep umbilicus, scales and woolly tufts later deciduous. Seeds large, helmet-shaped, with large basal hilum; seedcoat matt black, verrucose, with large depressions. 2 species in W Argentina.

Denmoza erythrocephala (K. Schumann) A. Berger □■ □□

Up to 1.5 m tall and 30 cm thick stems, with 20–30 blunt ribs. Areoles with over 30 stiff, pink or foxy-red spines, inner up to 6 cm long, outer modified to almost hair-like bristles. Flowers 7.5 cm long, red. Fruit a globose, berry 2 cm across, yellow. W Argentina.

ARROJADOA B. & R.

Upright or semi-prostrate, sparsely branching, slender stems, with jointed offsets, sometimes swollen at the ends of the shoots. Flowers from terminal cephalium of dense wool and brown bristles. Either the cephalium is grown through, or the offset forks from areoles further out. Flowers almost cylindric, completely pink or red. Pericarpel and receptacle-tube naked and glabrous. Fruit slender-turbinate, smooth, almost translucent, whitish to red, with dried floral-remains. Seeds small, irregular pear-shaped to kidney-shaped; seedcoat shiny black, verrucose with interstitial pits. 7 species in Brazil.

Arrojadoa rhodantha (Guerke) B. & R. □□ ■□

Upright, leaning or decumbent stems, up to 2 m long and 2–5 cm thick, jointed, mostly branching from base, dark green, 10–12 fairly shallow ribs. Areoles with short felt, 20 yellowish to brownish radial spines up to 1.2 cm long, and 5–6 stronger, dark brown central spines up to 3 cm long. Stems not thickened under the cephalium. Flowers up to 3.5 cm long and 1.2 cm wide, bluish red. Fruit turbinate, crimson. Brazil.

MICRANTHOCEREUS Backeb.

Upright, up to 1.25 m tall stems, branching from the base, with numerous densely spiny ribs. Flowers numerous, from a loose, lateral cephalium, very small, cylindric-tubed with very short perianth. Pericarpel and receptacle-tube naked, same colour as whole flower. Fruit small, naked, fleshy, with floral remains on lid. Seeds small, obliquely ovoid to almost kidney-shaped, slightly keeled; seedcoat dark brown, almost smooth, with interstitial pits. 3 species in Brazil.

Micranthocereus polyanthus (Werderm) Backeb. □□ □■

Stems up to 1.25 m tall and 3.5–5 cm thick, branching from the base only, with a bluish bloom, almost completely covered in white wool, with 15–20 low ribs. Areoles with white wool 1–2 cm long, with 20–30 needle-like, whitish to golden-yellow radial spines 0.5–1.2 cm long, and 3–7 golden yellow to almost reddish central spines sometimes up to 3 cm long. Flowers 1.6–1.8 cm long, pale pink to cream. Fruit rose-red. Brazil.

MATUCANA B. & R. (incl. SUBMATUCANA Backeb.)

Small to medium-sized, initially globose, later upright or decumbent stems, up to more than 50 cm long, solitary or branching from the base and forming cushions. Areoles with very diverse spines, initially often with more hairs. Flowers conspicuous, together with tube bright red to orange, violent pink or yellow, zygomorphic or regular. Pericarpel and receptacle-tube with numerous lanceolate scales, axils glabrous or hairy. Fruit small, globose to oblong, with adherent floral remains, ±scaly, semi-fleshy, opening lengthways. Seeds very variable, obliquely ovoid; seedcoat black, verrucose to wrinkled with interstitial pits. About 15 species, some very variable, in Peru.

Matucana haynei (Otto) B. & R.

Globose to short columnar, up to 60 cm tall and 10 cm thick, never branching, with 25–30 tuberculate ribs. Areoles close-set, white-felted, later glabrescent, with about 30 needle-shaped white radial spines up to 2 cm long, and on flowering plants usually 3, grey, dark-tipped central spines 3.5–5 cm long. Flowers near the apex, 6–7 cm long and 3.5 cm wide, scarlet to carmine. Fruit club-shaped, small. C Peru.

Matucana aurantiaca (Vaupel) F. Buxbaum
[= Submatucana aurantiaca (Vaupel) Backeb.]

Globose to flattened spherical, not elongate with age, up to 15 cm in height and diameter, unbranched or sprouting, with about 16 ribs. Areoles with 20–25 dissimilar, reddish brown, ±curving spines, outer up to 2.5 cm and a few central ones 2.5–4 cm long. Flowers 7–9 cm wide, pale orange. Fruit rounded-oblong, up to 2 cm thick, dark brown or purple. N Peru.

Matucana madisoniorum (Hutchison) Rowley
[= Submatucana madisoniorum (Hutchison) Backeb.]

Flattened down, globose or short columnar stem, up to 30 cm long and 8–15 cm thick, grey-green with velvety sheen, with 8–12 slightly elevated ribs, distinctly crenate when young. Areoles with grey hairs when young, becoming black with age, and 1–2(–5) easily detached, sturdy, curved, dark brown spines 5–6 cm long, or no spines. Flowers long-tubed, 8–10 cm long, almost regular, erect or slightly curved, bright vermilion. Pericarpel with leafy scales and tufts of long, blackish hair. Fruit globose, 2 cm across, with short hairs, splitting lengthways. N Peru.

OROYA B. & R.

Depressed globose, unbranched, rarely with several heads, with tuberous root. Ribs often divided into chin-shaped tubercles. Radial spines ±pectinate. Flowers in a ring round apex, vivid red, pink or yellow, regular, campanulate-funnelshaped, outer perianth-segments spreading wide, inner erect. Pericarpel and receptacle-tube with scales with decurrent podaria, with tufts of hair in the scale axils. Fruit a turbinate-globose berry, yellowish or reddish, with adherent floral-remains. Seeds helmet-shaped; seedcoat matt black, verrucose with large depressions. Probably only 2 species, Peru.

Oroya peruviana (K. Schumann) B. & R.

Depressed globose, unbranched or sprouting, 10–14 cm wide, bluish green, with up to 21 rather downward spiralling ribs divided into hexagonal tubercles by 2 notches above the areoles. Areoles 2–2.5 cm apart, with white wool, with about 18 needle-shaped, dark brown radial spines up to 1.3 cm long, and 1–3, barely differing central spines. Flowers numerous, apical, up to 3 cm long, perianth-segments light carmine to vermilion, lemon yellow to whitish at base. Fruit shortly clavate, reddish brown. Very variable species in stem shape, spination and flower colour. Peru.
Illustration shows *O. peruviana* var. *laxiareolata*.

ECHINOPSIS Zuccarini (incl. PSEUDOLOBIVIA (Backeb.) Backeb.)

Globose to short columnar, often freely sprouting; some species up to over 1 m high. Ribs straight, often somewhat crenate or with oblique cross-furrows. Flowers lateral, large, usually very long funnel-shaped, white or pale pink (night-blooming) or yellow or red (day-blooming). Pericarpel with tiny scales, receptacle-tube with long, narrow scales with long ±dense woolly hairs. Fruit semi-fleshy, bursting open, with flocky hair. Seeds almost globose or obovoid; seedcoat matt black, verrucose. About 50 species in South America: Uruguay, Argentina, Paraguay, and a few in Bolivia.

Echinopsis calochlora K. Schumann

Globose or somewhat elongate, 6–9 cm thick, glossy green, with 13, distinctly crenate ribs. Areoles in the notches, with pale grey felt and 14–20 thin, straight, yellowish radial spines 5–10 mm long, with 3–4 rather stouter and darker central spines. Flowers 16 cm long and 10 cm wide, white, tube narrow, greenish yellow. Brazil.

Echinopsis eyriesii (Turpin) Zucc.

Unbranched or moderately sprouting, globose, later elongate or cylindric, up to 30 cm high and 12–15 cm broad, dark green, with 11–18 sinuate, jointed ribs up to 2 cm high, separated by sharp furrows. Areoles 1.5–3.5 cm apart, grey-felted, with 7–14, conical, white or dark brown radial spines up to 5 mm long, and 4–8 very dark-brown central spines 5 mm long. Flowers lateral, solitary, 15–25 cm long, 8–12 cm wide, funnel-shaped, pure white, jasmine-scented. Fruit narrowly ovoid, 3 cm long. S Brazil, Uruguay, Argentina.

Echinopsis aurea B. & R.
[= Pseudolobivia aurea (B. & R.) Backeb.]

Globose to short cylindric, up to 10 cm high and 7 cm broad, dark green, with 14–15 sharp-angled ribs separated by deep furrows. Areoles brown-felted, with 8–10 spreading, light brown radial spines 1 cm long, and 4 stouter, dark brown to black central spines 2–3 cm long. Flowers low on the sides, 9 cm long, 8 cm wide, light to deep yellow, with greenish white tube. Argentina.

Echinopsis kermesina (Krainz) Krainz
[= Pseudolobivia kermesina Krainz]

Depressed globose, up to 8 cm broad, 6 cm high, sappy, dark green, with 15–23 ribs with ±hatchet-shaped tubercles. Areoles grey-felted, 12–15 mm apart, with 11–16 yellowish brown, later grey, radial spines, unequal, 6–12 mm long, and 4 (–6) rather darker central spines up to 25 mm long. Flowers near apex, 17.5 cm long and 9 cm wide, carmine pink to deep carmine red. Fruit oblong to globose, 15–20 mm long and wide. Argentina.

Echinopsis ancistrophora Spegazzini   ■□
[= **Pseudolobivia ancistrophora** (Speg.) Backeb.]   □□
Depressed globose, up to 8 cm broad, glossy dark green, with 15–16 ribs, 1 cm high. Areoles with 3–7(–9) flexible, reflexed, whitish, radial spines 15 mm long, and 1, light brown, hooked central spine up to 2 cm long. Flowers 12–16 cm long, slender-tubed, white, scentless. Fruit oblong, up to 1.6 cm across, green. Argentina.

Echinopsis kratochviliana Backeb.   □■
[= **Pseudolobivia kratochviliana** (Backeb.) Backeb.]   □□
Depressed globose, up to 5 cm high and up to 6 cm broad, dark green, sometimes brownish grey-green, with 18 sharp-angled ribs. Areoles up to 8 mm apart, with 12, whitish, radial spines up to 1.5 cm long, and 1–4 darker, curved or slightly hooked central spines 2–5 cm long. Flowers 6 cm wide, pure white with green tube. Argentina.

Echinopsis obrepanda (Salm-Dyck) K. Schumann   □□
[= **Pseudolobivia obrepanda** (Salm-Dyck) Backeb.]   ■□
Depressed globose, solitary, only seldom sprouting, 10 cm broad, glossy dark green or grey-green, with 17–18 sharp-angled ribs divided into off-set, hatchet-shaped tubercles. Areoles in the notches are up to 2 cm apart, grey-felted, with 7–11, white to brownish radial spines 1 cm long, and 1–3 central spines 1–3(–5) cm long; nearly all spines slightly curved. Flowers up to 20 cm long, 12–18 cm wide, white, parsley-scented. Bolivia.
Illustration shows *E. obrepanda* var. *purpurea*.

     □□
Echinopsis tubiflora Zucc.   □■
Initially globose, later columnar, up to 75 cm high and 12–15 cm thick, offsets sprouting when mature, dark green, with 11–12, sharp-angled, slightly sinuate ribs separated by deep furrows. Areoles up to 2 cm apart, with white, later grey or black felt, and numerous (up to 20) porrect, yellowish, dark-tipped radial spines, unequal, up to 2.5 cm long, and 3–4 stouter central spines sometimes up to 3.5 cm long. Flowers up to 24 cm long, 10 cm wide, white, green outside. Argentina.

LOBIVIA B. & R. (incl. ACANTHOCALYCIUM Backeb., ACANTHO-LOBIVIA Backeb. REICHEOCACTUS Backeb. p.p., SOEHRENSIA (Backeb.) Backeb., CHAMAECEREUS B. & R., HELIANTHOCEREUS Backeb. p.p.)

Medium-sized globose or shortly cylindric, unbranched or sprouting from the base. Ribs usually divided into hatchet-shaped tubercles by oblique cross-furrows above the areoles. Spines very diverse. Flowers at various heights from mature areoles, red, yellow or white, campanulate-funnelshaped, with short, wide tube. Pericarpel and receptacle-tube densely covered with scales and woolly hairs, occasionally with bristly spines in the axils of the lower scales. Stamens usually in 2 groups, the upper forming a ring round the throat (throat-circle), the filament-bases sometimes swollen and forming a 'hymen'. Fruit small, globose, hairy, occasionally also with bristly spines, semi-dry, with dried floral-remains. Seeds globose to ovoid; seedcoat matt or glossy black, ±verrucose. Over 70 species in Bolivia, Peru and the Argentinian Andes. In view of the extraordinary natural variability of these plants in their habitat, probably only a fraction should really be considered 'good' species (see the observations of Rausch, 1975).

Lobivia backebergii (Werderm.) Backeb. var. **hertrichiana** (Backeb.) Rausch ■□ □
[= **Lobivia hertrichiana** Backeb.] □□

Elongate-globose to somewhat oblong, unbranched or sprouting from the base, up to 10 cm high, 5—8 cm wide, vivid green, with 14—15 ribs divided by oblique cross-furrows above areoles. Areoles 1 cm apart, initially with sparse white woolly felt, with 5—12 or more yellowish to light brown, later grey, mostly curved radial spines, unequal, up to 1.5 cm long, and 1—3 porrect central spines up to 3 cm long. Flowers slender-tubed, 5.5 cm long, 4 cm wide, blood-red to madder-red with bluish lustre. Fruit almost globose, 7 mm thick, semi-dry, splitting horizontally. Bolivia (La Paz).

Lobivia maximiliana (Heyder ex. A. Dietrich) □■
Backeb. var. **corbula** (Herrera) Rausch □□

Stems cylindric, freely sprouting, often forming large clumps, light green, with 17 ribs divided by cross-furrows into hatchet-shaped tubercles. Areoles 2 cm apart, depressed, initially white felted, with 7—12, curved, honey-coloured radial spines, unequal, 3—5 cm long, and 1 upcurving central spine up to 7 cm long. Flowers lateral, 5—6 cm long, inner perianth-segments curving inwards, red outside, yellow inside, carmine-tipped. Fruit almost globose, up to 1.2 cm across, greenish red. S Peru, N Bolivia (Lake Titicaca).

□□
Lobivia pentlandii (Hooker) B. & R. ■□

Globose to slightly elongate stems, freely sprouting, mat-forming, dark green to grey, with 12—15 ribs divided by cross-furrows into hatchet-shaped tubercles. Areoles 2 cm apart, initially white felted, with 7—12 straight or slightly curving, brownish radial spines 1—3 cm long, and 1 upcurving central spine 3—4 cm long. Flowers lateral, 5—6 cm long, open funnel-shaped, lilac-coloured. Fruit globose, 1—2 cm across, green. As regards spination and flower colour (carmine-red, orange or yellow), this is an extraordinarily variable species. S Peru, N Bolivia (S shore of Lake Titicaca to Potosi).

□□
Lobivia cinnabarina (Hooker) B. & R. □■

Unbranched, depressed globose to globose, up to 15 cm across, dark green, with 18—21, spiralling ribs 1 cm high, divided towards the base into jutting, chin-like tubercles. Areoles in the notches, 10—12 mm apart, sparsely white-felted, with 8—10 slightly curved, light brown, later grey radial spines up to 1.5 cm long, and 2—3 stouter central spines. Flowers lateral, towards the apex, broad funnel-shaped with short tube, 6—7 cm long, up to 8 cm wide, scarlet to carmine red. Fruit globose, 2 cm thick, semi-dry, splitting vertically. Bolivia (Sucre, Potosi).

Lobivia pugionacantha Rose & Boed. var. **rossii** (Boed.) Rausch ■□
[= **Lobivia rossii** Boed.] □□

Globose to ovoid, usually unbranched, up to more than 7 cm broad, matt grey green, with thick tuberous root and 17–20 sharp ribs. Areoles 1.5 cm apart, white-felted, with 8–10 lateral, subulate, reddish horn-coloured to grey, radial spines 4–6 cm long, and up to 3 downward-pointing central spines up to 5 cm long. Flowers funnel-shaped, 4.5 cm long and wide, yellow, orange, carmine to blood-red, mostly perfumed. Fruit 1 cm thick, green, semi-dry, splitting lengthways and across. Bolivia (Potosi to La Quiaca).

□■
Lobivia tiegeliana Wessner □□

Unbranched, relatively small, depressed globose to globose, 6 cm across, glossy green, with ±well-developed rootstock and 18 slightly oblique ribs interrupted by cross-furrows. Areoles in cross-furrows 9 mm apart, with short woolly felt, with 8–12 flexible, needle-shaped, honey-yellow, russet-tipped radial spines up to 1 cm long, not appressed but curved right round so that they point towards the stem, and 1–3 chestnut or dark brown, overlapping central spines slightly curved at the tip. Flowers numerous, from the top third of the stem, 2.5 cm long, 4.2 cm across, shining violet-pink, outer perianth-segments curving well back. Fruit globose to ovoid, semi-dry, splitting lengthways and across. S Bolivia to N Argentina (Tarija to Iruya).

□□
Lobivia sanguiniflora Backeb. ■□

Depressed globose to globose, unbranched, up to 10 cm high and wide, with ±well-developed rootstock and up to 18 spiralling ribs with oblique, transverse notches. Areoles with 10, laterally appressed, mostly curved, dark, later grey radial spines, unequal, 8–15 mm long, and 1–3 hooked central spines 2 cm long (exceptionally up to 8 cm). Flowers short-tubed, 4–5 cm wide, pale to dark blood-red with white throat. Fruit small, semi-dry, splitting lengthways and across. N Argentina (Santa Victoria).

Lobivia haematantha (Speg.) B. & R. var. **kuehnrichii** (Frič) Rausch □□
[= **Lobivia kuehnrichii** Frič] □■

Unbranched or sprouting, globose to shortly cylindric, 3–8 cm broad, grey-green, with long tuberous root and about 12–15 spiralling, narrow, low ribs. Areoles with 10–12 whitish radial spines up to 1 cm long, appressed, and 1–4 yellow to black central spines, unequal, up to 6 cm long. Flowers shortly funnel-shaped, wide-opening, yellow to orange. Fruit ovoid, green to violet-brown. N Argentina.

Lobivia chrysantha (Werderm.) Backeb.

Unbranched, globose to shortly cylindric, 6–7 cm broad, matt grey-green, with tuberous rootstock, and 8–13(–26) straight or slightly twisting ribs. Areoles with 5–7(–14) thin, dark brown radial spines up to 2 cm long, and up to 3 sturdier central spines up to 3 cm long. Flowers bell-shaped, 5 cm long, yellow to orange with red throat. Fruit globose or ovoid. N Argentina.

Lobivia chrysantha (Werderm.) Backeb. var. **jajoiana** (Backeb.) Rausch
[= **Lobivia jajoiana** Backeb.]

Usually unbranched, globose to elongate-globose, up to 12 cm high and up to 8 cm wide, sap green, with 12–14 ribs divided into oblique tubercles. Areoles with 8–10 reddish-white radial spines up to 1 cm long, and 1 upwards projecting, darker to blackish, hooked central spine, 2.5 cm or more long. Flowers campanulate to broadly funnel-shaped, wine- or tomato-red or even yellow with deep purple throat, hymen and upper stamens. N Argentina.

Lobivia saltensis (Speg.) B. & R. var. **nealeana** (Backeb.) Rausch
[= **Lobivia nealeana** Backeb.]

Stems initially unbranched, later sprouting and forming colonies, up to 10 cm high and 5 cm wide, leaf-green or brownish green, with fleshy rootstock and 14–16 low ribs. Areoles with 10–12, laterally spreading, brown, radial spines up to 1 cm long, and up to 2 protruding, often twisting to almost hooked central spines up to 2.5 cm long. Flowers funnel-shaped, 3–6 cm long, 4–6 cm wide, brilliant red. Fruit rather small, rounded, reddish green. N Argentina.

Lobivia famatimensis (Speg.) B. & R.
[= **Reicheocactus pseudoreicheanus** Backeb.]

Globose, later cylindric and branching, 5–7 cm thick, with about 40 very narrow ribs divided up into very tiny tubercles. Areoles linear, with up to 9, tiny, pale spines up to 3 mm long, pectinately appressed. Flowers shortly funnel-shaped, up to 3.5 cm long and wide, yellow with red style, outer perianth-segments red-streaked. Fruit thick-walled, fleshy, 1.5 cm long, 1 cm thick, completely enveloped in light reddish-brown wool. N Argentina (Famatina and San José de Jachal to San Juan).

Lobivia formosa (Pfeiffer) Dodds ssp. **bruchii** (B. & R.) Rausch ■□ □□
[= **Soehrensia bruchii** (B. & R.) Backeb.]

Initially unbranched and globose, later up to 50 cm wide and forming broad colonies; with up to 50 rounded ribs with pronounced notches between the areoles. Areoles with 9–12, spreading, straight or ±curved, yellowish-brown radial spines up to 3 cm long, and 1(–3) porrect central spines. Flowers 4–5 cm long, blood-red. N Argentina.

Lobivia formosa (Pfeiffer) Dodds ssp. **bruchii** (B. & R.) Rausch
var. **kieslingii** Rausch □■ □□
[= **Soehrensia bruchii** (B. & R.) Backeb. var. **kieslingii** Rausch]

Unbranched, globose, up to 25 cm wide, fresh green, with up to 30 straight ribs divided into 2–2.5 cm long tubercles. Areoles white-felted, with 7–13 radial spines up to 2.5 cm long, curving towards the stem, and 1–2 upcurving central spines up to 3 cm long. All spines hard and pointed, brown with darker tips. Flowers 9 cm long and wide, orange-red with violet-pink outside. Fruit broadly globose, 3.5 cm long, 4 cm across, green. Argentina (Tucuman).

Lobivia violacea (Werderm.) A. Berger □□ ■□
[= **Acanthocalycium violaceum** (Werderm.) Backeb.]

Unbranched, globose or usually somewhat cylindric, up to 20 cm high and 15 cm across, bright green, sometimes yellowish, with about 15 ribs up to 2 cm high. Areoles 1.5–2 cm apart, at first with fluffy white wool, later glabrous with 10–12, (up to 20 on older areoles), straight, yellowish, brown-tipped spines up to 3 cm long, and later 4 stronger central spines up to 4 cm long. Flowers near the apex, 7.5 cm long and 6 cm wide, pale violet or lilac. Argentina.

Lobivia klimpeliana (Weidl. & Werderm.) A. Berger □□ □■
[= **Acanthocalycium klimpelianum** (Weidl & Werderm.) Backeb.]

Depressed globose, with depressed apex, up to 10 cm wide, dark green, with 19 straight ribs 1 cm high, somewhat tuberculate between the areoles. Areoles 2 cm apart, initially with yellowish-brown felt, with 6–8(–10) straight, subulate, radial spines, at first brownish to black, later grey- or brown-tipped, and 2–3 central spines, the lowest, longest of which point downward. Flowers 4 cm long, funnel-shaped, white. Argentina.

Lobivia silvestrii (Speg.) Rowley ■□
[= **Chamaecereus silvestrii** (Speg.) B. & R.] □□
Offsetting to form dense mats, light green, violet brown in full sunlight, finger-length, and up to 1.5 cm thick, with 8 ribs. Areoles with 10−15 white spines 1−1.5 mm long. Flowers lateral, 5−7 cm long, funnel-shaped, vivid vermilion. Fruit 7 mm long, dull red. W Argentina (Tucuman, Salta).

REBUTIA K. Schumann (incl. AYLOSTERA Spegazzini, CYLINDROREBUTIA Frič & Kreuz., DIGITOREBUTIA Frič & Kreuz. ex Buining, MEDIOLOBIVIA Backeb., PYGMAEOLOBIVIA Backeb.)
Dwarf, globose or shortly cylindric, simple at first, later usually sprouting from the base to form many-headed clumps, with straight or slightly spiralling ribs interrupted by cross-furrows or completely divided into low tubercles. Areoles usually with bristly spines. Flowers usually numerous, from areoles to the side or near the base, wide to narrow funnel-shaped, usually rotate, very occasionally opening to bell-shaped, vivid deep orange to yellow, with receptacle-tube coloured like perianth-segments. Pericarpel and receptacle-tube with numerous scales with wool or wool and bristly spines in the axils, or glabrous scales. Fruit small, globose, with adherent floral-remains, scales similar to those on flower, thin-walled, deliquescent or opening irregularly with an oblique split. Seeds pot-shaped to obliquely elongate, with straight basal hilum, often with white strophiole; seedcoat glossy black, verrucose or wrinkled, often with spiny tubercles at upper end. According to stem structure and flowers, the genus falls into 5 sections: *Cylindrorebutia*, with cylindric stem, ±flushed with violet, with tubercles on well-defined ribs. Flowers widely funnel-shaped to almost bell-shaped; *Digitorebutia*, with shortly cylindric stem, ±flushed with violet, with tubercles in well-defined ribs. Flowers narrowly funnel-shaped. Lower part of receptacle-tube fused with style-base. *Setirebutia*, with globose stem and less well-defined ribs. Hairs and bristly spines in the scale axils. Style free down to the base. *Aylostera*, with globose stem and less well-defined ribs. Hairs and bristly spines in the scale axils. Style fused with cylindric part of receptacle-tube. *Rebutia*, with globose stem and less well-defined ribs. Scale axils glabrous or with a few hairs, never with bristly spines. Style and receptacle-tube fused together only in lower part or not at all. About 40 species have been described from the High Andes or SE Bolivia and N Argentina, but probably not all really deserve the status of species.

Rebutia einsteinii Frič var. **rubroviridis** (Backeb.) Buining & Donald
[= **Mediolobivia schmiedcheniana** (Köhl.) Krainz var. **rubroviridis** Backeb.] □■
(*Cylindrorebutia*) □□
Narrowly cylindric, up to 8 cm high and 3.5 cm wide, sprouting, strongly red-tinted, with 13−16 weakly spiralling rows of tubercles. Areoles with 12 thin, grey and brown, erect spines 3−5 mm long. Flowers 3 cm long, 3.5 cm wide, yellow. N Argentina.

Rebutia eucaliptana (Backeb.) Buining & Donald □□
[= **Mediolobivia eucaliptana** (Backeb.) Krainz] (*Digitorebutia*) ■□
Stems 2 cm across, forming small groups, light green, with 8−9 ribs with only their upper half divided into tubercles. Areoles with 9−11 fine, curved, yellowish spines, up to 1.2 cm long, often bent at the tip. Flowers light-red with madder-red throat. Bolivia.

Rebutia pectinata (Backeb.) Buining & Donald □□
[= **Mediolobivia pectinata** (Backeb.) Backeb.] (*Digitorebutia*) □■
·Unbranched or sprouting, small, 1−3 cm long and 1.2−2 cm thick shoots, very slightly tapering at the top, green, with long, tuberous root, and small tubercles in 8−12 spirals. Areoles with some felt, with 6−9, often curved or twisted spines, 2−3 mm long, with dark, thickened base. Flowers sturdy, funnel-shaped, red. Bolivia.

Rebutia aureiflora Backeb.
[= **Mediolobivia aureiflora** (Backeb.) Backeb.] (*Setirebutia*)
Unbranched, globose, 6 cm across, forming groups, green, often reddish-tinged. Ribs divided into oval tubercles 6 mm long. Areoles with 15–20 white to brownish bristly spines 0.5–3 cm long. Flowers numerous, 4 cm across, apricot-yellow with white throat. N Argentina.

Rebutia aureiflora var. **rubelliflora** (Backeb.) Buining & Donald
This variety with over 10 radial spines and 1 slightly longer, usually somewhat darker central spine. Flowers deep orange.

Rebutia spinosissima Backeb.
[= **Aylostera spinosissima** (Backeb.) Backeb.] (*Aylostera*)
Unbranched, 4 cm wide and high, forming flat clumps, light green, with slightly depressed apex. Areoles very close-set, white-felted, with numerous bristly, whitish radial and central spines, the 5–6 most central stouter and horn-coloured with brown tips. Flowers from the base of the stem, funnel-shaped, 3 cm long and 2.5–3 cm wide, light orange. Fruit small, globose. N Argentina.

Rebutia kupperiana Boedeker
[= **Aylostera kupperiana** (Boed.) Backeb.] (*Aylostera*)
Somewhat depressed globose, up to 5 cm wide, very dark green, not vigorously sprouting, with slightly depressed violet or bronze apex. Tubercles 3–5 mm long and wide, in about 15 spiralling rows. Areoles 6–8 mm apart, with yellowish-white wool, with up to 15 fine, needle-shaped, straight, white, brown-tipped radial spines, unequal, 5–8 mm long, and 1–3 stronger, erect, straight or slightly curved, dark brown central spines up to 2 cm long. Flowers from the lowest areoles, 4–4.5 cm long, 4 cm wide, funnel-shaped, vermilion to brilliant orange. Fruit green. Bolivia.

Section *Rebutia* falls into 2 subsections:
Subsection *Rebutia*: Receptacle-tube hollow down to the base, not fused with the style. Scale axils glabrous or almost glabrous, never with bristles. Flowers self-fertile.
Subsection *Mediorebutia* Buining & Donald: Receptacle-tube fused at the base to some extent with the style. Scale axils with a few very short hairs. Flowers self-sterile.

Rebutia senilis (Backeb.) var. **kesselringiana** Bewerunge. (subsect. *Rebutia*)
Globose, freely sprouting, up to 6 cm wide, rich green. Tubercles conical, 6 mm apart. Areoles white-felted, with 30–35 fine, bristly, white spines 8–12 mm long. Flowers up to 4.5 cm wide, golden yellow. Fruit olive-green. N Argentina.

168

Rebutia violaciflora Backeb. (subsect. *Rebutia*) ■☐ ☐☐

Globose, up to 2 cm wide, with depressed apex, strong yellowish-green. Areoles with about 20 stiff, radiating, bristly, protruding, deep golden-brown spines 3–25 mm long. Flowers from base of stem, 3–3.5 cm long, 2.5–3 cm wide, funnel-shaped, light magenta. Fruit globose, orange-yellow. N Argentina.

Rebutia marsoneri (Werderm.) (subsect. *Mediorebutia*) ☐■ ☐☐

Depressed globose, 4.5 cm wide and 3 cm high, light green, with depressed apex, covered with nest-shaped clusters of young spines; rarely or never sprouting. Tubercles 2 mm long, 3.5–4.5 mm apart. Areoles with short brownish-white woolly felt and 30–35 bristle-shaped, flexible spines, the lower 20 white and 3–5 mm long, the upper 9–15 somewhat stouter, 8–15 mm long, fox-brown or golden-yellow or white, with long brown tips. Flowers usually one after the other from lower areoles, 3.5–4.5 cm long, 3–3.5 cm wide, golden-yellow to orange. Fruit globose, 5 mm thick, brownish. N Argentina.

Rebutia calliantha Bewerunge (subsect. *Mediorebutia*) ☐☐ ■☐

Oblong, hardly sprouting; tubercles 3 mm long; areoles 6 mm apart, with a little white felt and 15–18 bristling, vigorously spreading, white spines 6–10 mm long. Flowers up to 4.5 cm wide, carmine red. N Argentina.

SULCOREBUTIA Backeb.

Small, globose to oblong, sprouting laterally and forming dense clumps, with thick tuberous roots. Ribs divided into hatchet-shaped tubercles. Areoles narrowly elongate to oval, depressed, with sturdy, often black spines, pectinate to spreading. Flowers usually numerous, solitary from lateral areoles, funnel-shaped, long and short tubed, mostly opening rotately, vivid yellow, orange and red. Pericarpel and receptacle-tube with broad scales and small hairs and bristles in the scale axils. Fruit small, globose to oblong, scaly. Seeds elongate-ovoid; seedcoat black, finely to coarsely verrucose. Of the approximately 40 species described in NE Bolivia, only a fraction really deserve the status of species.

Sulcorebutia lepida Ritter ☐☐ ☐■

Stem hardly sprouting, with depressed apex, very dark green, with 16 ribs completely divided into tubercles 3 mm high and wide. Areoles up to 3 mm long with a furrow above, with 14–20 black to reddish brown or golden-yellow spines 3–7 mm long, spreading laterally and downwards almost pectinately appressed. Flowers vermilion to carmine red. Bolivia.

Sulcorebutia steinbachii (Werderm.) Backeb. ■□ □□

Solitary or forming clumps, green with tuberous root and up to 13 indistinct ribs divided into alternating oblong, rhomboidal tubercles. Areoles elongate, white-felted with 6–8 thin or stouter black, radial spines up to 2.5 cm long, and 1–3 greyer, later whitish central spines, unequal, 1–2 cm. Flowers 3.5 cm long, scarlet. Bolivia.

Sulcorebutia kruegeri (Card.) Ritter □■ □□

Initially globose, later oblong, sprouting laterally and forming clumps, light to dark green with 10–12 spiralling ribs divided into narrow, alternating tubercles. Areoles very elongate, with creamy-felt, with about 20, fine, up to 3 mm long, radial spines, white, a few brownish, pectinately appressed, and 1–2 short, fine, erect, brownish central spines. Flowers campanulate-funnelshaped, up to 2.5 cm long, golden-yellow to orange. Fruit 3 mm across, reddish purple. Bolivia.

Sulcorebutia cylindrica Donald & Lau □□ ■□

Up to 12 cm high and 4.5 cm wide, ±columnar, later sprouting from the base, dark green with 16 ribs divided into rectangular tubercles. Areoles 10 mm apart, 5 mm long, with white or brown felt, with 10–12, appressed or erect radial spines, 5–10 mm long, and up to 4, stouter, central spines up to 15 mm long. All spines often slightly curved, white or yellow with russet or black tips. Flowers lateral, near apex, 3 cm long, 3.5–4 cm wide, rich yellow. Fruit a depressed globose, 5 mm across, scaly berry, orange-brown, papery when ripe, splitting at base. Bolivia (Cochabamba).

Sulcorebutia rauschii G. Frank □□ □■

Unbranched or sprouting, 1.5 cm high and 3 cm wide, blackish green to violet, with tuberous root and up to 16 oblique ribs divided into low tubercles 5 mm across. Areoles oblong, up to 2 mm long, sparsely white-felted, with up to 11, subulate, black, radial spines 1–1.5 mm long, appressed and curving downward like claws; no central spines. Flowers shining carmine-red with white throat. Fruit globose, up to 4 mm across. Bolivia.

Sulcorebutia muschii Vasquez

Globose, 6 cm across, green, with ribs divided into tubercles 6 mm high and 8 mm wide. Areoles 7 mm apart, 5 mm long, woolly, with 12—16 sitff, slightly curving, yellow radial spines 4 mm—3 cm long, and usually 1 central spine. Flowers numerous from the base, 3.5 cm long, golden yellow. Bolivia.

Sulcorebutia arenacea (Card.) Ritter

Depressed globose, up to 3.5 cm high and 5 cm wide, with depressed apex, solitary or forming clumps, brownish green. Tubercles in about 30 spirals. Areoles elliptic, with silky, cream-coloured felt, 1 upward-pointing central spine, and 6—7 pairs of pectinately appressed, white, bristly, radial spines 5 mm long. Flowers funnel-shaped, 3 cm long and wide, yellowish orange. Bolivia (Cochamba).

Sulcorebutia crispata Rausch

Unbranched or sprouting, 2.5 cm high and up to 3.5 cm wide, grey-green, with tuberous root and up to 13 oblique ribs divided into 5 mm long tubercles. Areoles 4 mm long, with 24 fine, strongly curving, glassy-white to pinkish-brown, radial spines up to 8 mm long, interwoven round the stem like a web; no central spines. Flowers 3 cm long and wide, light to dark magenta. Bolivia.

Sulcorebutia mizquensis Rausch

Unbranched or sprouting, 2.5 cm high and 3 cm wide, with tuberous root and up to 17 oblique ribs divided into 4—5 mm long tubercles, reddish-violet at the base. Areoles 4 mm long, white-felted, with up to 20 radial spines up to 4 mm long, appressed, white-tipped, pink in the middle, black at the thickened base; no central spines. Flowers 3 cm long, 2.5 cm wide, light to dark magenta, often with white throat. Bolivia.

WEINGARTIA Werdermann

Solitary, more rarely several-headed, globose to shortly columnar (up to 30 cm high), sometimes with a narrow neck above the stout, tuberous root. Ribs largely or completely divided into tubercles. Flowers near the apex, relatively small, narrowly or widely funnel-shaped, occasionally several from one areole, yellow or orange. Short pericarpel and receptacle-tube with naked scales. Fruit small, globose to ovoid, with small scales, drying and splitting at the base. Seeds cap-shaped and seedcoat matt black, finely verrucose, or seeds elongate-ovoid and seedcoat shallowly verrucose.

According to seed-structure and vegetative characteristics 3 groups can be distinguished, which are also separated geographically:

To the south, the *W. fidaiana* group with cap-shaped seeds, round, raised areoles, and 1 long, narrow-tubed flower to each areole.

To the north, the *W. neocumingii* group with elongate-ovoid seeds, oval, slightly depressed areoles, and up to 4 short-tubed, widely funnel-shaped flowers to each areole.

In the centre, the *W. riograndensis* group, more closely related to the northern *W. neocumingii* group, with elongate, slightly convex seeds with stouter strophiole, broad, sturdy tubercles, and very large, broad oval areoles with dense wool, and up to 4 shortly funnel-shaped flowers from each areole.

About 20 (?) species in S Bolivia and N Argentina. Pending final clarification of the mutual connections between the closely related genera *Sulcorebutia* and *Weingartia*, which is currently being undertaken by Donald, the two genera must be retained in their hitherto accepted grouping.

Weingartia fidaiana group ■□
Weingartia fidaiana (Backeb.) Werderm. □□
Usually solitary, globose to oblong, up to 30 cm high and 15 cm across, grey-green, with thick tuberous root and thin neck. Ribs almost entirely divided into round tubercles. Areoles thick felted, with 9 radial spines up to 3 cm long and 3–4 central spines up to 5 cm long. All spines upcurved, densely covering stem, straw-yellow to blackish violet. Flowers up to 3 cm long, pale or egg-yolk yellow. Fruit small, rounded-oblong, brownish. S Bolivia.

□■
Weingartia neumanniana (Backeb.) Werderm. □□
Small, depressed globose, up to 7 cm high, 5 cm across, velvety grey to blue-green, with tuberous root and single or several segment neck thus forming groups, and 14 ribs divided by cross-furrows into almost 6-sided, round-topped, lower tubercles. Areoles 1 cm apart, at first white-felted, with 6–8, stiff, pointed, spreading, erect, radial spines up to 3 cm long, and 1 slightly upcurving central spine up to 3 cm long. All spines straw-yellow, brownish to violet-brown or black. Flowers up to 2.5 cm long and wide, yellow to reddish orange. Fruit small, globose to ovoid, brownish. N Argentina.

□□
Weingartia kargliana Rausch ■□
Solitary, globose, up to 5 cm wide, dark grey-green, with fleshy root up to 15 cm long, and narrow root neck, and up to 10 twisting ribs divided into flat, hexagonal tubercles. Areoles white-felted, with 1–7 needle-like to subulate, brown, black-tipped spines up to 15 mm long, protruding in tufts. Flowers near apex, 2.5 cm long, 3.5 cm wide, yellow to orange-yellow with yellow throat. Fruit globose, 6 mm across, very dark green with broad, lighter-rimmed scales. Bolivia.

Weingartia neocumingii group □□
Weingartia neocumingii Backeb. □■
Globose to oblong, up to 10 cm thick, and 20 cm long, fresh green, with ribs in a complete spiral, divided into tubercles protruding in a short chin below areoles. Areoles with about 20 honey-coloured, later white, radial spines up to 1 cm long, and 2–8 rather brownish central spines. Flowers numerous round the apex, 2.5 cm long, golden to reddish yellow. Bolivia, Peru.

Weingartia hediniana Backeb.

■□
□□

Solitary, somewhat oblong, up to 10 cm high and 6 cm wide, strong green, with thick white wool on apex, and 16 ribs mostly divided into rounded tubercles, roots not tuberous. Areoles with thick white wool, with 12–14 laterally spreading, ±curved, whitish, brown-tipped when young, radial spines up to 2.5 cm long, and 4 similar but clearly distinguishable central spines. Flowers numerous, round the apex, 2.5–3 cm long and wide, golden yellow. Bolivia.

Weingartia riograndensis group
Weingartia platygona Card.

□■
□□

Cylindric, tapering towards the top, up to 12 cm long and 5.5 cm wide, flushed with deep purple, with 12 ribs divided into broad, low, rounded tubercles. Areoles 1 cm apart, grey, with 12–14 appressed to somewhat erect, radial spines and 2 upward-pointing central spines up to 1.2 cm long. All spines thin, needle-like, whitish. Flowers 2.5 cm long, golden yellow. Bolivia.

GYMNOCALYCIUM Pfeiffer (incl. BRACHYCALYCIUM Backeb., NEOWER-DERMANNIA Frič)

Unbranched, rarely sprouting from the base, globose to depressed globose, very occasionally cylindric-elongate, of widely differing size. Ribs usually broadly rounded, separated by diagonal grooves and usually jutting chin-like below the areoles. Areoles very variably spined. Flowers mostly near the apex, white or pink, some yellow or, more rarely, vivid red. Pericarpel elongate, seldom short, receptacle-tube campanulate to wide goblet-shaped. Pericarpel and receptacle-tube with large, glabrous scales with no hairs but bristles or spines in the axils. Scales gradually merging into perianth-segments. Fruit with floral remains, oblong, scaly, fleshy and deliquescent or semi-fleshy and bursting open or drying. Seeds oblong to ovoid or almost lenticular, often with conspicuous strophiole; seedcoat glossy brown or black, verrucose, smooth or with fine prickles. According to seed structure the genus may be divided into numerous series and subseries. About 60 species in South America: S Brazil, Bolivia, Argentina, Uruguay, Paraguay.

Gymnocalycium uruguayense (Arech.) B. & R.

□□
■□

Depressed globose, rich green, with depressed apex and 12–14 ribs divided into hexagonal tubercles jutting out chin-like below the areoles. Areoles roundish, grey-felted, with usually 3, thin, yellowish, later whitish, rough-haired spines 1.5–3 cm long. Flowers round the apex, bell-shaped, 4 cm long, 5.5–6 cm wide, inner perianth-segments whitish with flesh-coloured centre. Fruit oblong to ovate, 2 cm long, 1 cm across, dark green. C Peru.

Gymnocalycium denudatum (Link & Otto) Pfeiffer

□□
□■

Depressed spherical to globose, 3–8 cm wide, glossy dark green, with 5–8 completely flat ribs, at first almost without tubercles. Areoles far apart, with usually 5, whitish-yellow, appressed and ±twisted, radial spines 1–1.5 cm long. Flowers slender-tubed, up to 5 cm long, 7 cm wide, pure white, almost giving the impression of being double. Fruit oblong. Rather variable species. S Brazil, N Uruguay, Argentina.

Gymnocalycium bruchii (Speg.) Hosseus

Freely-sprouting, mat-forming, with small, up to 3.5 cm high and up to 6 cm wide stems, dark green, with 12 low ribs divided into rounded, chinless tubercles. Areoles close-set, with short white felt, with 12–14 backward-curved, thin, bristle-shaped radial spines up to 6 mm long, white with brown at the base, and 1 erect, darker central spine. Flowers near apex, 3 cm long, 3.5 cm wide, delicate violet-pink to almost white. Fruit globose, 5–7 cm thick, whitish. Argentina (Cordoba).

Gymnocalycium baldianum (Speg.) Speg.

Depressed globose, up to 7 cm wide and up to 4 cm high, blue-grey, with tuberous root and 9–11 ribs divided into tubercles. Areoles with 5, thin, appressed, grey, radial spines, or sturdier, erect, horn-coloured to brown ones up to 15 mm long. Flowers apical, 3–5 cm long and wide, deep pink to purple. Fruit spindly, dark grey-green. Argentina (Catamarca).

Gymnocalycium andreae (Boedeker) Backeb.

Globose, up to 5 cm wide, freely sprouting from the base, dull glossy dark blue-green, with 8 flat ribs divided by sharp cross-furrows into roundish tubercles with areoles in the centre. Areoles with 7, thin, spreading, radial spines up to 8 mm long, whitish with brownish base, and 1–3 somewhat upcurved, dark brown central spines. Flowers near apex, 3 cm long, up to 4.5 cm wide, greenish outside, sulphur-yellow inside. Fruit globose, 12 mm thick, bluish-green. Argentina.

Gymnocalycium platense (Speg.) B. & R.

Globose, with depressed apex, 6–10 cm wide and 8–10 cm high, grey-green, with 10–14 ribs divided into jutting, somewhat chin-like tubercles, 5-sided at the base. Areoles grey-felted, with usually 7, appressed, radial spines, whitish with reddish base, up to 15 mm long. Flowers with long narrow tube, white with red throat. Argentina.

Gymnocalycium oenanthum Backeb.　■□

□□

Depressed globose, up to 12 cm wide and 8 cm high, matt grey-green, with 11−13 ribs divided into tubercles by cross-furrows. Areoles with 5(−7), downward-curving, grey, dark brown-tipped, radial spines, unequal, up to 1.5 cm long, and no central spines. Flowers, several at the apex, bell-shaped, 5 cm long, 4 cm wide, magnificent wine-red. Fruit about 18 mm thick, light green, slightly bloomed. Argentina (Mendoza).

Gymnocalycium quehlianum (F. Haage) A. Berger　□■

□□

Depressed globose, 4 cm high and up to 15 cm wide, grey-green to reddish, with thick, tuberous root and 11 ribs divided by cross-furrows into chin-like tubercles. Areoles felted, with 5, horn-coloured, radial spines 5−12 mm long, curved downwards and sideways towards the body; no central spines. Flowers narrowly tubular, up to 6 cm long, white with red throat. Argentina (Córdoba).

Gymnocalycium castellanosii Backeb.　□□

■□

Elongate-globose, up to 15 cm high and 10 cm wide, velvety matt blue-green, with felted apex and 10−12 ribs divided into small, sharply separated tubercles. Areoles 2 cm apart, initially with thick tufts of yellowish, flocky felt, with 5−7 stout, porrect, white, dark-tipped radial spines up to 2.5 cm long, and 1 similar central spine. Flowers campanulate-funnelshaped, 4.5 cm long, white, pink-tinted. Fruit roundish, 15 mm thick, green, slightly bloomed. Argentina (La Rioja).

Gymnocalycium horridispinum Frank　□□

□■

Shortly cylindric, 6−8 cm high and wide, dark green, with 10−13 ribs divided by deep, sharp furrows into strong chin-like jutting tubercles. Areoles grey-felted, later brownish, with 10−12 sturdy, straight, subulate, grey, often dark brown tipped, radial spines 20−25 mm long, curving slightly towards the stem, and 4 very stout, erect central spines 30−40 mm long, in cross-formation. Flowers in a ring round the apex, widely funnel-shaped, 6 cm long and wide, inner perianth-segments violet-pink outside and white inside, with violet-pink edge and midstripe. Fruit ovoid, 20 mm long, 15 mm across, dark green tinged with red. Argentina (Córdoba).

Gymnocalycium spegazzini B. & R.

Depressed globose, 6–12 cm high and 10–14 cm wide, brownish green, with yellowish-grey wool in the depressed apex, with 11–13(–15) broad ribs, somewhat notched between the areoles. Areoles 6–10 mm apart, with 5–7(–9) rigid, brownish radial spines up to 5.5 cm long, usually rather curved and bent towards the stem, and no central spines. Flowers funnel-shaped, 6–7 cm long and 5 cm wide, whitish to pink. Fruit globose-oblong. N Argentina (Salta).

Gymnocalycium zegarrae Card.

Globose, 6–10 cm high and 11–18 cm wide, grey-green, with 13 ribs divided into irregular, convex-tetragonal, 5–6-angled, tubercles 2 cm × 3 cm. Areoles 1.5–2.5 cm apart, with light grey felt, with 8 subulate, strongly curved, radial spines, somewhat pectinate, whitish with reddish to black tips, 1.5–2.5 cm long, and 1 central spine 2.5–3 cm long. Flowers numerous round the apex, goblet-shaped with oblique limb, 3–4.5 cm long, white with magenta throat. Fruit round, 1.5 cm long, 1 cm thick, orange. Bolivia (Prov. Campero).

Gymnocalycium joossensianum (Boed.) B. & R.

Solitary, depressed globose, dark green or leaf-green, slightly depressed on top, with 6–9 straight ribs with shallow diagonal notches between somewhat roundish tubercles. Areoles with 6–9 protruding, needle-like radial spines (lower ones longer than upper ones) and usually 1 rather shorter central spine. Flowers near the apex, up to 5 cm long, wine-red. Fruit spindly, up to 2.5 cm long, with a few red-tipped scales. Paraguay or N Argentina.

Gymnocalycium mihanovichii (Frič & Guerke) B. & R.

Broadly globose, 3–5 cm across, grey-green, usually red-tinged, with 8 blunt-angled ribs only slightly notched between the areoles, and lighter-coloured side-ribs running into the furrows on either side of the areoles. Areoles 1 cm apart, with 5–6 curved, greyish-yellow, radial spines 8–10 mm long; no central spines. Flowers 4–5 cm long, narrowly tubular, light olive-green with yellowish-green inside. Paraguay.

Rather variable species. A well-known mutation is the bright carmine-red, chlorophyll-free var. *friedrichii* and a brilliant golden-yellow mutant of that; both can only be cultivated by grafting.

Gymnocalycium vorwerkii (Frič) F. Buxbaum ■□ □□
[= **Neowerdermannia vorwerkii** Frič]
Depressed globose, with tuberous root and about 16 ribs divided into triangular tubercles. Areoles deep between the tubercles, with about 10, curved spines up to 2 cm long. Flowers campanulate-funnelshaped, 18 mm long and wide, violet-pink with brownish midstripe and whitish throat. Fruit globose, 5 mm thick, green, later reddish. Bolivia, N Argentina at altitudes of 4000–5000 m.

MILA B. & R.
Dwarf columnar cacti forming colonies, with straight or ±curved soft-fleshed stems and very variable spination. Flowers small, funnel-shaped, short-tubed, usually yellow. Pericarpel and receptacle-tube with small scales with woolly hairs in the axils. Fruit gooseberry-like, green, almost naked, with persistent floral-remains. Seeds small, oblong cap-shaped; seedcoat glossy black, verrucose. About 12 species in C Peru.

Mila caespitosa B. & R. □■ □□
Forming lax clusters, stems 10–15 cm tall, 2–3 cm thick, usually 10-ribbed. Areoles with 20 or more yellowish, later brown radial spines 1 cm long, and 1–3 central spines up to 3 cm long. Floswers up to 1.5 cm long, 2–3 cm wide, yellow to reddish yellow. Fruit 5–10 mm thick, shiny green. Peru.

Mila nealeana Backeb. □□ ■□
Lax clusters of decumbent stems up to 30 cm long and 3–4.5 cm thick, with 11–13 ribs. Areoles with 12–30 very fine, transparent radial spines up to 8 mm long, and 1–6 straw-coloured central spines up to 2 cm long, somewhat downward-pointing. Flowers up to 3.5 cm long, 2.5 cm wide, funnel-shaped to rotate, light to bright yellow. Fruit small, 1.5 cm thick, green. C Peru.

LEOCEREUS B. & R.
Slender, upright or decumbent stems, usually branching from the base, 1–2 m long, with numerous thin ribs. Areoles initially felted, later glabrescent, with numerous bristly or long needle-shaped spines. Flowers rather small, tubular-campanulate to narrowly campanulate-funnelshaped with short corolla, white to reddish. Pericarpel and receptacle-tube with numerous pointed scales with abundant long, curly, dark-brown, woolly hairs and bristles in the axils, and also, in the lower part, the first needle-shaped spines to develop. Fruit small, globose, green, resembling the stem, densely spiny, with considerable adherent floral-remains. Seeds obliquely ovoid, strongly compressed laterally; seedcoat shiny black or dark brown, lightly tessellate, with small interstitial pits. 3 species in Brazil.

Leocereus bahiensis B. & R. □□ □■
Upright or leaning, moderately branching stems, up to 2 m long and 1–1.5 cm thick, with 12–14 ribs. Areoles close-set, with initially 10, later 20 or more needle-like, yellow radial spines, and 1(–2) longer, outward-pointing, central spines up to 3 cm long. Flowers 4 cm long, white. Fruit globose, 10–12 mm thick. Brazil (Bahia).

ARTHROCEREUS (A. Berger) Backeb.
(incl. PYGMAEOCEREUS H. Johnson & Backeb.)
Small, with short, unbranched or branching, semi-upright to decumbent, rarely longer, short-jointed stems. Flowers elongate funnel-shaped, night-blooming, opening widely with slender, pointed, white to reddish perianth-segments. Pericarpel and receptacle-tube with pointed scales with tufts of wool in the axils. Fruit globose to inverted pear-shaped, with usually tiny tufts of felt on the bulges of the pericarpel scales, thin-

walled, green, not bursting open, with dried floral-remains. Seeds obliquely ovoid; seedcoat matt black, with low warts, with wavy depressions between them.

According to flower-structure the genus may be divided into 3 subgenera: *Praearthrocereus* F. Buxbaum: Columnar, unbranched or sparsely branching stems up to 50 cm long. Flowers sturdy. Scale-axils with abundant curly hair. Stamens numerous, very unequal, lower ones set at the same height, the rest getting shorter towards the throat, the anthers all at the same height. *Arthrocereus*: Dwarf plants with decumbent, freely-branching, short-jointed shoots. Flowers long funnel-shaped. Stamens all equal, lower ones inserted at very different heights and finishing well below the throat. *Pygmaeocereus* (Johnson & Backeb.) F. Buxbaum: Dwarf plants branching from the base into unjointed stems. Flowers narrowly tubular. Pericarpel scales not sharply pointed. All stamens with extremely short filaments, most of them set in the widened part of the receptacle-tube. 4 species in Brazil and S Peru.

Arthrocereus rondonianus Backeb. & Voll (*Praearthrocereus*)
Semi-erect, slender, branching stems up to 50 cm long and 2.5 cm thick, fresh light green, with 14–18 low, rounded ribs. Areoles 5–10 mm apart, with a little grey felt at first, and 40–50 needle-fine, greenish to golden-yellow spines 5 mm long, a few up to 2 cm long, and 1–2 central ones up to 7 cm long. Flowers 8 cm long, 6 cm wide, lilac pink, inner perianth-segments ±trumpet-shaped. Brazil. (Photo turned anticlockwise 90°.)

Arthrocereus microsphaericus (K. Schumann) A. Berger (*Arthrocereus*)
Dwarf, freely-branching, with glossy fresh green annual growth 5 cm long and 3 cm thick, with 8–11 low, slightly crenate ribs. Areoles with about 12 bristly, white, radial spines 2 mm long, about 12 white bristles, and 4–12 brownish central spines. Flowers lateral, funnel-shaped, 7 cm long, 5 cm wide, white. Fruit globose. Brazil (Minas Gerais).

Arthrocereus bylesianus (Andreae & Backeb.) F. Buxbaum
[= **Pygmaeocereus bylesianus** Andreae & Backeb.] (*Pygmaeocereus*)
Branching from the base, forming small groups, up to 8 cm long and 2 cm thick stems, with 12–14 ribs. Ribs at first barely notched, later almost divided into tubercles. Areoles initially pale-felted, with numerous dark spines, later grey, radiating in all directions; no definite central spines. Flowers very slender, long-tubed, 6 cm long, widening to funnel-shaped, white, night-blooming. S Peru.

SETIECHINOPSIS Backeb.

Erect, shortly cylindric, up to 15 cm tall. Flowers near apex, large, narrowly elongate tubular, perianth-segments straight, narrow, opening radially, night-blooming, strongly perfumed. Pericarpel and receptacle-tube with numerous scales almost reduced to bristles, densely hairy in the axils. Lower half of the style fused with the receptacle-tube. Stamens with very short filaments inserted at different heights. Fruit spindly, gradually merging into remains of receptacle-tube, densely covered with bristle-pointed scales, semi-juicy, bursting open lengthways. Seeds almost globose with broad, truncate, basal hilum; seedcoat matt black, finely verrucose. 1 species in Argentina.

Setiechinopsis mirabilis (Speg.) De Haas
Usually unbranched, upright, 12–15 cm tall and 2 cm thick stems, dark brownish green, with 11 straight or slightly twisting, somewhat notched ribs. Areoles 4–5 cm apart, with a little white wool, long curly felt, and 9–14 fine, almost bristle-shaped, erect, nearly transparent, radial spines 3–5 mm long, and 1 stouter, brown, central spine 10–15 mm long. Flowers near apex, narrowly funnel-shaped, 11–12 cm long, 3 cm wide, white, delicately perfumed. Fruit 3–4 cm long, 5–6 mm thick, brownish-green to reddish, splitting laterally. Argentina.

Tribe VII **Notocacteae** F. Buxbaum
CORRYOCACTUS B. & R. (incl. ERDISIA B. & R.)
Stout-stemmed, erect, 1–2(–5) m tall, branching from the base and forming large groups, or thin-stemmed shrubs, freely-branching from the base, with erect or pendent stems; some species with creeping or underground stolons. Areoles strongly spiny. Flowers campanulate or campanulate-funnelshaped, wide-opening, vivid yellow, orange or scarlet. Pericarpel and receptacle-tube densely covered with tiny scales with dark, curly, woolly hair and young spines. Fruit globose, juicy, without floral-remains, with tufts of deciduous needle-shaped spines. Seeds small, obliquely ovoid, with large lateral hilum; seedcoat black or brownish, wrinkled and verrucose. About 20 species in C and S Peru, W Bolivia and N Chile, sometimes up to 3300 m. Two subgenera: *Corryocactus*: Upright, shrub-like, thick-stemmed, up to 4 m tall. Flowers yellow or orange, up to 7 cm across, lateral. Fruit up to apple-sized, spiny. *Erdisia*: Slender-stemmed, upright or decumbent, producing stolons or climbing, rarely up to 3 m tall. Flowers yellow, orange or vermilion, sometimes terminal. Fruit small.

Corryocactus melanotrichus (K. Schumann) B. & R. (*Corryocactus*)
Freely-branching shrub, up to 1.2 m tall with yellowish green stems up to 6 cm thick, with 7–9 ribs. Areoles with 10–11 light brown, later grey spines 0.7–2 cm long, with 1 central spine up to 3 cm long. Flowers 5 cm long, 6 cm wide, purplish-red. Fruit globose, 4–8 cm thick, soft, with tufts of 9–12, thin spines 1 cm long. Bolivia.

Corryocactus brachypetalus (Vaupel) B. & R. (*Corryocactus*)
Up to 4 m tall and 6–10 cm thick, with often very numerous, 7–8-ribbed stems rising almost vertically from the base. Areoles with up to 20, initially black, often twisting spines, mostly under 1 cm, the longest 10–16 cm. Flowers broadly funnel-shaped, 4–6 cm wide, deep orange. Fruit globose, 6–7 cm thick, greenish-yellow, with tufts of spines, later deciduous. Peru.

Corryocactus apiciflorus (Vaupel) P.C. Hutchison
[= **Erdisia apiciflora** (Vaupel) Werderm.] (*Erdisia*]
Shrub-like, with decumbent or ascending stems up to 50 cm long and 2.5 cm thick, densely spiny, with 8 very low ribs. Areoles with 10 almost horizontally spreading, radial spines up to 1 cm long, and 1 central spine up to 2 cm long. Flowers, several at the apex, terminal or lateral, up to 4 cm long, scarlet. S Peru.

AUSTROCACTUS B. & R.
Shortly columnar, 30–60 cm long, unbranched or branching from the base, soft-fleshed. Ribs low, divided into tubercles bearing areoles. Radial spines needle-shaped, central spines shaped like fish-hooks or straight needles. Flowers near apex, small, bowl-shaped to bell-shaped, reddish-yellowish. Pericarpel with very reduced scales with tufts of wool and small prickly bristles. Receptacle-tube with sharp-pointed scales with wool and very stout bristly spines. Fruit globose to oblong, soft, greenish, with floral-remains and tufts of hairs. Seeds oblique ovoid, laterally compressed; seedcoat matt black, radially ridged, finely reticulate. About 4 species in S Argentina and S Chile.

Austrocactus gracilis Backeb.
Slender, often decumbent stems, usually sprouting towards the base, 12–16 mm thick and 10–35 cm long, with 8–9 ribs almost completely divided into verrucose tubercles. Areoles with 10–11, whitish, yellowish-tipped radial spines, plus 1–3 tiny, upward-pointing spines 2–5 mm long, and 1–3(–4) sometimes hooked, yellowish, brown-tipped central spines up to 2 cm long. Flowers campanulate-funnelshaped, brownish yellow. S Argentina (Patagonia).

ERIOSYCE Philippi

Large, solitary, globose, with age columnar, up to 1 m high and over 30 cm thick, apex with white wool and yellow spines. Areoles felted, with straight to often claw-like spines. Flowers from the woolly apex, bell-shaped, small, red. Pericarpel and receptacle-tube with pointed scales, scale axils with thick woolly hair and often bristles. Fruit oblong, becoming dry, upper part stoutly spiny, breaking off at the base. Seeds large, broad and oblique ovoid, laterally compressed; seedcoat black, finely structured. Probably only 1, very variable species in Chile and Argentina.

Eriosyce ceratistes (Otto) B. & R.

Solitary, globose to ±elongate, up to 1 m high and up to 50 cm wide, with 20—30 or more somewhat sinuate ribs 2—3 cm high, with numerous yellow spines and abundant white wool on the apex. Areoles large, up to 2 cm long, 2.5—4 cm apart, with abundant felt and 18—20 straight or ±curved, thickly subulate, brown spines 2.5—3.5 cm long. Flowers 3.5 cm long, red. Fruit up to 4 cm long. Very variable species in stem-shape and in spine development and colour. Chile.

PYRRHOCACTUS (A. Berger) Backeb.

Usually solitary, occasionally forming clusters, depressed globose stems, with age often short-columnar, with straight, notched ribs. Areoles large, felted, with numerous stiff, subulate, ash-grey, red-brown or blackish spines. Flowers near apex, urn-shaped to campanulate-funnelshaped, deep yellow to red-tinged. Pericarpel and receptacle-tube densely covered with narrowly lanceolate scales, reduced on the pericarpel to a tiny sharp point, with hairy tufts in the scale axils, and bristly spines more strongly developed in the upper axils, sometimes lacking in more highly evolved species. Fruit gooseberry-like, with attached floral-remains, splitting round the base. Seeds oblique ovoid, often with coarse folds; seedcoat black, finely verrucose. About 11 species in N and W Argentina and C Chile.

Pyrrhocactus bulbocalyx (Werderm.) Backeb.

Solitary, depressed globose, light grey-green, with 12—20 blunt, lightly cross-furrowed ribs. Areoles 1.5—2 cm apart, oblong, with pale grey felt and 7—12 radial spines 1.5—2 cm long, strongly curved, appressed, and 4, ash-grey, central spines somewhat over 2 cm long, upcurving only. Flowers 4 cm long, straw-coloured with red throat. N Argentina.

Pyrrhocactus catamarcensis (F.A. Weber) Backeb.

Solitary, elongate-globose, later columnar, 10—50 cm high and 8—12 cm wide, with 13—17 ribs thickened round the areoles. Areoles 2—3 cm apart, white-felted, with about 10 light brown, often white, stiff, subulate, curved, radial spines 2 cm long, with 4 stouter and more curved, yellow to glossy dark-brown central spines over 2 cm long. Flowers 4.5 cm long, lemon- or golden-yellow. N Argentina.

Pyrrhocactus umadeave (Frič) Backeb.

Matt green, ±globular, later even columnar, 10(—40) cm high and 11 cm wide, with 18 rather spiralling ribs. Areoles oblong, with white felt and 30—35 piercing, subulate, whitish to brownish-pink, dark-tipped, somewhat bloomed spines, 3—4 cm long, upcurving, covering the whole stem. Flowers at the apex, 3—3.5 cm long, pale yellow. Fruit oblong-ellipsoid, 3—4 cm long, up to 2 cm across, with small tufts of wool. N Argentina (Salta).

EULYCHNIA Philippi

Freely-branching tree or shrub, with straight, ascending or decumbent, ribbed stems. Areoles with woolly felt or long hairs, short radial spines, and very long, stout central spines. Flowers small, campanulate-funnelshaped, white to pink. Pericarpel and very short receptacle-tube densely covered with scales, their axils full of woolly hairs or woolly felt. Fruit large, globose, fleshy, hairy or woolly-felted. Seeds small, oblique ovoid; seedcoat matt black, verrucose. About 6 species in N Chile and S Peru.

Eulychnia saint-pieana Ritter

Trees up to 4 m tall, stems 7.5 cm thick, with 12 ribs. Areoles on older stems with long, snow-white, woolly hairs standing out from the stem, and about 20 radial spines up to 18 mm long and central spines up to 15 cm long. Flowers 6–7.5 cm long, 5–7.5 cm across, white. Fruit almost pear-shaped, 8 mm long. N Chile.

NEOPORTERIA B. & R. (incl. CHILENIA Backeb., CHILEOREBUTIA Frič, HORRIDOCACTUS Backeb., NICHELIA Bullock, DELAETIA Backeb., HILDMANNIA Kreuz & Buining, REICHEOCACTUS Backeb.)

Solitary or very rarely group-forming, globose to shortly cylindric stems, some up to 1.5 m long, decumbent or pendent, or dwarf, with large root and thin, neck-like epicotyl. Stem usually dark brown to almost black. Ribs tuberculate to almost entirely divided into tubercles. Areoles often dark-coloured and strongly spiny. Flowers solitary, or in some species 2–3 together, from areoles near the apex, narrow-tubed and funnel-shaped to widely funnel-shaped or ±bell-shaped. Pericarpel and receptacle-tube with ±pointed to much-reduced scales with soft tufts of wool to long, thick, woolly hairs and needles in their axils. Pericarpel and receptacle-tube separated by a constriction. Fruit elongate, berry-like, hollow, with seeds only in the upper part, with attached floral-remains, breaking off by a basal opening. Seeds almost globose, broad ovate or oblique ovate, with small hilum; seedcoat matt black, ±heavily wrinkled, coarsely or finely verrucose. About 40 species in Chile and N Argentina.

Neoporteria subgibbosa (Haw.) B. & R.

Initially globose, later cylindric stem, decumbent with age, 10 cm across and up to 1 m long, later grey, with about 20 ribs divided by cross-furrows into protruding, chin-like tubercles. Areoles with white wool at first, with about 24 thin, amber-yellow radial spines 2–3 cm long, and 4 stouter central spines. Flowers 4–5 cm long, pink. Chile.

Neoporteria gerocephala Y. Ito

Solitary, globose, later columnar stem, up to 18 cm high and up to 10 cm thick, initially light green, later grey with age, with 16–18 straight, slightly crenate ribs divided by cross-furrows into ±distinct tubercles oblique at the top and protruding chin-like, at the base. Depressed apex with abundant white woolly felt. Areoles with blackish woolly felt, about 25 twisting, hair-shaped, radial spines 2–5 cm long that completely envelop the stem, and 6–8 stouter central spines. Spine colour varies between white, yellow, brown and dense black. Flowers singly or in pairs, funnel-shaped, up to 6 cm long and 2.5 cm wide, light carmine-red. Fruit an oblong-ovoid or almost cylindric, brownish pink berry, 3 cm long and 1.3 cm across. N Chile.

Neoporteria nidus (Soehrens) B. & R.

Stem initially globose, later clavate-cylindric, up to 30 cm high and 5–9 cm wide, red-brown, with 16–18 deeply crenate ribs completely enveloped in upcurving spines. Areoles with about 30 greyish or yellowish white spines 2–3 cm long. Flowers 4 cm long, reddish, with narrow, pointed perianth-segments. Chile.

Neoporteria napina (Phil.) Backeb. ■□ □□
[= **Neochilenia napina** (Phil.) Backeb.]
Depressed globose to somewhat elongate, up to 10 cm high and 5 cm thick, grey-green to reddish grey, with long, tuberous root and about 14 ribs completely divided by cross-furrows into rounded, spiralling, protruding chin-like, tubercles 8 mm across. Areoles at tip of tubercles, with 3–9 radiating, appressed, black spines no more than 3 mm long. Flowers 3–3.5 cm long, light yellow with reddish stigma. Fruit globose, slightly elongate. Chile.

Neoporteria odieri (Lem.) var. **mebbesii** (Hildm.) Backeb. □■ □□
[= **Neochilenia mebbesii** (Hildm.) Backeb.]
Globose or somewhat elongate stem, 5 cm across, pure green, with 13 ribs divided into low tubercles, protruding chin-like below areoles. Areoles in a small longitudinal furrow, somewhat felted, with 6–9 stout, spreading, light brown radial spines 2–5 mm long, and sometimes 1 central spine. Flowers near apex, up to 5 cm long, funnel-shaped, white to pink, outside with reddish midstripe. Chile.

Neoporteria aspillagai (Soehrens) Backeb. □□ ■□
[= **Neochilenia aspillagai** (Soehrens) Backeb.]
Depressed globose, up to 15 cm across, dark green stem, with up to 14 ribs up to 1.6 cm wide, with plump, protruding tubercles above the areoles. Areoles initially white-felted, later glabrescent, with 4–12 curved, needle-like radial spines up to 2 cm long, white and dark-tipped at first, later grey, and 1–4 stouter, mostly straight, dark central spines 2–3 cm long. Flowers funnel-shaped, 4 cm long, pink outside to pale yellow inside. Fruit ovate or oblong, 1 cm long. Chile.

Neoporteria paucicostata (Ritter) Donald & Rowley □□ □■
Solitary, semi-globose, later somewhat columnar, light blue-grey, with thick tuberous root and 8–10 ribs divided into protruding, chin-like, tubercles. Areoles white-felted, with 5–8, initially dark grey, later pale grey, ±recurved, radial spines 2–4 cm long, and 1–4 similar central spines. Flowers funnel-shaped, 3.5 cm long and wide, reddish white. Fruit reddish with white hairs. Chile.

Neoporteria krausii (Ritter) F. Buxbaum   ■□
[= **Neochilenia krausii** (Ritter) Backeb.   □□
Small, globose, up to 4 cm thick, freely sprouting, grey-green to greyish yellow, with long, tuberous root and ribs divided into small tubercles. Areoles with copious, white, hairy felt, confluent into a white tuft on the apex, with about 10, tiny, subulate, spreading, porrect, glassy, dark-tipped, radial spines, and 1, slightly longer, porrect central spine. Flowers 3.5 cm long and wide, pale yellow or greenish yellow, sweet-smelling. Fruit pale red, very woolly. Chile.

Neoporteria esmeraldana (Ritter) Donald & Rowley   □■
[= **Neochilenia esmeraldana** (Ritter) Backeb.]   □□
Broad globose, 5–7 cm thick, freely-sprouting from the base to the middle, brownish to black, with ribs completely divided into rather chin-like tubercles. Areoles white-felted, with 4–12 yellow, brown or (rarely) black radial spines 2–7 mm long, and 1 or several central spines. Flowers 4.5–5 cm long, pale greenish-yellow. Fruit red. N Chile.

Neoporteria pilispina (Ritter) Donald & Rowley   □□
[= **Neochilenia pilispina** (Ritter) Backeb.]   ■□
Solitary, semi-globose, 4–5 cm thick, blackish green, with long tuberous root and 13–16 spiralling ribs with protruding, chin-like tubercles. Areoles depressed, with 6 very thin, spiralling, upcurving, brown or black, radial spines 0.5–2 cm long, and 2–3 similar central spines 1–3 cm long. Flowers near apex, 2.5–3 cm long, white, scented. Fruit globose, reddish to olive-brown above, white-flecked. Chile.

Neoporteria wagenknechtii Ritter   □□ / □■
Solitary, oblong with age, up to 30 cm high and up to 11 cm wide, grey-green, with 11–17 blunt ribs with chin-like tubercles; no tuberous root. Areoles with 10–14 straight, dark grey radial spines up to 2.5 cm long, and 3–6 grey-brown central spines 2–3 cm long. Flowers 2.2 cm long, light purple. Fruit oblong, green or reddish. N Chile.

ISLAYA Backeb.

Solitary, globose to shortly columnar, 10–20 cm high [*I. grandis* 30(–50) cm], rarely branching from the base. Ribs cross-furrowed above the areoles to tuberculate. Areoles in the apex with long, dense, woolly, pale yellow hairs and ±densely spiny. Flowers near apex, campanulate-funnelshaped, with thin little stalk, yellowish or yellowish-green, rarely red. Pericarpel and receptacle-tube densely covered with pointed scales with long, dense hairs in the axils and bristles, especially towards the tip. Fruit extending, shortly before ripening, to a hollow, red, clavate bladder with a few dry seeds, with hairy tufts from the axils of the scale-remains, and in part bristly also, with attached floral-remains, breaking off when ripe with a circular split at the base. Seeds oblique ovoid, seedcoat matt or glossy black, finely verrucose. About 12 species from the coastal regions of S Peru.

Islaya grandiflorens Rauh & Backeb.

Often buried in the ground up to the apex, up to 10 cm high and wide, grey-green to green, with tuberous root, woolly apex, and (16–)20–21 rounded to almost angular ribs distinctly swollen round the areoles. Areoles with 10–12(–15) thin, up to 1 cm long, sometimes pectinate, radial spines, blackish at first with red at the base, soon horn-coloured, and 2–3 rather longer and stouter central spines up to 2.5 cm long, soon ash-grey with black tips. Flowers large, 4 cm across, covering the entire apex, pure yellow, outside greenish yellow with reddish tips. Fruit up to 3 cm long, carmine red. S Peru.

Islaya bicolor Akers & Buining

Short columnar, up to 20 cm high and 10 cm wide, purplish green, with white, woolly felt on apex and 20 ribs slightly swollen between the areoles. Areoles with 12–14 stout, radial spines 3–10 mm long, initially grey with brown tips, protruding, and 4 sturdier central spines up to 1.25 cm long. Flowers from the apex, 2 cm long and wide, not widely opening, yellow with reddish brown tips, reddish outside. Fruit inverted-conical, reddish, 1 cm long. S Peru.

Islaya paucispina Rauh & Backeb.

Solitary or forming few-headed groups, stem globose, up to 8 cm thick, sap-green to grey-green, with yellow-felted apex and 12–16 ribs. Areoles 1 cm apart, with 5–8 ±divided, very sturdy radial spines 0.5–1.5 cm long, pale reddish brown with dark brown tips, grey with age, usually pointing obliquely downwards, and 1 (often absent) stout central spine, 2.5–3 cm long, red-brown with dark brown tip, later grey, protruding horizontally or downward-pointing. Flowers numerous, 1.5 cm long and wide, vivid yellow, scented. Fruit elongate-clavate, up to 3.5 cm long, 1.5 cm thick, pale carmine-red. S Peru.

Islaya copiapoides Rauh & Backeb.

Solitary to forming few-headed groups, globose stem, up to 10 cm high, 8 cm wide, set deep in the ground, grey-green, with yellowish felt on the apex and 17–21 blunt ribs. Areoles set on tubercles, those in the apex with dense woolly felt, with 8–13 stout, 5–7 mm long radial spines, reddish with violet-grey tips, turning grey with brown tips in age, in a regular formation around the areoles, and 1–2 sharp-pointed central spines up to 1.5 cm long, reddish with blackish-violet tips. Flowers small, up to 1.5 cm long, 1.2 cm wide, greenish-yellow. Fruit up to 3 cm long, carmine red. S Peru.

COPIAPOA B. & R. (incl. PILOCOPIAPOA Ritter)

Solitary or often sprouting to form large colonies, globose or columnar stems, up to more than 1 m high. Apex densely woolly-felted. Ribs ±tuberculate and thickened round the areoles. Spination very diverse. Flowers from the apex, almost tubeless, wide bell-shaped to almost bowl-shaped, yellow. Pericarpel and receptacle-tube with a few narrow scales, their axils mostly naked, rarely with white wool. Fruit small, globose to ovoid, with dried floral-remains, splitting at the top. Seeds ovoid; seedcoat glossy black, verrucose. About 30 species in N Chile.

Copiapoa cinerea (Phil.) B. & R.

■□
□□

Broadly globose, columnar with age, up to 1 m high and 10 cm wide, forming large colonies, with a chalk-white bloom, up to 30 ribs, with dense, pale brown wool on the apex. Areoles with usually 1–7, black, radial spines up to 2 cm long, and 1–2 central spines up to 3.5 cm long. Flowers up to 3.5 cm long and wide, pale yellow. Chile.

Copiapoa solaris (Ritter)
[= Pilocopiapoa solaris Ritter]

□■
□□

Forming many-headed, hemispherical clumps 1 m high and 2 m in diameter. Individual heads up to 12 cm thick, grey-green, with flat, woolly apex and usually 9–10 non-tuberculate ribs. Areoles at first brown-felted, with 7–10 straight to curved, brownish radial spines 1.5–5 cm long, and 2–5 central spines 2–6 cm long. Flowers 2.5–3 cm long and wide, funnel-shaped, rosy-yellow to carmine. Fruit green to red, 1.5 cm long, with white wool. N Chile.

Copiapoa pepiniana (K. Schumann) Backeb.
var. fiedleriana (K. Schumann) Backeb.

□□
■□

Mat-forming. Individual stems depressed globose, up to 8 cm high, 7 cm wide, with thick rootstock, ash-grey, with brown spines rising among tufts of white felt on the apex, and 13 straight, deeply notched ribs divided into laterally compressed tubercles, lower part protruding chin-like. Areoles with grey woolly felt and 4–6 straight or slightly curved spines up to 3 cm long, initially light chestnut-brown, later grey. Flowers funnel-shaped, 5 cm long, pure yellow, greenish-yellow outside with purple midstripe. Chile.

Copiapoa krainziana Ritter

□□
□■

Globose, later elongate stems, up to 12 cm wide, sprouting to form clumps 1 m in diameter, grey-green, with grey woolly apex and 13–24 slightly crenate ribs. Areoles with 10–12 white, fine, usually curving, radial spines 1–2 cm long, and 14–20 central spines 2–3 cm long. Flowers up to 3.5 cm long, yellow. Fruit yellow or red. N Chile.

NOTOCACTUS (K. Schumann) Backeb. & F.M. Knuth (incl. BRASILI-CACTUS Backeb., ERIOCACTUS Backeb., WIGGINSIA D.M. Porter [= MALACOCARPUS Salm-Dyck])

Stems globose, usually elongate in age, some species columnar up to over 1 m tall, solitary or more rarely sprouting from the base, some species producing stolons. Ribs few, fairly high and sharp, or numerous, bluntly-rounded and low, frequently spiralling, often cross-furrowed or tuberculate. Young areoles very woolly, later glabrescent, usually with needle-shaped or bristly spines. Flowers often numerous, near the apex, funnel-shaped or widened to bell-shaped, yellow, rarely red. Stigma-lobes usually red. Pericarpel and receptacle-tube densely covered with narrow scales, abundant wool and bristly spines in the axils. Fruit small, floral remains conspicuous, often much elongated before ripening, and with seeds in the upper part only, dry, splitting open lengthways, or breaking off by a basal opening, or berry-like, soft and deliquescent. Seeds straight or

slightly oblique bell-shaped to semi-globose, hilum basal, strophiole large, incorporating part of seedcoat; seedcoat proper black or dark brown, verrucose. (Compare *Parodia*.) 5 subgenera: *Notocactus:* Receptacle-tube narrowly to widely funnel-shaped, never bell-shaped. Fruit initially soft-fleshed, short or elongate and drooping, later drying. *Malacocarpus* (Salm-Dyck) F. Buxbaum: Ribs very pronounced, thickened round the areoles, young areoles with copious woolly hairs. Flowers relatively small, bell-shaped. Fruit concealed in the apical wool, berry-like and soft-fleshed, usually with small tufts of wool, usually deliquescent. *Neonotocactus* Backeb: Receptacle-tube widely bowl-shaped, only the lower group of stamens present (all other subgenera have 2 groups). Fruit before ripening very elongate at the base and drooping limply, breaking off by a basal opening. *Eriocactus* (Backeb.) Buining: Stems up to over 1 m tall, apex thickly woolly often oblique. Flowers widely bell-shaped. Fruit dry, strongly hairy and bristly, breaking off by a basal opening. Seeds numerous and very small. *Brasilicactus* (Backeb.) F. Buxbaum: Ribs divided into tiny tubercles, very densely covered with fine spines. Flowers small, greenish or orange-red, short campanulate-funnelshaped, individually very variable, their internal structure often very simplified. Fruit globose, small, not woolly, but with bristly spines. About 30 species in Uruguay, Paraguay, S Brazil and N Argentina.

Notocactus scopa (Sprengel) A. Berger (*Notocactus*)
Usually unbranched, seldom sprouting, later columnar to club-shaped stem up to 50 cm high and 8–10 cm thick, with 30–35 ribs. Apex depressed, with erect spines rising through short, white, woolly felt. Areoles with short, white, woolly felt, later glabrescent, with up to 40 thin, needle-shaped, snow-white radial spines 5–7 mm long, and 3–4 rather longer, reddish or brown to black, central spines. Flowers, several near apex, shortly funnel-shaped, 4 cm long, canary-yellow. Fruit almost globose, 7 mm across. Uruguay and S Brazil. The illustration shows *N. scopa* var. *nigrispinus.*

Notocactus ottonis (Lehm.) A. Berger (*Notocactus*)
Depressed globose or somewhat elongate stem, 5–11 cm across, fresh green with depressed, somewhat felted apex and 10–13 ±crenate ribs. Areoles depressed, short-felted with 10–18 short, straight or curved, thin, yellow radial spines, and 3–4 rather stouter, brown or red, light-tipped central spines up to 2.5 cm long. Flowers 4–6 cm long and wide, rich shining yellow with cherry-red stigma. Very variable species as regards spination and flower structure. S Brazil, Uruguay, Paraguay, Argentina.

Notocactus minimus Frič & Kreuz. (*Notocactus*)
Shortly cylindric stem, columnar with age, 2–4 cm across, mostly unbranched, only rarely sprouting from the base, dark blue-greem to reddish-violet with somewhat depressed, white woolly apex, and about 15 ribs with shallow cross-furrows, protruding chin-like below the areoles. Areoles 4 mm apart, initially white-woolly, later glabrescent, with about 17(–26) thin, chalk-white, radial spines 3–4 mm long, curved towards the stem or protruding, and 4 erect, dark red-brown, central spines 6–10 mm long, the lowest, strongest of which with strongly hooked, lighter tip. Flowers near apex, 3 cm long and 4 cm wide, yellow. Fruit ovoid, 1 cm thick, dry. Uruguay.

Notocactus sessiliflorus (Mackie ex Hooker) Krainz
[= **Malacocarpus sessiliflorus** (Mackie ex Hooker) Backeb.] (*Malacocarpus*)
Depressed globose stem, up to 20 cm across, dark green to grey-green, with few ribs at first, later up to 30 sharp ones thickened round the areoles. Areoles initially with 3, later 4, radial spines up to 2 cm long, of which the lower 3 are often slightly curved, and, rarely, 1 central spine. Flowers up to 4 cm long, canary-yellow. Uruguay, Argentina.

Notocactus mammulosus (Lem.) A. Berger (*Neonotocactus*) ■□ □□
Globose, later elongate stem, up to 10 cm high and 5—6 cm wide, dark green, with depressed, white-felted, unarmed apex and 18—20 low, deeply crenate ribs. Tubercles protruding chin-like. Areoles depressed, 4—6 mm apart, felted, with 10—13, thin, radial spines barely 5 mm long, yellowish, brownish at base and tip, and 2 stouter, upward- or downward-pointing central spines 10—14 mm long, yellow with darker tip. Flowers near apex, 3.5—4 cm long, canary-yellow, darker at base, with crimson stigma. Argentina, Uruguay.

Notocactus rutilans Daeniker & Krainz (*Neonotocactus*) □■ □□
Globose to oblong-columnar stem, 5 cm or more in diameter, matt blue-green, with depressed apex and 18(—24) ±spiralling ribs divided into small, chin-like, protruding tubercles. Areoles 6—7 mm apart, initially with abundant white wool, later glabrous, with 14—16, hard, radial spines 3—5 mm long, sometimes white, sometimes russet-tipped, yellowish in age, spreading on all sides or very rarely pectinate, and 2 sharp-pointed, straight or slightly down-curved, bright red-brown, central spines 5—7 mm long. Flowers 3—4 cm long, up to 6 cm wide, carmine pink with egg-yellow throat, pale yellow at the base, and purple stigma. Fruit 1.5 cm long, soft and green. Uruguay.

Notocactus schumannianus (Nicolai) A. Berger □□
[= **Eriocactus schumannianus** (Nicolai) Backeb.] (*Eriocactus*) ■■
Initially globose, with age clavate-cylindric stem, decumbent to ascending, over 1 m long and 12 cm thick, light green, later dark green and becoming corky with age, with somewhat oblique apex with white wool and spines, and about 30 sharp-edged, serrate ribs. Areoles 6—8 mm apart, felted at first, with 4—7 thick-based, bristly, straight or somewhat curved spines up to 5 cm long, initially red-brown, later grey. Flowers near apex 4—5 cm long and rather wider, yellow with yellow stigma. Fruit a pale yellow, fleshy berry. Paraguay, N Argentina.

Notocactus floricomus (Arech.) A. Berger ■□
var. **rubrispinus** A. Berger (*Neonotocactus*) □□
Initially globose, later columnar stem, up to 30 cm high and 13 cm wide, with depressed, woolly apex and 20 ribs divided into conical tubercles. Areoles 3 mm apart, with 20 or more diverse radial spines, protruding, whitish or grey, reddish at the base, and 4–5 stout, bright red central spines 2–2.5 cm long, spreading, the middle one porrect. Flowers numerous, in a ring round apex, 5.5–6 cm long, yellow. Uruguay.

Notocactus leninghausii (F. Haage) A. Berger □■
[= **Eriocactus leninghausii** (F. Haage) Backeb.] (*Eriocactus*) □□
Solitary, in age freely branching from the base, columnar, up to 1 m high and 10 cm thick, upright at first, later often bending and almost decumbent, bright green, apex usually oblique, with golden-yellow spines rising through white wool. Over 30, blunt, weakly crenate ribs. Areoles close-set, 4–5 mm apart, initially densely white-felted, with 15–20 bristly, spreading, honey-coloured, radial spines 0.5–1 cm long, and 3–4 somewhat stouter, backward-pointing, golden-yellow, central spines up to 4 cm long. Flowers often several near apex, up to 5 cm long and 6 cm wide, shining yellow with pale yellow stigma. Fruit a top-shaped berry, 2 cm across. S Brazil.

Notocactus graessneri (K. Schumann) A. Berger □□
[= **Brasilicactus graessneri** (K. Schumann) Backeb.] (*Brasilicactus*) ■□
Solitary, globose stem, 5–10 cm high and usually rather wider, leaf-green, almost covered by golden-yellow spines, usually with obliquely flattened and depressed apex, and 50–60 rather spiralling, low ribs almost completely divided into small tubercles. Areoles very close-set, 3–5 mm apart, yellow-felted, with very numerous, thin, needle-shaped, pale yellow, somewhat translucent, interlacing, radial spines, and up to 6 rather stouter, golden brownish-yellow central spines up to 2 cm long. Flowers in a ring round the apex, up to 2.5 cm long, yellowish green to emerald green with pale green stigma. Fruit small and round. S Brazil.

Notocactus haselbergii (F. Haage) A. Berger □□
[= **Brasilicactus haselbergii** (F. Haage) Backeb.] (*Brasilicactus*) □■
Solitary, depressed globose stem, up to 15 cm across, light green, covered in delicate, silvery-white spines, with slightly oblique apex, densely woolly-felted, with erect spines, and 30 or more ribs almost entirely divided into small, hemispherical tubercles. Areoles 5–7 mm apart, white-felted, with 20 or more needle-shaped, at first yellowish, then white, nearly erect, radial spines up to 1 cm long, and usually 4 erect, rather stronger, yellowish central spines. Flowers round apex, 1.5 cm long, 1 cm wide, fiery orange with deep yellow stigma. Fruit globose, at first green, then yellow. S Brazil.

PARODIA Spegazzini

Solitary or sprouting from the base, small to medium-sized, globose, rarely shortly columnar. Ribs often spiralling, tuberculate or competely divided into tubercles. Young areoles often with copious woolly hair. Central spines straight or curved to hooked. Flowsers numerous, near the apex, narrowly campanulate to funnel-shaped. Pericarpel naked and glabrous in species with a woolly apex, otherwise pericarpel and receptacle-tube with small, pointed scales and abundantly hairy, sometimes with bristles in the scale axils. Fruit small, globose to ovoid, with floral remains, dry, hairy, and bursting open, or red and strongly elongate-tubular. Seeds small, semi-globose to globose, with a spongy, corky strophiole usually larger than the seed itself. Seedcoat glossy brown, smooth (compare *Notocactus*). According to the seed- and flower-structure, the genus may be divided into 3 subgenera:

Parodia: Flowers funnel-shaped and usually widely opening. Pericarpel naked or pericarpel and receptacle-tube scaly with woolly hair and bristles. Fruit thin-walled and dry. Seeds extraordinarily numerous, very small (0.2 mm in diameter), globose with very large strophiole. Seedcoat smooth, brown.

Protoparodia F. Buxbaum: Flowers various. Bristles produced in much greater number in the upper scale-axils (except in *P. chrysacanthion*). Fruit thin-walled and dry. Seeds mostly over 0.5 mm in diameter, black or dark brown, verrucose (*P. columnaris* brown and smooth). Strophiole usually small.

Obtextosperma F. Buxbaum: Flowers very strongly hairy; only the uppermost receptacle-tube scales with bristles. Fruit red, hairy, tube-shaped. Seeds in the lower part only, nearly 1 mm in diameter, hemispherical, covered with a brown arillar membrane, strophiole large hemispherical (1 species only).

About 50 (?) sometimes very variable species from N Argentina and S and C Bolivia at altitudes of 4000 m and more.

Parodia nivosa Frič ex Backeb. (*Parodia*)

Solitary, globose to weakly cylindric, 15 cm high, 8 cm wide, dull green, with thick white wool on apex, and spiralling ribs divided into tubercles. Areoles initially white-felted, with about 18 pure white radial spines 1 cm long, and 4, pure white, straight, cruciform, central spines up to 2 cm long. Flowers near apex, funnel-shaped, 3 cm long, 2.5–3 cm wide, light blood-red. Fruit small. N Argentina.

Parodia sanguiniflora Frič ex Backeb. (*Parodia*)

Solitary, globose, up to 8 cm across, fresh green, with spiralling ribs entirely divided into tubercles. Areoles at first very woolly, with about 15 bristly, white radial spines, and 4 brownish central spines up to 2 cm long, the lowest curving into a hook. Flowers 3–4 cm across, shining bluish-red to carmine. Bolivia.

Parodia catamarcensis Backeb. (*Parodia*)

Initially globose, later cylindric, sometimes rather curved stem, strong green, ribs divided into low, flatly-rounded tubercles. Areoles initially strongly white-woolly, with 9 thin, white, radial spines, and 4 often fairly stout, pure dark-red central spines, the lowest hooking round claw-like towards the stem. Flowers light yellow, medium-sized. N Argentina.

Parodia mutabilis Backeb. (*Parodia*)

Globose, up to 8 cm across stem, with spiralling ribs entirely divided into tubercles. Areoles with about 50 hair-fine, white radial spines, and 4 strong, sometimes hooked, yellow, red- to orange-brown, central spines up to 1.2 cm long. Flowers large, pale- to golden-yellow with white or pink throat. Rather variable species with several varieties. N Argentina.

210

Parodia maassii (Heese) A. Berger (*Protoparodia*)

Globose to shortly cylindric stem, up to 20 cm high, 7—15 cm wide, yellowish green, apex tufted with brown spines; ribs 13—21, spiralling, tuberculate, flattened towards the base. Areoles on the tubercles, with white wool, with 8—10(—15), protruding, fine, sometimes curving, radial spines, honey-coloured at first, later whitish, and 4 stronger, initially light brown central spines bulbous at the base, downward-curving and hooked, 3(—7) cm long. Flowers 3—4 cm long, 1.5 cm wide, orange. red. Fruit 5—6 cm thick. S Bolivia to N Argentina.

Parodia comarapana Card. (*Protoparodia*)

Solitary, or more usually sprouting, globose stem, up to 5 cm high and 8 cm across, with 18—20 straight ribs devided by cross-furrows into tubercles. Areoles 6 mm apart, white-felted, with 18—23 thin, needle-like, straight, pale yellow to whitish spines up to 2 cm long. Flowers tubular, up to 2.5 cm long, 0.5 cm wide, orange-yellow. Fruit globose, 8 mm thick, greenish white. Bolivia.

Parodia schwebsiana (Werderm.) Backeb. (*Protoparodia*)

Solitary, rarely sprouting from the base, globose, weakly cylindric with age, up to 12 cm high, 7 cm thick, fresh green, with somewhat depressed apex, with dense white wool, and 13—20 weakly tuberculate, usually straight ribs. Areoles 5—7 mm apart, initially with long, dense, white wool, later glabrescent, with 10 yellowish to brownish, almost straight or only slightly curved radial spines 5—7(—12) mm long, and 1, hooked central spine up to 2 cm long, pointing obliquely downwards. Flowers 3 cm long, brilliant blood-red, consecutive from the woolly apex. Fruit globose, 3—4 mm across. Bolivia.

Parodia chrysacanthion (K. Schumann) Backeb. (*Protoparodia*)

Solitary, depressed globose, oblong with age, up to 12 cm high, 10 cm wide, light green, the apex somewhat depressed, very woolly, topped with golden-yellow spines, with about 24 spiralling ribs divided into tubercles. Areoles 3—5 mm apart, with tufts of white wool and 30—40 thin, bristly, golden or brownish-yellow spines, the longer middle ones up to 3 cm long. Flowers from the woolly apex, almost 2 cm long, 1—2 cm wide, golden yellow. Fruit a small, ovoid berry. N Argentina.

Parodia schuetziana Jajó (*Protoparodia*) ■□□□
Broadly globose, over 11 cm wide stem, with spiralling tubercles. Areoles initially strongly woolly-felted, with numerous fine, white, radial spines, and pale yellow to brown or red central spines, one of which is hooked. Flowers red, 2 cm long. N Argentina.

Parodia mairanana Card. (*Protoparodia*) □■□□
Sprouting, globose stem, 3–4 cm high and 4–5.5 cm across, fresh green, with depressed apex and 13–14 ribs divided into tubercles. Areoles 8–10 mm apart, grey-felted, with 9–14 needle-shaped, whitish or straw-coloured radial spines, spreading or appressed, unequal, 3–8–12 mm long, and 1, not hooked, central spine, or 2–3 with 1 of them hooked, 1–2 cm long. Flowers from white woolly apex, urn-shaped to shortly funnel-shaped, 3–3.5 cm long, 2 cm wide, gold inside, dark orange outside, lilac-tipped. Fruit elliptic, up to 8 mm long, light magenta. Bolivia (Prov. Florida).

Parodia ayopayana Card. (*Obtextosperma*) □□■□
Solitary, rarely sprouting, globose stem, 6–8 cm high, 6–9 cm wide, fresh green, with 11 fairly sharp-edged, weakly tuberculate ribs. Areoles 12 mm apart, initially densely white-felted, later greying, with 10–11 needle-shaped, whitish radial spines 1.2–2 cm long, appressed to somewhat pectinate, and 4 spreading, subulate, light brown or whitish central spines, thicker at the base, 3–3.5 cm long. Flowers several at a time from the dense white wool on the apex, 3 cm long, golden yellow. Fruit 1–4 cm long, reddish. Bolivia.

BLOSSFELDIA Werdermann

Small, depressed globose stem, with tuberous root, often forming extensive cushions through dichotomous division, side-shoots and suckers. Stem without ribs and tubercles. Areoles spiralling, with tiny tufts of wool and no spines. Flowers solitary or several at once from the middle of the apex, very variable in size and shape, companulate to pointed funnel-shaped. Pericarpel on ±long stalk, the lower part naked or with tiny scales only, with decurrent podaria and small tufts of hair in the axils, the upper part and the very short receptacle-tube with larger, triangular, fairly dense scales, sometimes without wool. Fruit globose to narrowly pear-shaped, sculptured by the decurrent podaria, with floral remains and small tufts of hair, splitting laterally and deliquescing. Seeds tiny, globose, with large spongy strophiole; seedcoat glossy red-brown, lightly areolate and densely covered with fine papillae. 1 species with a series of varieties in N Argentina. This is the smallest known cactus.

Blossfeldia liliputana Werderm. □□□■
Tiny, up to 16 mm across, flat, disc-shaped stem, grey-green, sprouting to form small clusters from many-headed, thickened rootstock. Apex slightly depressed, densely felted. Ribs and tubercles absent. Areoles without spines, in an irregular spiral. Flowers solitary from woolly apex, 1 cm long, yellowish white. Fruit globose, 5 mm thick. N Argentina.

FRAILEA B. & R.

Dwarf cacti, globose or shortly cylindric, often mat-forming. Ribs divided into tubercles. Areoles with thin spines. Flowers near the apex, medium-sized, campanulate-funnel-shaped, yellow, usually only opening in full sunlight, otherwise cleistogamous. Pericarpel naked in the lower part, the upper part like the receptacle-tube with small scales, woolly hairs, and a few bristles, more pronounced in upper scale axils. Fruit small, globose, pea-sized, with floral remains and hairs and bristles, drying, thin-walled and brittle. Seeds hemispherical or cap-shaped, with large, concave hilum, with or without strophiole; seedcoat glossy brown or blackish, verrucose, sometimes finely verrucose or almost smooth with darker reticulate marking. About 35 species from central South America: Paraguay, Argentina, Uruguay, Bolivia, S Brazil.

Frailea schilinzkyana (F. Haage) B. & R.

Globose, 2–4 cm high and equally wide, light green with grey underside, with conical root, ±strongly sprouting from the base and of mat-forming habit, with depressed and almost unarmed apex, and 10–13 shallow ribs divided into hexagonal or rounded tubercles 1.5 mm high. Areoles 2–4 mm apart, sparsely woolly-felted, with 12–14 radiating, recurved and flat-lying, thin, black spines 2–3 mm long, later deciduous. Flowers up to 3.5 cm long, sulphur-yellow. Fruit globose, 5 mm thick. Paraguay, Argentina.

Frailea horstii Ritter

Slender cylindric, up to 18 cm high, 2–2.5 cm wide, dark green, with 20–33 straight ribs completely divided into rounded tubercles. Areoles with 15–20, yellowish brown to russet, radial spines 2–3 mm long, and 3–6 only slightly stronger central spines 4–6 mm long. Flowers 4 cm long, 5 cm wide, sulphur-yellow, with white wool and long brown bristles on the outside. Brazil (Rio Grande do Sul).

Frailea gracillima (Monv. ex Lem.) B. & R.

Cylindric up to 10 cm high, 2–2.5 cm wide, frequently sprouting laterally, ash-grey green, with 13 straight or oblique ribs completely divided into rounded tubercles 2 mm high. Areoles initially white-felted, with up to 16 thin, slightly curved, ±appressed, transparent radial spines 1–1.5 mm long, and usually 2 somewhat stronger and darker, protruding, central spines. Flowers 3 cm long, light yellow, carmine red at the base, with white wool and brown bristles on the outside. Fruit globose, 6 mm across, greenish, hairy, Paraguay.

Frailea colombiana (Werderm.) Backeb.

Solitary or sprouting from the base and many-headed to cushion-forming, stem depressed globose or ovoid, up to 4 cm high and wide, glossy matt leaf-green, with deeply umbilicate, sparsely woolly, spiny apex, and 17–18 straight or somewhat spiralling, very shallow ribs almost completely divided into barely elevated tubercles. Areoles 3–5 mm apart, weakly brownish-white felted, soon glabrescent, with 16–20 brown-tipped, yellowish, later pale grey radial spines 3–4 mm long, ±spreading horizontally, usually pectinate, and (without a sharp distinction) 2–5 central spines up to 6 mm long, ±spreading out. Flowers 2.5 cm long, 2–2.5 cm wide, pure yellow. Fruit oblong-ovoid, 5 mm thick, green to brown, splitting at the base. Originally said to have been from Colombia, but not found there subsequently.

Frailea castanea Backeb.　　　　　　　　　　　　　■☐
[= **Frailea asterioides** Werderm.]　　　　　　　　☐☐
Solitary, depressed globose, up to 4 cm high, 4.5 cm or more wide, dark-red to chocolate-brown, often even blue-green or grey-green, with slender, conical, tuberous root and 9–11(–14) very shallow, low-convex ribs. Areoles 2.5–3 mm apart, with 7–11 tiny, dark or very-dark brown spines 0.5–1.5 mm long, pointing downwards and appressed. Flowers up to 4 cm long, over 4 cm wide, pale yellow. Fruit a yellowish green, 1 cm berry. Brazil.

Frailea cataphracta (Dams) B. & R.　　　　　　☐■
　　　　　　　　　　　　　　　　　　　　　　　　☐☐
Depressed globose, up to 4 cm thick stem, sprouting from the base, dull green, with depressed apex and 15 low ribs divided into flat tubercles, characterised by crescent-shaped, brown or violet marks below the areoles. Areoles 3 mm apart, with sparse woolly felt at first, and usually 5 thin, initially golden yellow, later greying radial spines up to 2 mm long, pointing laterally and downwards and appressed; central spines absent. Flowers 3.8 cm long and wide, light yellow. Fruit globose, 4 mm thick. Paraguay.

UEBELMANNIA Buining
Solitary, globose, later cylindric, sometimes up to 75 cm high, upright. Ribs numerous, sharp or divided into tubercles. Areoles mostly strongly spiny. Flowers near the apex, funnel-shaped, yellow. Pericarpel and receptacle-tube with solitary, very small scales with abundant hairs and a few bristles in the axils. Fruit an oblong-cylindric, red or yellowish-green berry, without floral remains, with a few tiny scales with hairs and bristles, together with a mop of hairs and bristles on the apex, drying. Seeds cap-shaped; seedcoat glossy black to red-brown, wrinkled, tuberculate or smooth, hexagonally areolate. 5 species, some rather variable, in Brazil (Minas Gerais).

Uebelmannia pectinifera Buining　　　　　　　☐☐
　　　　　　　　　　　　　　　　　　　　　　　　■☐
Solitary, not sprouting, ±cylindric, up to 75 cm high and up to 15 cm thick, upright, dark red-brown, ±covered with waxy white scales, with 15–18 sharp ribs. Areoles almost touching one another, shortly pale-grey felted, forming a 4 cm wide woolly-cap on the apex, later glabrescent, with 3–4 dark brown to almost black, later black-tipped grey spines, 12–15 mm long, standing out at a right angle, interlacing, pectinate and vertical from the ribs. Flowers slenderly funnel-shaped, from the woolly apex, 1.5 cm long and 1 cm wide, greenish-yellow. Fruit oblong-pear-shaped to cylindric, 1.5–2.5 cm long, bright carmine-red. Brazil.

Uebelmannia buiningii Donald　　　　　　　　　☐☐
　　　　　　　　　　　　　　　　　　　　　　　　☐■
Solitary, shortly cylindric, up to 8 cm thick, greenish or reddish brown, with a rough surface, the 18 straight ribs divided into downward-pointing tubercles 5 mm apart. Areoles with sparse woolly-hair, with 2–4 spines up to 5 mm long, and 4 longer, cruciform, red-brown, later white spines. Flowers up to 2.7 cm long and 2 cm wide, yellow. Brazil.

ASTROPHYTUM Lemaire

Solitary, depressed globose, shortly columnar with age (up to 1.5 m high), with few ribs ±densely covered with fine white hairy tufts. Areoles woolly, spineless or with straight or spiralling spines. Flowers large, funnel-shaped, yellow or yellow with red throat. Pericarpel and receptacle-tube densely covered with narrowly lanceolate scales with long, dense, woolly hair in the axils. Fruit with floral remains, semi-fleshy, later dessicated with dry scales and dense, felty hair, splitting in various ways. Seeds cap-shaped, edge curved over the deep cavity of the hilum; seedcoat shiny dark brown, almost smooth. 4 species with numerous varieties in N and C Mexico.

■□
□□

Astrophytum ornatum (DC.) F.A.C. Weber

Solitary, globose, cylindric with age, up to 1 m or more high, 30 cm across, dark green, with sparse white or yellow woolly flakes in bands, with 8 straight or frequently spiralling, strongly compressed, ±sinuate, crenate ribs. Areoles at first yellowish-white felted, later glabrescent, with 6–8 very stout, 2–4 cm long radial spines laterally compressed, amber yellow, later brown and finally grey, and usually 1 rather larger central spine. Flowers 7–8 cm long, canary-yellow with bright silken sheen. Fruit almost globose, 1.5 cm long, bursting midway to the base into a star shape. Mexico (Hidalgo, Querétaro).

□■
□□

Astrophytum myriostigma Lem.

Globose, cylindric with age, up to 60 cm high, densely covered with pure white woolly flecks, with depressed apex and usually 5, rarely 4–8–10 sharply-edged, broadly triangular ribs. Areoles woolly and spineless. Flowers 4–6 cm long and wide, pale yellow with silken sheen. Fruit oblong-ovoid, opening into a star shape. C Mexico.

□□
■□

Astrophytum capricorne (A. Dietr.) B. & R.

Globose, elongate with age, up to 25 cm high, light green, densely covered with white woolly flecks, and 8 sharply-edged, slightly crenate ribs. Areoles with 5–10 ±flattened, weak, irregularly pointing, yellow to brownish black, 3–7 cm long spines tangled over the top. Flowers 6–7 cm long, wide opening, pale yellow with carmine-red throats, sweet-smelling. Fruit opening at the base. Very variable species. N Mexico.

□□
□■

Astrophytum asterias (Zucc.) Lem.

At first ±spherical, later disc-like, quite flat, up to 5.5 cm high, 10 cm across, grey-green, glabrous with white woolly-flecks, with a slightly depressed apex and 7–8 very wide, quite flat ribs separated by sharp longitudinal furrows. Areoles grey-felted and spineless. Flowers 3 cm long, straw-yellow with rush-brown to carmine-red throat. Fruit reddish-grey, not opening above the base. N Mexico (Nuevo Leon, Tamaulipas).

DISCOCACTUS Pfeiffer

At first ±globose, later disc-shaped and prostrate. Ribs few to numerous, widening round the aroles and often elongate like tubercles. Spines very strong, often horny. Flowers from a true terminal cephalium, chiefly growing in breadth with copious hair and sharp, bristly spines; vegetative growth still possible after the formation of the cephalium, by means of an intervening (intercalary) ring-meristem surrounding the cephalium and the formation of new rib-tubercles. Flowers large, funnel-shaped or salver-shaped, white or pink, night-blooming and strongly perfumed. Pericarpel small naked, slender lower part of the receptacle-tube naked or with a few tiny scales, funnel-shaped upper part with ±recurved lanceolate scale-leaves grading into outer perianth-segments. Fruit a pear-shaped, yellow, green, white or red berry, later drying and concealed in the woolly cephalium, floral remains deciduous later. Stalk-like base of fruit with dense, long hairs. Seeds nearly globose with large ±straight hilum; seedcoat black, minutely prickly, with short conical tubercles. 12 species from Brazil, Paraguay and E Bolivia.

Discocactus silicicola Buining & Brederoo ■□ □□
Depressed globose to globose, 15 cm wide, 5 cm high, grey-green, with 10 ribs divided into tubercles. Areoles with 3–5(–6) cream, later brownish-grey, radial spines (1 pointing downwards, up to 4 cm long, and always 2 laterally up to 2.7 cm long), central spines absent; older plants have 2 more small spines on the upper edge of the areoles. Cephalium relatively narrow, 2.5 cm across and 2 cm high, with white wool and brown to grey bristles protruding up to 3 cm mainly from the edge. Flowers up to 7 cm long, 3.5–4 cm wide, white, strong-smelling. Brazil (Mato Grosso).

Discocactus horstii Buining & Brederoo □■ □□
Depressed globose, up to 6 cm wide and 2 cm high, brownish green, with 15–22 rounded ribs. Areoles 4–5 mm apart, initially white-felted, later glabrous, with somewhat curving, ±club-shaped, brown, later pale grey spines 3–3.5 mm long, pectinately appressed, '3–4 pairs pointing laterally and 1 straight downwards). Cephalium up to 2 cm wide and 1.5 cm high, with white wool and a few brown bristles up to 2 cm long, surrounded by stiff, vertical, brown-tipped spines up to 1 cm long all round the edge. Flowers up to 7.5 cm long, 6 cm wide, white. Fruit cylindric, 3 cm long, 4 mm thick, white. Brazil (Minas Gerais). In the illustration, the main stem is hidden by young offsets with juvenile spination.

MELOCACTUS Link & Otto
Globose to elongate, often large cacti with distinct ribs, usually strongly spiny, with an extensive superficial root-system. Flowers from a true terminal cephalium that terminates vegetative growth and later produces a dense, cylindric, reddish to blackish mop of wool and bristles, which can reach a length of 1.5 m. Flowers small, tub ular, hardly emerging from the cephalium, mostly pink to red, occasionally violet, day-blooming, not scented. Pericarpel and receptacle-tube demarcated by a constriction, glabrous or sometimes with a few small scales, coloured. Fruit oblong-clavate, berry-like, with flower-remains, coral or carmine red to whitish or violet. Seeds obovoid, with truncated hilum; seedcoat glossy black, ±verrucose. About 30 fairly variable species (about 300 described) from Central America to Peru and Brazil.

Melocactus neryi K. Schumann □□ ■□
Depressed globose, 10–11 cm high, 13–14 cm wide, dark green, with 10 straight, somewhat tuberculate ribs separated by broad furrows. Areoles 2–2.5 cm apart, with 7–9 straight or upcurving, terete, dark-tipped, grey radial spines up to 2.7 cm long. Cephalium 5 cm high and 7 cm wide, with white wool and 2 cm long red bristles. Flowers 22 mm long, 8–10 mm wide, carmine red. Fruit club-shaped, 18 mm long, light carmine-red. Brazil (Amazonas).

Melocactus curvispinus Pfeiffer □□ □■
[= **Melocactus delessertianus** Lem.]
Globose, up to 10 cm high, 9 cm wide, grey-green, with 15 straight or slightly spiralling ribs, sometimes with folds across them. Areoles somewhat grey-felted, with 9–10 strong, subulate, greyish pink, russet-tipped radial spines 1.5–2 cm long, somewhat curving towards the stem, and 2 stouter central spines up to 2.8 cm long, situated one below the other. Cephalium 4 cm high, 5 cm wide, with white wool and orange-red bristles. Flowers 2.5 cm long, purplish pink. Fruit 3 cm long, purple. Mexico.

Melocactus azureus Buining & Brederoo

Solitary, up to 17 cm high, 14 cm wide, azure blue-pruinose, with 9–10 fairly sharp, vertical ribs somewhat elevated between the areoles. Areoles initially white-felted, soon greying and glabrescent, with usually 7 radial spines (1 pointing downwards 4 cm long and 3 each side 3–3.5 cm long) together with a few smaller, upward-pointing secondary spines 18 mm long, and 1(–3) central spines up to 2.5 cm long. All spines very sturdy, pale grey, dark-brown tipped. Cephalium up to 3.5 cm high, 7 cm wide, with pure white wool and fine, red bristly hairs. Flowers tubular, 14 mm long, 4.5 mm wide, carmine red, darker above. Fruit club-shaped, 20 mm long, 7 mm across, glossy pale-pink. Brazil (Bahia).

Melocactus albicephalus Buining & Brederoo

Solitary, up to 12 cm high, 15 cm wide, green, with 9–10 fairly acute ribs with sharp, hatchet-shaped, protruding tubercles between the areoles. Areoles with white wool, soon glabrescent, with usually 9 radial spines (1 porrect, 4.5 cm long, always 3 laterally, 2-3 cm long, and 2 above, 4–7 mm long), together with 1(–2) central spines, 3 cm long. All spines very sturdy, often slightly curved, light brown at first, soon light greyish-pink with light brown tips. Cephalium 4 cm high, up to 7.5 cm wide, with dense white wool and red bristles becoming visible only in the lower part. Flowers 23 mm long, 9 mm wide, glossy carmine-red. Brazil (Central Bahia).

Melocactus giganteus Buining & Brederoo

Solitary, up to 50 cm high, 20 cm wide, green, with 15 ribs usually spiralling to the left. Areoles initially grey-felted, then glabrous, with 8 spreading, somewhat curved, radial spines 11–18 mm long, and 1 obliquely upcurving central spine 15–17 mm long and 4 mm thick at the base. All spines very sturdy, initially brownish pink, later grey-brown. Cephalium up to 26 cm long, 9 cm wide, with white wool and red bristles. Flowers tubular, 6–8 mm long, bright lilac. Fruit 18 mm long, 7 mm across. Brazil (Bahia).

Melocactus zehntneri (B. & R.) Werd.

Solitary, up to 18 cm high, 15 cm wide, green, with 12–16 fairly sharp ribs with strong, hatchet-shaped protruberances between the areoles. Areoles initially with yellowish grey felt, later glabrous, with 8 radial spines 20 mm long, often somewhat depressed, with a bloom along the upper side, and 1 central spine 17–22 mm long, protruding obliquely upwards. All spines sturdy, ±strongly curved towards the stem, at first horn-coloured, then brown and later violet-grey with dark brown tips. Cephalium 10 cm high, 8.5 cm wide, with white wool and red bristles. Flowers tubular, 18 mm long, 8 mm wide, violet. Fruit club-shaped, 12 mm long, 4.5 mm across, reddish pink. Brazil (Bahia).

Tribe VIII Echinocereeae (B. & R.) F. Buxbaum
WILCOXIA B. & R.

Slender-stemmed, dwarf, shrub-like, with turnip-like or tuberous roots. Stems no longer than 60 cm, sparsely branching. Ribs very shallow. Areoles with delicate spines and hairs or with dense hair only. Flowers conspicuous, near the apex, lateral or truly terminal, tubular to flatly campanulate, opening throughout the day. Pericarpel and lower part of receptacle-tube with dense, tiny scales on pronounced podaria, upper part more sparsely so, scales on receptacle-tube lanceolate and merging into the perianth-segments; bristly spines and hairs in the scale axils. Fruit oblong to ovoid to pear-shaped, juicy, berry-like, with floral remains and spiny tufts, both deciduous. Seeds small, almost globose, with large, protruding, basal hilum; seedcoat black, verrucose, with large, rounded pits. 4 (?) species in S Texas and N Mexico.
This genus is considered by some experts to be part of *Echinocereus*.

Wilcoxia poselgeri (Lem.) B. & R. ■□ □□

[= **Wilcoxia tuberosa** Kreuz.]

Upright or leaning shrub, 30–60 cm high, with tuberous thickened roots and very slender, dark green, terete, 8-ribbed branches 7–15 mm thick. Areoles white-felted, with 9–12, straight, thin, white radial spines 2 mm long, and 1 upward-pointing, subulate, white or darker, even black central spine 4–5 mm long. Flowers terminal or lateral, almost rotate, 4.5–5 cm long, 3 cm wide, light purple, segments with darker midstripe. Fruit ovoid, 1.5 cm long, 1 cm thick, green. USA (Texas), Mexico (Coahuila).

Wilcoxia albiflora (Backeb.) □■ □□

Small, freely-branching shrub, with almost cylindric, bright green stems 15–20 cm long and 6 mm thick. Areoles with 9–12 tiny, appressed, bristly white spines 1 mm long. Flowers terminal and lateral, 2 cm long, 2.5 cm wide, white to delicate pink with darker, greenish-brown throat. Fruit ovate, 15 mm long, 8 mm across, olive-green, with floral remains and about 20 easily shed spine-areoles, later drying. Probably N Mexico.

ECHINOCEREUS Engelmann

Low, globose to shortly-columnar, upright, or elongate, decumbent, usually freely-branching from the base and forming dense mats or clumps of soft-fleshed stems. Ribs sometimes divided into deep tubercles. Areoles with very diverse spines, sometimes banded with different colours. Flowers mostly near the apex, breaking through the epidermis above an areole, very large, shortly (rarely longly) funnel-shaped, or narrowly to broadly campanulate, pink to red, scarlet to purplish violet or yellow to greenish white. Pericarpel and receptacle-tube ±densely scaly, the scale-areoles with needle-shaped spines, hairs and felt. Stigma-lobes usually emerald green. Fruit globose to ovoid, with floral remains, mostly red-purple or green, berry-like, opening, with easily shed prickly tufts. Seeds obliquely ovoid to almost globose, with sunken basal hilum; seedcoat black, roundly verrucose, rarely wrinkled with conspicuous interstitial pits. According to the structure and branching habit of the stems, 4 series may be distinguished: *Subinermes*: Upright, vigorously sprouting or freely branching and mat-forming. Ribs not very prominent. Areoles without spines or with only a few thin ones. *Prostrati*: Very freely sprouting from the base and mat-forming. Branches decumbent and ascending. Areoles with very sharp spines (plus 5 subseries). *Erecti*: Freely sprouting from the base and mat-forming. Branches mostly upright and much stronger than those of *Prostrati*: Always very spiny (plus 2 subseries). About 60 species in Mexico and SW USA. Depending on the habitat these plants are extraordinarily variable, so various groups of 'species' certainly ought to be combined. A new classification of *Echinocereus* has recently been published by Taylor (1985).

Echinocereus subinermis Salm-Dyck (*Subinermes*) □□ ■□

Solitary, rarely sprouting, initially globose, later columnar stem, 10–15(–20) cm high , .7–9 cm wide at the base, vivid green when young, later blue-green or dark green, with 5–8 ribs separated by shallow furrows and, often creased horiztonally. Areoles with 6–8 thin, yellowish radial spines up to 5 mm long and 1 similar central spine; older areoles with only 3–4 conical spines 1 mm long. Flowers from upper part of stem, usually several together, 7 cm long and wide, pure yellow. Fruit olive-shaped, 2 cm long, 1.3 cm across, dark green. Mexico.

Echinocereus pulchellus (Mart.) K. Schumann (*Subinermes*) □□ □■

Shortly cylindric, 4 cm thick, often up to 10 cm long stem, blue-green, later grey, clustering, with 12–13 shallow ribs ±divided into tubercles by cross-furrows. Areoles with 3–4 radiating, weakly curved, yellowish, eventually grey spines only a few millimetres long. Flowers 4 cm long, funnel-shaped, whitish to deep pink. Mexico.

Echinocereus scheeri (Salm-Dyck) Scheer (*Prostrati*) ■□ □□
[= **Echinocereus salm-dyckianus** Scheer]
Sprouting from the base, forming thick mats, ascending stems, 15–20 cm long, 2–2.5 cm thick, dark green, with 7–9 straight or somewhat spiralling, slightly sinuate ribs. Areolés 5–8 mm apart, initially yellow-felted, with 8–9 yellowish, reddish-tipped radial spines 7 mm long, and 1 subulate, horn-coloured or red central spine up to 1.5 cm long. Flowers lateral, solitary or several together, 10–12 cm long, 5–6 cm wide, tubular-funnelshaped, carrot-coloured, only fully opening in the evening. Fruit almost globose, 2 cm across, green. Mexico (Chihuahua, Durango).

Echinocereus berlandieri (Engelm.) Hort. F.A. Haage (*Prostrati*) □■ □□
Freely-branching, decumbent or ascending, light to dark green stems 6–10 cm long, 1.3–2 cm thick, with 5–6 spiralling ribs almost completely divided into conical tubercles. Areoles 1–1.5 cm apart, with 6–8, protruding, bristly, translucent white or light brown, radial spines 8–10 mm long, and 1 yellowish-brown central spine up to 2 cm long. Flowers lateral, broadly funnel-shaped, 6–8 cm long, carmine-pink. Fruit ovoid, 2–2.5 cm long, 1.5 cm thick, green. USA (Texas), Mexico.

Echinocereus pentalophus (DC.) Lem. (*Prostrati*) □□ ■□
Freely-branching from the base, mat-forming, semi-decumbent, fresh green stems, sometimes red-tinged, finger-thick, up to 15 cm long, with usually 5 straight or somewhat spiralling, sinuate ribs divided into tubercles. Areoles 1 cm apart, with 3–5, needle-shaped, brownish, then whitish, darker-tipped radial spines up to 7 mm long, and 1 rather darker and stouter central spine 1 cm long. Flowers 10–12 cm long, 8 cm wide, rotate-funnel-shaped, carmine red to violet with lighter base. Fruit ovate, 1–1.5 cm long, green. USA (Texas), N Mexico.

Echinocereus enneacanthus Engelmann (*Prostrati*) □□ □■
Sprouting from the base, forming thick, irregular mats, soft-fleshed, light or dark green, ascending stems, 7–20 cm long, 3–3.5 cm thick, with 8–10 straight ribs divided into tubercles by broad cross-furrows and separated by sharp longitudinal furrows. Areoles 8–15 mm apart, with 7–12 (usually 8) protruding, white radial spines, bulbous at the base, unequal, 2–15 mm long, and 1(–3) straight, rather darker and stouter central spines up to 4 cm long. Flowers lateral, broadly funnel-shaped, 4.5–6 cm long, 7 cm wide, red. Fruit globose, 2–2.2 cm thick, green, red-tinged. USA (Texas, New Mexico), Mexico (Chihuahua, Coahuila).
The illustration shows var. *brevispinus* (W.O. Moore) L. Benson.

Echinocereus ferreirianus H. Gates (*Erecti*)

Sprouting stems, up to 30 cm high and up to 8 cm thick, with 9–13 tuberculate ribs. Areoles with 9–13 needle-like, grey to brown radial spines up to 2 cm long, and a few central spines 3–5 cm long, the lowest, longest 1 porrect to downward-pointing. Flowers up to 6 cm long, and 4 cm wide, pink, brown to purplish-pink outside. Fruit globose. Mexico (Baja California).

The plant illustrated is not true to type and may be a hybrid of *E. triglochidiatus* Engelm.

Echinocereus stramineus (Engelm.) Ruempler (*Erecti*)

Forming huge colonies of several hundred heads, up to 1 m high and 2 m wide; stems ovoid to cylindric, 10–20 cm long, 4–6 cm thick, fresh green, strongly spiny, the apex topped with long spines, and with 11–13 blunt, sinuate ribs separated by sharp furrows. Areoles 8–25 mm apart, with 7–10 protruding, radial spines 2–3 cm long, and 3–4 central spines 5–9 cm long; spines initially rosy red, then straw-coloured and finally white. Flowers widely funnel-shaped, 8–12 cm long, purple. Fruit almost globose, 3–4 cm thick, purplish red. USA (Texas, New Mexico), N Mexico (Chihuahua).

Echinocereus fendleri (Engelm.) Ruempler (*Erecti*)

Sprouting from the base, upright stems 10–20 cm high, 5–7.5 cm thick, somewhat narrowed towards the top, with 9–12 straight or twisting ribs, somewhat divided into tubercles by cross-furrows. Areoles 8–15 mm apart, with 5–10 straight or gently curved, protruding, light or dark, often very dark brown radial spines 1–2 cm long, and 1 usually dark central spine up to 4.5 cm long, bulbous at the base. Flowers up to 8 cm long, 10–12 cm wide, light to dark carmine-violet. Fruit ovoid, 3 cm long, edible. N Mexico to USA (Texas, Arizona, Utah).

Echinocereus viridiflorus Engelm.
var. **davisii** (A.D. Houghton) W.T. Marshall (*Erecti*)

Very small, globose, never cylindric, almost always solitary stem up to 1.5 cm high, with 6–7 lowish ribs. Areoles with 9–12 white, brown-tipped radial spines up to 6 mm long, curved or slightly depressed; no central spines. Flowers 2.5 cm long, greenish-yellow. Fruit globose, 1 cm long. USA (Texas).

Echinocereus pectinatus (Scheidw.) Englem. (*Erecti*)

Upright, usually unbranched, 10–15 cm high and 3–6 cm thick stem, almost completely enveloped in spines, with up to 23 straight, blunt ribs. Areoles close-set, with 16–30 white or pink-flushed, pectinate spines up to 9 mm long, and 2–6 short, conical, central spines standing in a row. Flowers 6–8 cm long, deep pink. Fruit globose, 2–3 cm thick. The spine colour in this species varies considerably from white or yellowish to reddish-purple. C Mexico (San Luis Potosi to Chihuahua).

Echinocereus reichenbachii (Terscheck ex Walp.) Hort. F.A. Haage
var. **fitchii** (B. & R.) L. Benson (*Erecti*)
[= **Echinocereus melanocentrus** Lowry]

Shortly-cylindric, up to 4 cm thick stem, with 12 low ribs divided into tubercles. Areoles with about 17 brown marginal spines, those on the apex blackish, without central spines or very rarely with short ones. Flowers rotate, up to 6 cm wide, purple with much darker centre. USA (Texas).

Echinocereus chloranthus (Engelm.) Hort. F.A. Haage (*Erecti*)

Sparsely sprouting, upright, cylindric stem, 5–7 cm thick and up to 15 cm high, with 13–18 low, straight or spiralling, tuberculate ribs. Areoles 12 mm apart, orbicular, with 12–20 sturdy, needle-shaped, protruding, later pectinate, white, red-tipped radial spines 1 cm long, and 3–4, white or red, central spines, unequal, 2–3 cm long, standing in a vertical row. Flowers 2–3 cm long, barely opening, brownish green. Fruit almost globose. N Mexico, USA (SW Texas and SE New Mexico).
The illustration shows var. *russanthus* (Weniger) G. Rowley

Echinocereus longisetus (Engelm.) Ruempler (*Erecti*)

Branching from the base, initially dark green, later more yellowish, up to 20 cm long and 4.5 cm thick stems, with 11–14 ribs. Areoles 1 cm apart, with 15–25 bristle-thin, lax, not interlacing, white to light-toned, radial spines 1.5 cm long, and 5–7 central spines up to 4 cm long, white, darker-tipped, brownish and thickened at the base. Flowers up to 6 cm long and wide, light purple. Mexico (Coahuila).

Tribe IX **Cacteae** F. Buxbaum

ECHINOCACTUS Link & Otto (incl. HOMALOCEPHALA B. & R.)

Usually very large, solitary or freely-branching from the base, globose to shortly columnar (some up to 1 m in diameter and 3 m high), or depressed globose to disc-shaped, usually with very numerous, sharp, occasionally tuberculate ribs. Spines extraordinarily stout, often flattened, transversely striate, often highly coloured. Areoles usually connected to the one above by a groove full of felt. Apex densely woolly-felted. Flowers in a ring deeply-embedded in the apical wool, campanulate to campanulate-funnelshaped, yellow or pink. Pericarpel and receptacle-tube united, the tube either very short and thick-walled or turbinate and only hollow around the nectar chamber, densely covered with oblong, pointed scales and with dense, long-haired wool in the axils; also the outer perianth-segments spine-tipped. Style thick, grooved longitudinally. Fruit densely woolly, with dried floral-remains, dry and breaking off at the base, or fleshy and glabrescent and bursting open irregularly. Seeds large, orbicular to kidney-shaped or obovoid, ±compressed; seedcoat glossy or matt black to dark brown, smooth or finely verrucose with folds. According to stem and flower structure the genus may be divided into 2 subgenera: *Echinocactus*: Very large, globose to columnar, solitary or forming groups. Flowers yellow. Fruit densely woolly, dry, breaking off at the base. *Homalocephala*: Small, disc-shaped. Flowers pink. Fruits soon drying and breaking off, or fleshy, glabrescent and bursting open. 6 species, some with several local forms, from the S USA and Mexico.

Echinocactus grusonii Hildm. (*Echinocactus*) ■□ □□
Initially broadly globose, shortly cylindric with age, up to 80 cm wide and up to 1.3 m high, vivid green, with white woolly apex, and 20−27 sharp-angled ribs separated by sharp furrows, tuberculate on young plants, later straight. Areoles 1.2 cm apart with dense yellow woolly-felt, with 8−10 subulate, radial spines up to 3 cm long, nearly erect, golden yellow at first, later paler, and 4 broader, curved, cruciform central spines up to 5 cm long. Flowers numerous, from woolly-felted apex, funnel-shaped, 4−6 cm long, 5 cm wide, silky yellow, only opening in full sunlight. Fruit oblong to globose, thin-skinned, 12−20 mm long. Besides the normal form there is another with pure white spines. C Mexico.

Echinocactus platyacanthus Link & Otto (*Echinocactus*) □■ □□
Very large, globose, later elongate columnar, grey-green stem, 1−2 m high (or more), 0.5−1 m thick, with strongly woolly apex and numerous (up to 40) narrow ribs. Areoles oblong, almost touching each other towards the top, the older ones separate or confluent, with 4−8 stout, straight, yellow to brown, radial spines 3−5 cm long, and 1−4 straight central spines 4−8 cm long. Flowers numerous, 2−5 cm long, yellow. Fruit ovoid to cylindric, 3−5 cm long. The plants described as individual species under the names *E. ingens* Zucc., *E. grandis* Rose, *E. palmeri* Rose and *E. visnaga* Hook. are only local forms of *E. platyacanthus*; at the most, the oblong fruits of *E. visnaga* might justify treating it as a variety of *E. platyacanthus*. Mexico.

Echinocactus texensis Hopffer □□
[= **Homalocephala texensis** (Hopffer) B. & R.] (*Homalocephala*) ■□
Depressed globose, 10−15 cm high and up to 30 cm wide, dark green, with concave woolly apex and 13−27 sharp ribs. Areoles far apart, white-felted, with 6 somewhat flattened, reddish, annulate radial spines 1−4 cm long, protruding or recurved, and 1 very flattened and annulate central spine 3−6 cm long. Flowers widely bell-shaped, 5−6 cm long and wide, silky pink and yellowish, reddish at the base; perianth-segments fringed with fine cilia. Fruit ovoid, up to 4 cm thick, red, juicy at first, then dry. USA (Texas, New Mexico), N Mexico.

Echinocactus horizonthalonius Lem. (*Homalocephala*) □□ □■
Globose to conical stem, up to 25 cm high, blue-green, with weakly felted apex topped with spines, and 8−10 broad, blunt ribs. Areoles 1.5−2 cm apart, with 7−8 very stout, straight or weakly curved, amber-yellow radial spines up to 3 cm long. Flowers from the apex, funnel-shaped, 5.5 cm long, 6 cm wide, pale to pinkish red, sweet-smelling. Fruit cylindric to ellipsoid, 3 cm long, red. USA (W Texas, S New Mexico to Arizona), N Mexico.

SCLEROCACTUS B. & R.
Solitary, rarely sprouting, globose to oblong, occasionally cylindrical, up to 45 cm high. Ribs straight or spiralling, strongly sinuate to ±tuberculate. Areoles rather elongate, with woolly felt, later glabrescent. Spines numerous, central spines partly flattened and leaf-like, straight or weakly curved. Flowers usually several on the apex, widely campanulate-funnelshaped, white, pink, greenish red or purple. Pericarpel and receptacle-tube thick-fleshed, with isolated tough-fleshed scales with angular podaria and sparse hairs in the axils. Fruit cylindric, globose or club-shaped, with floral remains, greenish pink, red or purple, thin-walled, drying, with occasional scales and hairs, breaking off at the base. Seeds semi-globose, flattened; seedcoat black, finely verrucose. 6 species in the USA.

Sclerocactus polyancistrus (Engelm. & Big.) B. & R. ■□ □□

Solitary, globose to cylindric, 8—40 cm high, 5—10 cm wide, with 13—17 blunt ribs. Areoles yellowish woolly-felted, with 10—15(—20) white radial spines 1—2.5 cm long, and 6—8 central spines 3—12 cm long, upper white and flattened, others round, dark red and often hooked. Flowers funnel-shaped, to 8 cm long, 5 cm wide, pinkish purple. Fruit long cylindric, 3.5 cm long, 1.6 cm thick, fresh green. USA (California, Nevada).

Sclerocactus intermedius Peebles □■ □□

Ovoid to cylindric, up to 20 cm high with 13 low, slightly spiralling ribs. Areoles with 12 white, straight or twisted radial spines, and 4 cruciform central spines 3--5 cm long, upper ones white and flattened, lower ones reddish, 4-sided, often hooked. Flowers 4—5 cm long, purple. USA (Arizona).

ANCISTROCACTUS B. & R.

Solitary, rarely forming groups, globose to elongate, with neck-like constriction above a tuberous root. Ribs almost completely divided into tubercles. Areoles with hooked central spine. Flowering areoles with a woolly furrow running to the middle or base of the tubercle. Flowers near the apex, small, campanulate-funnelshaped, greenish-yellow or reddish. Pericarpel with a few, small, naked scales, receptacle-tube scales merging into perianth-segments. Fruit a small, ovoid, green berry with floral remains. Seeds obovoid; seedcoat brown to almost black, finely verrucose. 4 species in S Texas and N Mexico.

Ancistrocactus scheeri (Salm-Dyck) B. & R. □□ ■□

Globose to club-shaped, green to blue-green, 5—8 cm high and 3—7 cm across, with 13 straight or rather oblique ribs almost completely divided into tubercles. Areoles with 11--18 needle-shaped, whitish or yellowish radial spines 8—10 mm long, a nd 3—4 stouter central spines 2—5 cm long, the lowest one hooked. Flowers from the furrow behind the areoles, 2.2 cm long, greenish-yellow and inconspicuous. Fruit a small green berry. USA (S Texas) and N Mexico.

HAMATOCACTUS B. & R. (incl. GLANDULICACTUS Backeb.)

Stem solitary, globose, to shortly cylindric. Ribs protruding at the areoles to almost tuberculate. Spines mostly long, one or more central spines hooked. Flowering areoles extended into a furrow, from which arise glands (modified spines) and flowers. Flowers conspicuous, companulate to narrowly funnel-shaped, wide-opening, yellow to purple. Pericarpel and receptacle-tube evenly covered with naked scales, gradually merging into the outer perianth-segments. Fruits small, oblong to almost globose, scarlet, juicy with appressed scales and floral remains. Seeds oblique broad-ovate to almost globose with basal hilum; seedcoat glossy black, shallowly verrucose.

The genus falls into 2 subgenera: *Hamatocactus* B. & R.: Ribs somewhat wavy and only slightly swollen at the areoles, with short areole furrows. Flowers narrowly funnel-shaped with very long perianth-segments. *Glandulicactus* (Backeb.) F. Buxbaum: Ribs pronouncedly tuberculate at the areoles. Areoles furrows very elongate. Flowers widely funnel-shaped with short perianth-segments. There are further differences in the structure of the seeds. 3 species in N and C Mexico and S texas.

Hamatocactus setispinus (Engelm.) B. & R. (*Hamatocactus*) □□ □■

Globose to shortly cylindric, 10—20 cm high and 8—12 cm wide, fresh green to blue-green, soft-fleshed, with 13 wavy, tuberculate ribs. Areoles with 12—15 needle-shaped, brown or white radial spines up to 4 cm long, and 1—3 stouter, hooked, dark brown central spines. Flowers very numerous near apex, 5.5—7 cm long, funnel-shaped, yellow with reddish throat. Fruit globose to ovoid, 6—18 mm thick, red. Mexico and SE USA. The illustration shows *H. setispinus* var. *cachetianus*.

Hamatocactus uncinatus (Galeotti.) F. Buxbaum ■☐
[= **Glandulicactus uncinatus** (Galeotti.) Backeb.] (*Glandulicactus*) ☐☐
Oblong or shortly cylindric, 10–20 cm high, blue-green, with usually 13 ribs divided into tubercles by sharp cross-furrows. Areoles white-felted, with 7–8 radial spines 2.5–5 cm long, upper ones straight, somewhat flattened, straw-coloured, lower ones spreading, rounded and hooked, purple, together with 1–4 erect, 4-sided, hooked, central spines often up to 12 cm long, yellow underneath, red above. Flowers 2–2.5 cm long, reddish brown, from the base of the furrow running from the areole to the base of the tubercle. Fruit small, oblong-ovoid, 1.5–2 cm long. USA (W Texas) to C Mexico.

ECHINOMASTUS B. & R.
Solitary, globose to oblong. Ribs divided into tubercles. Areoles with ±long furrow and densely spiny. Flowers from the furrows, apical, solitary or several together, campanulate-funnelshaped, whitish, pink to purple. Pericarpel and receptacle-tube with naked scales. Fruit globose to cylindric, drying, splitting at the base or side after shedding the floral remains. Seeds ovoid or kidney-shaped, with large, recessed, ventral hilum; seedcoat glossy brown to black, very finely verrucose. 8 species from USA and N Mexico.

Echinomastus macdowellii (Rebut.) B. & R. ☐■
☐☐
Globose or oblong, 8–13 cm high and wide, light green, almost totally covered with white, glassy spines, and with 20–25 ribs 5–7 mm high, divided into conical tubercles, rhomboidal at the base. Areoles initially very woolly, with 15–20 white, glassy, radial spines 1.5–2 cm long, interlacing, and 3–4 straw-coloured central spines 3–5 cm long. Flowers 4 cm wide, rosy red. Mexico (Nuevo Leon and Coahuila).

Echinomastus intertextus (Engelm.) B. & R. ☐☐
■☐
Globose to ovoid, up to 10 cm high, 7 cm thick, depressed apex with short, dense woolly felt and oblique spines, and with 13 straight or somewhat oblique ribs divided by cross-furrows. Areoles 8–11 mm apart, initially with abundant white woolly felt, with 16–25 straight, radial spines 9–15 mm long, white at the base, reddish and brown above, projecting horizontally and intertwining, also 4 erect central spines up to 2 cm long, lower ones much shorter, 2–4 mm long, porrect. Furrows behind the areoles short and woolly. Flowers crowded at the apex, shortly funnel-shaped, 2–2.5 cm long and wide, reddish purple. Fruit a globose, dry, green berry 8–10 mm thick. USA (SW Texas, SE Arizona), N Mexico.

Echinomastus erectocentrus (J. Coulter) B. & R. ☐☐
☐■
Shortly cylindric, 7–20 cm high, up to 10 cm wide, pale bluish-green, sometimes almost entirely covered in spines, with 15–20 low, tuberculate ribs. Areoles with 13–15 spreading, needle-shaped, white radial spines 13 mm long, and 1–2 upward-pointing, reddish to purple, central spines up to 25 mm long. Flowers usually several together at apex, shortly funnel-shaped, 2–4 cm long, 4 cm wide, pink with darker centre. Fruit shortly-cylindric to almost globose, 1 cm long and thick. USA (Arizona).
The specimen illustrated shows juvenile spination.

THELOCACTUS (K. Schumann) B. & R. (incl. GYMNOCACTUS Backeb. p.p.)
Usually solitary, depressed globose, globose to elongate, medium-sized. Ribs divided into tubercles. Areoles on the tips of the tubercles with ±long woolly furrow, densely spiny. Spines very diverse. Flowers clustered out of the furrow on the apex, broadly funnel-shaped to campanulate, large, white, pink-carmine to purple or yellowish. Pericarpel and receptacle-tube densely covered with large, naked, overlapping scales, merging gradually into the outer perianth-segments. (In more highly evolved forms pericarpel naked and only receptacle-tube with a few scales.) Fruit oblong to ovoid, dry, scaly like the pericarpel, with floral remains, splitting at the base or even laterally. Seeds oblong-ovoid with large basal hilum; seedcoat glossy black to dark brown, verrucose. 25 species in Mexico and S USA.

Thelocactus lophothele (Salm-Dyck) B. & R.
Globose to shortly-columnar stem, up to 25 cm high and wide, fresh green to grey-green, on a thick tuberous root, with depressed woolly apex and 15—20 narrow ribs thickened at the areoles into tubercles 2 cm long. Areoles 4—5 cm apart, with 3—5 slightly curved, almost erect, amber-yellow, red-based radial spines up to 4 cm long, and 0—1 central spine up to 4.5 cm long. Flowers from areoles near apex, funnel-shaped, 4 cm long, 5 cm wide, variable in colour, often green outside with red midstripe and light yellow inside. Fruit somewhat oblong, 10 mm long, 8 mm across, green. Mexico (Chihuahua).

Thelocactus hexaedrophorus (Lem.) B. & R.
Globose, up to 15 cm high and wide, blue-green to grey-green, with densely woolly apex, and 13 ribs entirely divided into large, stout, ±hexagonal tubercles. Areoles with 4—9 straight, minutely-annulate, yellowish-white, brown-tipped radial spines 12—22 mm long, and 1 stouter, erect central spine up to 3 cm long. Flowers appear solitary or in clusters on apex, campanulate-funnelshaped, 3.5—6 cm long, up to 8 cm wide, outside pinkish-red rimmed, inside white. Fruit oblong, 10 mm long, 6 mm across, light brown. Mexico (San Luis Potosi, Tamaulipas).

Thelocactus bicolor (Galeotti) B. & R.
Globose to shortly-cylindric or conical, up to 20 cm high, 6—8 cm wide, blue-green or grey-green, depressed apex with white woolly felt, topped with spines; whole stem strongly spiny, with 8 straight or slightly oblique ribs divided by cross-furrows into tubercles 1.5 cm high. Areoles with 9—18 spreading, whitish radial spines up to 3 cm long, on new growth ruby-red with amber-yellow tips, and usually 4 red, yellow-tipped central spines up to 5 cm long. Flowers funnel-shaped, 5—6 cm long and wide, purple. Fruit 1 cm long, red-brown. C Mexico.

Thelocactus schwarzi Backeb.
Oblong-globose, 6 cm high, 5.5 cm wide, blue-green stem, with 13 ribs almost entirely divided into tubercles 13 mm long and 9 mm wide. Areoles with 13—14 yellowish, red-based, radial spines up to 17 mm long, spreading horizontally and curved towards the body, the uppermost one flattened, curved towards the tip, up to 27 mm long. Central spines none. Flowers up to 8.5 cm wide, reddish purple with scarlet throat. Fruit roundish, 12 mm across, brownish violet. Mexico (Tamaulipas).

Thelocactus leucacanthus (Zucc.) B. & R.

■□
□□

Sprouting from the base or sides and forming clumps, shortly-cylindric, 10—15 cm high, 6—8 cm wide, light green stems, with thick, tuberous root and with 8—13 somewhat spiralling, uniformly thick ribs divided into tubercles. Areoles on the tubercles, with 7—20 radial spines up to 2.5 cm long, pale yellow at first, later white or grey, and 1 straight, stouter central spine 4—5 cm long. Flowers 5 cm long, pale yellow, with finely toothed perianth-segments. Mexico (Zimpan, Ixmiquilpan).

Thelocactus knuthianus (Boed.) Kladiwa
[= Gymnocactus knuthianus (Boed.) Backeb.]

□■
□□

Solitary or sprouting from the base, globose, up to 6 cm wide, glossy dark green stems, with somewhat woolly, spiny, depressed apex, and over 20 ribs entirely divided into conical tubercles 9 mm long. Areoles with white wool, with 18—20 silvery white, fine, needle-shaped radial spines 8 mm long, somewhat curving towards the stem, and 1 upcurving central spine up to 10 mm long. Axils glabrous. Flowers very numerous at the apex, broadly funnel-shaped, up to 2.5 cm long and wide, pale lilac-pink. Fruit ovoid, 7 mm long, 5 mm wide, glossy green to brown. Mexico.

NORMANBOKEA Kladiwa & F. Buxbaum

Usually solitary, rarely sprouting, globose to oblong dwarf cacti, with tubercles in oblique rows. Areoles oblong to strongly elongate. Radial spines ±pectinate, delicate, feathery. No central spines. Flowers from upper end of elongate areole, narrowly to widely funnel-shaped, pale pink to violet-pink. Pericarpel naked, receptacle-tube coloured, with small, naked scales. Fruit turbinate to oblong, with floral remains, dry, splitting at the base or laterally. Seeds elongate-globose to ovoid, with very pronounced basal hilum; seedcoat black or dark russet, verrucose. 2 species in Mexico.

Normanbokea valdeziana (Möller) · Kladiwa & F. Buxbaum
[= Gymnocactus valdezianus (Möller.) Backeb.]

□□
■□

Solitary, rarely sprouting, globose to oblong, up to 3.5 cm high, 3.3 cm wide, on a strong, tuberous root. Tubercles satiny blue-green, 3 mm long, rectangular at the base, truncate at the top, with about 30, almost hair-like, white spines 1-5—2 mm long, at first in a circle, then pectinate, spreading horizontally to somewhat backwards. Axils glabrous. Flowers solitary or several at the apex, up to 2 cm long, funnel-shaped, lilac-pink. Fruit turbinate, 7 mm long, 6 mm thick. Mexico (Coahuila).

Normanbokea pseudopectinata (Backeb.) Kladiwa & F. Buxbaum
[= Pelecyphora pseudopectinata Backeb.]

□□
□■

Globose to oblong, not sprouting, dark green stem, up to 6 cm high and 4.5 cm wide. Tubercles almost rectangular at the base, completely flattened at the top. Areoles 5 mm long and 0.6 mm wide, with 28 or more, translucent white spines 1.5 mm long, pectinate to either side, slightly curving towards the stem. Flowers, 1—3 from the apex, 2 cm long, perianth-segments very pale pink with a wide violet-pink midstripe. Fruit turbinate, dark olive-green, 10 mm long. Mexico (Tamaulipas).

PEDIOCACTUS B. & R. (incl. PILOCANTHUS B.W. Benson & Backeb., UTAHIA B. & R., NAVAJOA Croizat, TOUMEYA B. & R.)

Solitary or sprouting, globose to oblong, ribs divided into spiralling tubercles. Spines numerous, diverse. Flowers solitary or several together near the apex, campanulate, white, pink or greenish-yellow. Pericarpel and receptacle-tube thick-fleshed. Pericarpel naked or ±covered with fleshy, glabrous scales mostly on the upper edge, receptacle-tube with similar scales. Fruit globose to ovoid or shortly-cylindric, pale pink, green or greenish-yellow, breaking off leaving an opening in the base, or splitting irregularly lengthways, with deciduous or persistent floral remains. Seeds globose to ovoid; seedcoat black, ±coarsely verrucose. 6 species in the USA.

Pediocactus paradinei B.W. Benson
[= **Pilocanthus paradinei** (B.W. Benson) B.W. Benson & Backeb.]

Globose, 2.5–5 cm high, 2.5–8 cm wide, green or blue-green, on a narrowly conical, tuberous root up to 15 cm long, with ribs divided into tubercles 5 mm long and 3 mm thick. Areoles with 20 hair-like, flexible, white radial spines 2.5–7 cm long, and 4–6 barely distinguishable central spines with brown flecks on the upper part. Flowers round the apex from tubercles of previous growth period, campanulate and 19–22 mm long, or widely campanulate and shorter (16 mm), perianth-segments white with a pink midstripe. Fruit ovoid, 10 mm long, 6 mm across, dry. USA (N Arizona).

Pediocactus knowltonii L. Benson
[= **Pediocactus bradyi** L. Benson. var. **knowltonii** (L. Benson) Backeb.]

Very small, solitary or barely sprouting, up to 3.8 cm high, 1.9 cm wide, with cylindric, conical or pyramidal tubercles 1.5–2.5 mm long. Areoles with 18–23 dense, slightly curved spines round the edge, pectinate, 1–2 mm long, white or pinky-red, ultimately pale grey. Flowers squat-campanulate, 15 mm long and 9 mm wide, pink. Fruit turbinate, 5 mm long, off-white tinged with dark carmine-red. USA (Colorado, New Mexico).

Pediocactus papyracanthus (Engelm.) L. Benson
[= **Toumeya papyracantha** (Engelm.) B. & R.]

Usually solitary, matt dark green, stem up to 10 cm high, 2.5 cm wide, strongly tapering from tip to root, ribs almost entirely divided into tubercles 5 mm high. Areoles initially woolly, with 8–9 white radial spines up to 4 mm long, spreading horizontally, and 3–4 flat, papery, flexible, white to brown central spines, 2–3 pointing upwards, up to 2 cm long, and 1 porrect and down-curving, up to 5 cm long. Flowers solitary near apex, 2.9 cm long, 1.25 cm wide, ivory-white. Fruit globose, 4–5 mm thick, red-brown. USA (New Mexico).

Pediocactus peeblesianus (Croizat.) L. Benson
[= **Navajoa peeblesiana** Croizat.]

Small, usually solitary, rarely branching, globose to shortly cylindric, blue-green stem, 2.5–7 cm high and up to 2.5 cm across, deep in the ground, with globose to ±cylindric tubercles. Areoles densely felted, with 3–5 radial spines curving towards stem, the longest pointing downwards, with 1 upcurved central spine 5–15 mm long, curved over the apex. All spines flexible, corky, sometimes with cross-furrows and fissures, horn-coloured, later greying. Flowers 1.7 cm long, whitish with pink midstripe. Fruit turbinate, 8–10 mm long, semi-dry, with floral remains. There are 2 varieties:— var. fickeiseniae L. Benson: usually branching. Central spine up to 3.5 cm long, erect and curving strongly inwards and bending together over the apex. Flowers yellow. — var. *maianus* L. Benson: unbranched, no central spine, the uppermost, longest radial spine somewhat recurved towards the centre. Flowers yellow. USA (Arizona).

NEOLLOYDIA B. & R. (incl. GYMNOCACTUS Backeb. p.p., CUMARINIA F. Buxbaum, RAPICACTUS F. Buxbaum & Oehme)

Globose or cylindric, solitary or sprouting from the base and forming clumps, or developing a long shoot from a thick tuberous root, club-shaped at the end and sprouting. Ribs spiralling, divided into cylindric or conical tubercles, these with either a short furrow or one reaching to the axil. Axils with ±dense, short hair. Radial spines numerous, often pectinate. Central spines occasionally hooked. Flowers near apex from the end of the furrow nearest the axil, large, funnel-shaped or campanulate-funnel-shaped, greenish-yellow, yellowish-pink, yellow or red to purple. Pericarpel naked or with 1−3 small scales, receptacle-tube with a few scales, with or without woolly hair in their axils. Fruit globose to club-shaped, naked or with a few small scales, berry-like or thin-walled and drying to paper-like, splitting at the base and laterally, floral remains deciduous. Seeds obovoid or curved-ovoid; seedcoat glossy black, smooth or ±strongly verrucose. About 8 species from Mexico to Texas, 1 species in Cuba.

Neolloydia odorata (Boed.) Backeb.
[= Cumarinia odorata (Boed.) F. Buxbaum]

■□
□□

Sprouting from the base and mat-forming, globose to somewhat elongate offsets, up to 3 cm wide, apex without wool, topped with spines. Tubercles cylindric, 10 mm long, 4 mm thick. Areoles with 7−9 thin, needle-shaped, radial spines 8−10 mm long, whitish, brown-tipped, and 3−4 stouter, spreading central spines 20−25 mm long, hooked at the tip, light to dark brown. Flowers near apex, from axillary end of furrows in tubercles, 15−20 mm long, 10 mm wide, narrowly funnel-shaped, pale yellowish-pink. Fruit small, pale green to reddish. Mexico (Tamaulipas and San Luis Potosí).

Neolloydia conoidea (DC.) B. & R.

□■
□□

Solitary, shooting from the base when older, conical to cylindric, 7−10 cm high and 5−7 cm wide, pale green to yellowish-green. Tubercles fairly laxly arranged, ovoid. Areoles with 13−20 thin, stiff, radial spines 6−13 mm long, translucent white with dark brown or black tips, grey when old, and 1−6 spreading, straight or somewhat curved, dark brown central spines 2−3 cm long. Flowers 3 cm long, up to 6 cm wide, reddish-violet. Fruit ovoid to club-shaped, 10 mm long, 8 mm wide, light green to reddish tinged. USA (Texas) and E Mexico.

Neolloydia smithii (Muehlenpfordt) Kladiwa & Fittkau
[= Gymnocactus beguinii (F.A.C. Weber.) Backeb.
var. smithii (Muehlenpfordt) Backeb.]

□□
■□

Globose to cylindric, leaf-green to blue-green stem, 12 cm long, 6 cm wide, with 21 ribs almost completely divided into bluntly-conical tubercles. Areoles 1.5−2 cm apart, initially white-felted, with 20−27 white radial spines up to 1.6 cm long, curved towards stem, and 3−4 white, brown to black-tipped central spines up to 2.5 cm long, 3 pointing upwards and one porrect. Furrows 5−6 mm long, with white woolly felt. Flowers 3.5 cm long, reddish. Fruit globose, 8 mm thick. Mexico.

Neolloydia subterranea (Backeb.) H.E. Moore
[= Rapicactus subterraneus (Backeb.) F. Buxbaum & Oehme]

□□
□■

Arising from a tuberous root, with a neck up to 10 cm long and 2−4 mm thick, and a club-shaped head 2.5−5 cm high and up to 3 cm thick, sprouting, leaf-green. Ribs divided into symmetrical, rectangular tubercles up to 5 mm high, slightly spiralling. Areoles with about 16 translucent, white, radial spines 2−6 mm long, and 2 dark brown, up to 2 cm long, central spines, upper ones appressed, lower ones standing out stiffly. Flowers from apical axils, funnel-shaped, 3 cm long, 3.5 cm wide, pale violet. Fruit globose, 5 mm thick, wine-red. N Mexico.

COLORADOA Boissevain & Davidson

Small, globose to shortly-cylindric, usually solitary, rarely sprouting. Ribs usually spiralling, divided into large tubercles. Areoles ending in a short woolly furrow. Flowers solitary or several together around apex, campanulate-funnelshaped, usually large, yellowish to yellowish-green. Pericarpel naked or with a few small scales on upper part. Receptacle-tube covered with a few glabrous scales. Fruit shortly cylindric to oblong, naked, with floral remains, dry, slitting irregularly. Seeds kidney-shaped, with pronounced crest; seedcoat black to dark brown, shallowly verrucose. 1 species in the USA (Colorado and New Mexico).

Coloradoa mesae-verdae Boissevain & Davidson

Solitary, rarely sprouting, 3.8—17.5 cm high, 3.8—8 cm across, pale green to grey-green, with 13—17 ribs divided into tubercles. Areoles with 8—10 irregularly spreading, erect or slightly curved, straw-coloured radial spines up to 12 mm long, and usually 1 smaller, straight or hooked, grey, dark-tipped central spine 10—12 mm long. Flowers up to 3.5 cm long, 2.5 cm wide, yellowish with light green throat. Fruit 4—5 mm long, 6—8 mm thick, green. USA (Colorado, New Mexico).

TURBINICARPUS F. Buxbaum & Backeb.

Small, globose to shortly-cylindric, occasionally sprouting from the base. Tubercles low. Areoles often with curved or twisted, sometimes papery, flexible central spines. Flowers solitary or several together around the apex, funnel-shaped, white to pink or yellowish. Pericarpel with a few scales, rarely with a few woolly hairs and bristles in their axils, usually naked and glabrous. Fruit globose to ovoid, berry-like, later dry, occasionally with isolated scale-remains, otherwise naked, splitting at the base or laterally, floral remains deciduous or persistent. Seeds ovoid, often with pronounced crest; seedcoat black, verrucose. 5 species, some variable, in Mexico.

Turbinicarpus macrochele (Werderm.) F. Buxbaum & Backeb.

Solitary, occasionally sprouting, depressed-globose to semi-globose, dark green to carmine-brown stem, on tuberous root. Axils hairless. Areoles initially white woolly, with usually 4(—5) fairly strongly curved and ±compressed, yellowish, dark brown-tipped spines, unequal, from 1.5 to 2.5(—4) cm long, densely interlaced over the apex. Flowers 2—3 cm long, 3.5 cm wide, white flushed with pink. Fruit globose, 6—7 mm long and 4—5 mm wide. Mexico (San Luis Potosí).

Turbinicarpus lophophoroides (Werderm.) F. Buxbaum & Backeb.

Depressed semi-globose or conical, 2.5—3.5 cm high, 4—4.5 cm across, dark green stem, on a sturdy tuberous root, apex with thick white wool interspersed with spines, ribs entirely divided into laxly arranged, broad tubercles. Areoles initially white woolly, with 2—3(—4) stout, needle-shaped, almost black radial spines 4—8 mm long, often somewhat curving towards the stem, and 1 straight upward-pointing central spine up to 1 cm long. Flowers 3.5 cm wide, silky white with faint violet-pink sheen. Fruit a light green berry. Mexico (San Luis Potosí).

Turbinicarpus krainzianus (G. Frank) Backeb.

Shortly cylindric, solitary, occasionally sprouting with age, dark green, 3—4 cm high, 2—3 cm across stem, on a thick tuberous root, with a white woolly apex topped with curving spines, and 11 spiralling ribs entirely divided into tubercles. Areoles at first white woolly, later glabrescent, with 6—8 flexible, blunt spines 12—30 mm long, twisted like wire, initially yellowish brown, later greying and dark tipped. Flowers apical, narrowly funnel-shaped, 2 cm long, creamy yellow to almost white, yellowish-green outside. Fruit naked, ovoid to globose, green at first, later reddish on top, with dry floral-remains. Mexico.

STROMBOCACTUS B. & R.

Depressed-globose to very shortly columnar, apex depressed, ribs entirely divided into flat, rhomboid tubercles, overlapping in spiral rows. Areoles with a few bristly spines, later broken off. Flowers near the apex, funnel-shaped, white to yellowish. Pericarpel with only a few scales on upper part, receptacle-tube scaly. Fruit dry, almost glabrous, splitting irregularly at the sides. Seeds very tiny (0.3 mm in diameter), almost globose, with large aril; seedcoat glossy red-brown with scattered warts. 1 species in Mexico.

Strombocactus disciformis (DC.) B. & R.

Solitary, depressed-globose or very shortly columnar. blue-green or grey-green, 2–3 cm sometimes up to 8(–18) cm high, 3–8.5 cm wide, with spiralling ribs entirely divided into tubercles. Tubercles rhomboidal, shallow-domed or low-pyramidal, 10–18 mm wide, overlapping. Areoles small, initially white woolly, with 4–5 bristly, upright spines up to 15 mm long, usually soon falling off. Flowers near apex, funnel-shaped, 2.5–3 cm long, white to yellowish white. Fruit 7 mm long, dirty brown. Mexico (Hidalgo and Querétaro).

AZTEKIUM Boedeker

Small, depressed-globose stem, with tuberous rootstock sprouting above the base, grey-green, very slow-growing. Tubercles thick and horny, compressed together and flattened, laterally, so forming 9–11 false ribs, low, secondary ribs also formed where the bases of tubercles on adjacent ribs touch; false ribs with densely overlapping areoles, secondary ribs without areoles, both cross-furrowed. Areoles felted, with 1–3 short, twisted spines, soon falling off. Flowers apical, small, salver-shaped (widening from a slender cylindrical tube into a funnel and opening flat), whitish to pale pink. Pericarpel naked, also the distinct, slender, cylindric, receptacle-tube, the lower part buried in the woolly apex. Fruit very small, berry-like, bottle-shaped, pink, buried in the woolly apex, where it decays. Seeds small, elongate hemispherical, with massive strophiole on the basal hilum; seedcoat black, very coarsely verrucose. 1 species in Mexico, growing on vertical slate rock-faces.

Aztekium ritteri (Boed.) Boed.

Depressed-globose, sprouting from the base, grey-green, 5 cm wide, 3 cm high stem, on a short tuberous root, with 9–11 ribs of compressed tubercles with many furrows and cross-folds and secondary ribs without areoles. Areoles close-set, almost forming a continuous band of felt, the younger ones with 1–3 twisting spines, 3–4 mm long, soon falling off. Flowers from the apex, campanulate-funnelshaped, 10 mm long, 8 mm wide, white, touched with red. Fruit a very small pink berry. Mexico (Nuevo León).

LOPHOPHORA J. Coulter

Depressed-globose, later shortly cylindric cacti with thick tuberous root, solitary or freely sprouting and forming clumps, blue-greygreen, matt. Apex depressed, full of yellowish-grey wool on the areoles. Ribs 5–13, broadly rounded, straight or somewhat spiralling, marked out or almost completely divided into tubercles by cross-furrows. Areoles with a few small spines only when young, later with a tuft like a paintbrush of yellowish or offwhite hairs. Flowers often several together with areoles near the apex, slenderly funnel-shaped, pink to carmine, white or yellowish; only their upper part emerging from the wool. Pericarpel and sharply distinct receptacle-tube smooth and without scales. Fruit a slenderly club-shaped, naked, pink berry, with floral remains, later breaking off. Seeds only in upper, hollow part of fruit, obovoid, with truncate, basal hilum; seedcoat black, coarsely verrucose. 1 very variable species in Mexico and the USA (S Texas and New Mexico).

Lophophora williamsii (Lem. ex Salm-Dyck) J. Coulter

■■
□□

Solitary, or later offsetting and colony-forming, depressed-globose to shortly cylindric stem, 5–7 cm high, up to 8 cm wide, blue-green to grey-green, on a thick tuberous root, with 5–13 broad, flat, straight or spiralling ribs, divided by cross-furrows into low, 5–6 sided tubercles. Areoles 3–15 mm apart, with stiff, upright, dirty grey, paintbrush-like tufts of wool 8–10 mm long, without spines in age. Flowers several together near apex, shortly funnel-shaped to almost rotate, 2.5–3 cm long, 1.5–2.5 cm wide, pale pink. Fruit club-shaped, up to 20 mm long, 4.5 mm thick, pink. Rather variable as regards stem shape and flower colour (pink, carmine, white, yellowish). C Mexico to USA (S Texas and S New Mexico).

LEUCHTENBERGIA Hooker

Solitary or branching, cylindric stem, up to 50 cm tall, with long, thick, often many-forked, tuberous root, and densely covered with very long, triangular, spiralling tubercles breaking off near the base in age. Areoles at truncate tip behind a distinct leaf-rudiment, with papery, very twisted spines, and with 2 more very small, horn-like spines at the flowering stage. Flowers solitary from upper edge of areoles of young tubercles, large, funnel-shaped, wide-opening, yellow, pleasantly-scented. Pericarpel and receptacle-tube with scales, of which only lowest may contain a little wool; silky hairs present between innermost perianth-segments and highest row of stamens. Fruit ovoid to pear-shaped, with floral remains, dry, with a heavy bloom, breaking off leaving an opening in the base. Seeds large, oblique cap-shaped, with very deep basal hilum; seedcoat matt, very dark grey or brown, finely verrucose. 1 species in C and N Mexico.

□□
■□

Leuchtenbergia principis Hooker

Cylindric, solitary stem, later sprouting and branching, up to 50 cm high and 5–7 cm thick with age, arising from a long, thick, tuberous root. Tubercles erect at first, later spreading, 10–12 cm long, sharply triangular, grey-green. Areoles with 8–14 curved, papery, straw-coloured, later greying radial spines up to 5 cm long, and 1–2 wider, twisted central spines up to 10 cm long, occasionally together with short, brown, horny spines. Flowers 8 cm long, up to 10 cm wide, yellow, sweet-scented. Fruit ovoid to pear-shaped, dry. C to N Mexico.

OBREGONIA Frič

Depressed-globose, with thick root, up to 20 cm in diameter, solitary or few-headed, grey-green, densely covered with almost leaf-like tubercles arranged in rosettes. Tubercles elongate-triangular, broad at base, narrowing to a recurved tip, sharply keeled on sides and underside, with woolly hairs in axil. Areoles on tubercle tip with thin, lightly curved caducous spines. Flowers in the woolly apical depression, shortly funnel-shaped, white or pink. Pericarpel and receptacle-tube naked; receptacle-tube grooved by the decurrent bases of the outer perianth-segments. Fruit white, berry-like, with floral remains, initially concealed in woolly apex, but club-shaped and exserted when ripe, drying and decaying after floral remains have dropped off. Seeds curved, pear-shaped; seedcoat black, verrucose. 1 species in Mexico.

□□
□■

Obregonia denegrii Frič

Depressed-globose to hemispherical, 8–12 cm across, grey-green or dark green, from a thick tuberous root. Tubercles 2–2.5 cm wide, 1–1.5 cm long. Areoles on the tubercle-tips, initially woolly, with 2–4 weak, slightly curved spines 1–1.5 cm long, caducous. Axils with woolly hairs. Flowers from areoles on woolly apex, funnel-shaped, 3 cm long, 2 cm wide, whitish to pale pink. Fruit ovoid, club-shaped when ripe, whitish, initially concealed in woolly apex. Mexico (Tamaulipas).

252

EPITHELANTHA F.A.C. Weber ex B. & R.

Small, globose to cylindric, solitary or very freely-sprouting, sometimes with thick, fleshy roots. Tubercles small, arranged spirally; areoles with numerous short, white spines, almost completely covering stem; at the flowering stage uppermost radial spines becoming very elongate, curved and gland-tipped. Flowers small, funnel-shaped, whitish to pinkish-red, solitary, apical, arising directly from the areoles. Pericarpel and receptacle-tube naked, the tube funnel-shaped, corolla-like. Fruit a long-clavate, naked, red berry without floral remains. Seeds few, large, rather cap-shaped, with recessed elongate, basal hilum; seeedcoat red-brown or black, verrucose. 3 very variable species in the USA (W Texas) to N Mexico.

Epithelantha micromeris (Engelm.) F.A.C. Weber ■■ □□

Solitary or offsetting and mat-forming, ±globose, 1.5–4 cm high and wide, completely covered with chalk-white spines. Tubercles small, barely 1 mm high, close-set in spirals, with up to 20 white spines 2 mm long. Flowers from apical areoles, up to 6 mm wide, whitish to rose-red. Fruit club-shaped, red. N Mexico, USA (W Texas).

PELECYPHORA Ehrenb. (incl. ENCEPHALOCARPUS A. Berger)

Globose to shortly cylindric clavate, with fleshy rootstock, offsetting and forming clumps. Tubercles in spirals, either hatchet-shaped, truncate, grey, with elongate areoles with numerous very short, smooth pectinate spines joined at the base, or scale-like, broad, overlapping, triangular, keeled, the point incurved, the areole on the inner side slightly below the tip with a few short, bristly spines, the upper ones lengthening into club-shaped glands. Spines and areole caducous, revealing a rudimentary groove, axils woolly. Flowers solitary or several together from axils near apex; campanulate or funnel-shaped, carmine-violet. Pericarpel and cylindric part of receptacle-tube naked and glabrous, lower half of tube fused with style-base. Fruit spindly, berry-like, later drying to paper-like, completely concealed in the axil. Seeds kidney-shaped with small hilum; seedcoat brown or blackish, almost smooth. 2 species in Mexico.

Pelecyphora aselliformis Ehrenberg □□ ■□

Slenderly-cylindric, later club-shaped, blue-green or grey-green, 10 cm high, 5.5 cm across, solitary or forming groups. Tubercles hatchet-shaped, up to 5 mm high, axils woolly. Areoles with about 40, pectinate, grey spines up to 4 mm long, connivent at the base. Flowers solitary or several together near apex, funnel-shaped to campanulate-rotate, 2 cm long, 3 cm wide, carmine-violet. Fruit a spindly berry deliquescent when ripe. Mexico (San Luis Potosí).

Pelecyphora strobiliformis (Werderm.) A. Berger □□
[= Encephalocarpus strobiliformis (Werderm.) A. Berger] □■

Depressed-globose to elongate-conical stem, up to 6 cm across, on thick tuberous root, with woolly apex, completely covered with appressed, scale-like, overlapping, grey-green, tubercles, broadly triangular, fairly thin and leaf-like, keeled on the back, the tips curved inwards. Young tubercles with woolly axils and areoles with 10–12 bristly white spines up to 5 mm long, later deciduous. Flowers apical, from very young axils, up to 3 cm long, 4 cm wide, bright violet-red. Fruit concealed in the apical wool, drying out. Mexico (Tamaulipas).

ARIOCARPUS Scheidweiler (incl. ROSEOCACTUS A. Berger, NEOGOMEZIA Castañeda)

Small, depressed-globose, solitary, hardly emerging from the ground, with large tuberous root and spirally arranged tubercles. Stem permeated by a system of mucilage ducts. Tubercles resembling triangular leaves, short or long, grey or green, with smooth

or deeply fissured surface. Depending on the position of the growing point and the elongation zone of the tubercles, 4 different arrangements are possible from the same areole position, (see fig.11). 1. The undivided areole remains in the axil of the elongated tubercle and produces hairs and flowers; 2. As the tubercle lengthens, the areole becomes divided into an axillary flowering areole and a subapical dot-shaped one with rudimentary spines. 3. The vegetative areole produces a woolly furrow starting from the axillary flowering areole and running all or partway along the tubercle. 4. After flowering, elongation from the base displaces the undivided areole from the axil to within the top quarter of the tubercle. Flowers solitary from the upper axils or the areoles of very young tubercles, short to slenderly funnel-shaped, medium-sized, whitish, pink to carmine or yellowish. Pericarpel and receptacle-tube naked and glabrous. Fruit a club-shaped, thin-walled, smooth berry with floral remains, white or pale green or red, concealed in the woolly hairs or emerging, later drying and decaying. Seeds pear-shaped with oblique-truncate hilum; seedcoat matt black, coarsely verrucose.

This genus is divided into 3 sub-genera according to the structure and position of the areoles. *Ariocarpus*: tubercles smooth on the upper side; vegetative areole either united with the flowering areole and axillary, or divided and situated on the upper side of the tubercle below the tip. *Roseocactus* (A. Berger) F. Buxbaum: tubercles with a furrow lined with woolly hairs situated on the upper side. *Neogomezia* (Castañeda) F. Buxbaum: with undivided areole in the upper quarter of the elongate tubercle. 6 species in Mexico and SW Texas.

Ariocarpus retusus Scheidweiler (*Ariocarpus*)
Solitary, rarely offsetting, 10–15 cm wide stem, blue-green to grey-green, apex with a densely-woolly top. Tubercles close-set, upright, sharply triangular, with horny tip, smooth, keeled underneath. Areoles short, below the tip, or lacking, mostly tiny and glabrous. Flowers numerous from woolly apex, funnel-shaped, 5–6 cm long, 5 cm wide, almost pure white. Fruit ellipsoid, up to 2.2 cm long, whitish to rose-red. Mexico (San Luis Potosí).

Ariocarpus trigonus (F.A.C. Weber) K. Schumann (*Ariocarpus*)
Solitary, rarely offsetting, brownish grey-green, 10–15(20–25) cm wide. Tubercles numerous, sharply triangular, upcurving, 3.5–5.5 cm long, 2–2.5 cm wide at the base, sharply keeled. Areoles on the horny tips, hardly visible. Flowers in a ring round the apex from the axils, widely funnel-shaped, 5 cm wide, light yellowish. Fruit up to 2 cm long, 1 cm thick, whitish. Mexico. (Nueva León and Tamaulipas).

Ariocarpus fissuratus (Engelm.) K. Schumann (*Roseocactus*)
Solitary or sometimes mat-forming, 10–15 cm wide, with depressed apex covered with white wool. Tubercles thickly fleshy, triangular, pointed, with furrowed and calloused, grey-green upper side, a furrow and ridge along the edges and a deep, felted furrow along the middle down to the axil. Axils naked. Areoles below the tubercle tips, without spines. Flowers several on the apex, campanulate, 3.5–4 cm long, pink to carmine-red. Fruit ellipsoid, 5–15 mm long, greenish. USA (SW Texas) and N Mexico (Coahuila).

Ariocarpus agavoides (Castañeda) E.F. Anderson
[= Neogomezia agavoides Castañeda] (*Neogomezia*)
Solitary, flattened 5–8 cm wide stem, tubercles dark green, later grey-green, up to 4 cm long, and 6 mm wide, semi-circular in section, wide-spreading, with recurved tips and horny surface. Areoles 1 cm from the tip, thickly woolly, occasionally with 1–3 small white to horn-coloured spines 3–5 mm long. Flowers emerging from the wool in areoles of young tubercles about 15 mm long, campanulate-funnelshaped, 4–5 cm long, pink. Fruit club-shaped, up to 2.5 cm long, red. Mexico (Tamaulipas).

FEROCACTUS B. & R.

Large to very large, depressed-globose, globose to thick columnar cacti, up to 3 m high, usually solitary or forming clumps or mats, with strong ribs, large, often elongate areoles, and very stout, usually colourful spines. Spines often hooked, 1 central spine frequently flattened like a ribbon and banded transversly. Uppermost spines often modified into glands. Flowers in profusion near the apex from the areoles, large, widely and shortly campanulate-funnelshaped, yellow to red. Pericarpel and receptacle-tube covered with overlapping, naked scales intergrading with the perianth-segments. Between the innermost perianth-segments and the uppermost stamens there are ±numerous hairs. Fruit oblong to ovoid, scaly, with floral remains, firm-fleshed and drying or fleshy, yellowish to reddish, breaking off to leave a basal opening. Seeds oblong, curved, with obliquely truncate hilum; seedcoat black, smooth, punctate or reticulate. Two sections are distinguished according to fruit and seed structure: section. *Bisnaga* (Orcutt) N.P. Taylor & J.Y. Clark: seeds mostly smooth and shiny, with abrupt edge to the hilum; fruit when ripe juicy, indehiscent or bursting irregularly near the apex, often red or purplish. 11 species in Mexico and S Texas; sect. *Ferocactus*: seeds mostly dull, with broad rim to hilum; fruit yellow (or red- or pink-tinged in a few species), soon becoming dry, and dehiscent by a basal pore. 12 species in Mexico and SW USA.

Ferocactus hamatacanthus (Muehlenpfordt) B. & R. (*Bisnaga*)

Solitary, globose to ovoid or conical, green to bluish green, up to 60 cm high and 30 cm wide stem, with 13–17 crenate ribs up to 5 cm high. Areoles on the tubercles, initially yellowish-white felted, with 8–12, protruding radial spines 5–7 cm long, red at first, later grey, and 4 central spines, the upper 3 straight or somewhat curved, the lower 1 up to 12 cm long and shaped like a fish-hook. Flowers 5.5–7 cm long, funnel-shaped, shining yellow with red throat. Fruit ellipsoid, 2–5 cm long, green to dark brown. C Mexico to the USA (S Texas and S New Mexico).

Ferocactus latispinus (Haw.) B. & R. (*Bisnaga*)

Solitary, globose, 25–40 cm high, up to 40 cm wide stem, blue-green or grey-green, with sparsely woolly apex and initially 8–14, later up to 21 sharp, narrow, shallowly sinuate ribs 1.5–2.5 cm high. Areoles large, grey-felted, with 8–12 radial spines 2–2.5 cm long, and 4 erect central spines up to 3.5 cm long, the lowest hooked and up to 7 mm wide. All spines orange to ruby-coloured at first, later reddish horn-coloured. Flowers near apex, funnel-shaped, 2.5–3.5 cm long, whitish, pink to deep purple. Fruit ovoid, 2–4 cm long. C Mexico.

Ferocactus robustus (Pfeiffer) B. & R. (*Ferocactus*)

Freely sprouting, forming colonies of hundreds of heads, 1 m high and several (3–5) m in diameter, stems ±globose to oblong, up to 20 cm high, 12 cm wide, dark green, with 8–10 sturdy ribs. Areoles initially white-felted, with 10–14 radial spines 1.5–3 cm long, bristly and white above, stouter and amber-yellow below, and 4 straight central spines 3.5–6 cm long. Flowers near apex, 3.5–4 cm long, and 4 cm wide, funnel-shaped, yellow. Fruit 2.2 cm long, 1.5 cm thick, yellow. Mexico (Puebla).

Ferocactus flavovirens (Scheidw.) B. & R. (*Bisnaga*)

Forming large colonies, stems oblong-globose, 30–40 cm high, 10–20 cm wide, pale green, with somewhat woolly and spiny apex and (11–12)13 sharp, slightly sinuate ribs 1–2 cm high. Areoles 2 cm apart, grey-felted, with 14 tough, annulate, protruding, red to brown, ultimately grey radial spines up to 2 cm long, and 4 similar central spines, the lowest 5–8 cm long. Flowers yellow. Mexico (Puebla, Tehuacán).

STENOCACTUS (K. Schumann) Backeb. & F.M. Knuth (incl. ECHINOFOSSULOCACTUS sensu Britton & Rose)

Globose to elongate, solitary, only a few species producing offsets, mostly small, usually with numerous (30–100) thin, lamellate, frequently undulating ribs, only rarely on a broad base. Young plants tuberculate for a long time, the tubercles only later confluent to form ribs. Areoles few to each rib, with very variable spination, the central spine frequently flattened dagger-like, very long, straight or upcurved, but never hooked. Flowers relatively large, in a cluster from areoles around the apex, campanulate to broadly funnel-shaped, white, brownish striate or violet. Pericarpel and receptacle-tube with thin, glabrous scales. Fruit globose to oblong, with a few thin scales, drying, splitting at the base or side. Seeds obovoid with truncate hilum, seedcoat black, finely punctate or reticulate.

Extraordinarily variable in all their characteristics and often separable from each other with great difficulty. The number of species usually quoted (about 30) is certainly far too large. Mexico.

Stenocactus lamellosus (A. Dietr.) A. Berger ex Backeb. & F.M. Knuth   ■□
[= **Echinofossulocactus lamellosus** (A. Dietr.) B. & R.   □□

Globose, later cylindric, up to 10 cm high and 6–8 cm wide stem, grey-green, with 30–35 or more, thin and irregularly wavy ribs. Areoles somewhat depressed, initially white-felted, with 5 flat, white, brown-tipped radial spines up to 2 cm long, and 1 flattened, straight or slightly curved central spine up to 3.5 cm long. Flowers 3.5–4 cm long, barely opening, carmine red. Mexico (Hidalgo).

Stenocactus coptonogonus (Lem.) A. Berger ex Backeb. & F.M. Knuth   □■
[= **Echinofossulocactus coptonogonus** (Lem.) Lawr.]   □□

Depressed-globose, 5–10 cm high, 8–11 cm wide stem, grey-green, forming small groups of 6–8 heads, with 10–14 broad, sharp, deeply crenate ribs 1.5 cm high. Areoles in the notches, 2–3 cm apart, initially woolly-felted, with 3–5 upcurving, flat, angular spines up to 3 cm long, red at first, later horn-coloured. Flowers 3 cm long, 4 cm wide, whitish with carmine-red midstripe. Mexico (San Luis Potosí).

Stenocactus obovallatus (DC.) A. Berger ex Backeb. & F.M. Knuth   □□
[= **Echinofossulocactus pentacanthus**] (Lem.) B. & R.   ■□

Depressed-globose to globose stem, grey-green, with about 30 fairly thin, wavy ribs, much broadened round the areoles, looking as though they are split. Areoles slightly grey-felted, with 5 stout, grey-brown, clearly annulate spines, the uppermost very broad, upcurving 5 cm long, and 3–4 mm wide, the side ones angular, spreading and 2 cm long, and the 2 lower ones 7–10 mm long, pointing downwards like pincers and appressed. Flowers pale yellow with reddish-violet midstripe. Mexico.

Stenocactus phyllacanthus (A. Dietr. & Otto) A. Berger
ex Backeb. & F.M. Knuth   □□
[= **Echinofossulocactus tricuspidatus** (Scheidw.) B. & R.]   □■

Globose to shortly cylindric, light green stem, 5–8 cm wide, with 30–35 thin, sinuate ribs. Areoles initially felted, with 5 or more spreading radial spines and 1 dagger-like, almost straight, central spine, reddish at first, later black-tipped. Flowers 1.5 cm long, greenish yellow. Mexico (San Luis Potosí). The illustration shows var. *tricuspidatus*, in which the principal spine is 3-pointed.

CORYPHANTHA (Engelm.) Lemaire (incl. LEPIDOCORYPHANTHA Backeb.)

Globose or elongate to cylindric, solitary or sprouting from the base. Tubercles sometimes very elongate, with a furrow ±reaching as far as the axil, often filled with wool, with or without fairly large, red or yellow glands. Flowers conspicuous, campanulate-funnelshaped, crowded at the apex from the furrows of the youngest tubercles. Pericarpel and receptacle-tube naked or the tube with a few to several scales with some wool in their axils. Fruit berry-like, naked, rarely with a few small scales, yellowish to greenish, with dried floral-remains. Seeds semi-ovoid to kidney-shaped; seedcoat brown, smooth or at most irregularly wrinkled. About 50 species have been described in SW USA and Mexico, but the total of 'good' species must be appreciably smaller.

Coryphantha radians (DC.) B. & R.

Solitary, globose to weakly elongate, green stem, 5–7 cm across, covered in spines and with felted apex, tubercles obliquely-ovoid, axils and areoles initially woolly. Areoles with 12–20, pectinate, slightly curved, appressed, yellowish, brown-tipped radial spines, central spines absent. Flowers 6–7 cm wide, lemon-yellow with a silky sheen, often flushed with red outside. C Mexico.

Coryphantha palmeri B. & R.

Oblong-globose, pale green stem, 6–8 cm across, apex very woolly, tubercles erect, conical. Areoles very woolly when young, with 11–14 thin, protruding, yellowish, black-tipped radial spines, and 1 stouter, hooked, brown central spine up to 2 cm long. Flowers near apex 3–4 cm long, yellow. Mexico (Durango, Tamaulipas).

Coryphantha salm-dyckiana (Scheer) B. & R.

Solitary or sprouting and clump-forming, light green, 10–15 cm wide stem, apex with white wool topped by spines, tubercles almost rhomboid, 1 cm long, obliquely-truncate, overlapping, furrows deep, glabrous. Areoles at first sparsely felted, with 7–15 grey or whitish radial spines 1–1.5 cm long, and 1–4 reddish to black central spines 2–2.5 cm long, the 3 upper ones ascending, the lowest, stoutest 1 slightly curved. Flowers up to 4 cm long, pale yellow, greenish and red-tinged outside. Mexico (Chihuahua).

Coryphantha werdermannii Boed.

Initially depressed globose, later ovoid to ±columnar, up to 8 cm high, 6 cm wide stem, occasionally producing lateral offsets in age, light grey-green, tubercles rectangular-pyramidal, rounded, 5 mm long, axils glabrous. Areoles glabrous, with 15–20 stiff, needle-like, appressed, pale greyish-white radial spines up to 6 mm long, and 4 brownish central spines up to 22 mm long, 3 of which are erect and 1 porrect and curved; central spines only on older plants, about 4 cm up from the base, at the same time radial spines increasing from 25–30. Flowers broadly funnel-shaped, 5 cm long, 6–7 cm wide, pale yellow, with reddish midstripe outside that soon disappears. Fruit large, thin. Mexico (Coahuila).

Coryphantha pallida B. & R.　■□
□□
Solitary or sprouting and forming clumps of up to 10 heads, stems globose, up to 12 cm wide, blue-green, tubercles close-set, short and thick. Areoles with 20 or more appressed, white radial spines, and 3 black or black-tipped central spines, the upper 2 erect, the lower 1 protruding and curving downwards. Flowers up to 7 cm long and wide, pale lemon-yellow. Fruit 2 cm long, greenish brown. Mexico (Tehuacán).

Coryphantha elephantidens (Lem.) Lem.　□■
□□
Depressed globose, up to 15 cm high, 18–20 cm wide stem, glossy dark green, with white wool on apex and in axils, tubercles very large, thick and stout, 4–5 cm long, deeply furrowed and felted, axils densely woolly. Areoles initially white-felted, with 6–8 stout, curving radial spines up to 2 cm long, yellowish at first, then brownish with darker tips, central spines absent. Flowers 8–10 cm wide, deep pink with darker base and midstripe. Mexico (Michoacán).

Coryphantha clavata (Scheidw.) Backeb.　□□
■□
Cylindric to clavate, 4–7 cm wide, dark leaf-green or violet-flushed stem, with woolly felted apex, tubercles distant, obliquely-conical, furrows shallow, with 1–2 red nectar-glands, axils white-woolly. Areoles initially with short white felt, later glabrous, with 6–12 straight, horizontally spreading radial spines 8–15 mm long, brown on new growth, then white with brown tips, and later 1 straight, yellowish to brownish central spine 2–3 cm long. Flowers 2–3 cm long, yellow. Mexico (San Luis Potosí).

Coryphantha erecta (Lem.) Lem.　□□
□■
Cylindric, initially upright and solitary, then decumbent and sprouting from the upper side to form colonies several square metres in area; stems up to 30 cm high and 6–8 cm thick, vivid green, apex white woolly-felted, topped with inward-curving yellow spines; tubercles rather openly arranged, conical, 7–8 mm long, 15 mm wide at the base; axils initially with profuse woolly felt. Areoles white-felted, later glabrescent, with 8–13 horizontally spreading, straight, subulate, golden-brown radial spines up to 12 mm long, and 2(–4) downward-pointing central spines up to 2 cm long. Flowers near apex, 5.5–6 cm long, 7.5 cm wide, shortly funnel-shaped to almost rotate, lemon-yellow with canary-yellow inside. Fruit clavate, 1.5 cm long, 5 mm thick, green. Mexico (Hidalgo).

ESCOBARIA B. & R. (incl. NEOBESSEYA B. & R. CORYPHANTHA (Engelm.) Lemaire p.p.)

Small, clustering cacti, globose or elongate to cylindric, branching from the base, without milky sap. Tubercles with a furrow on the upper side reaching from the areole to the axil. Areoles mostly densely spiny. Flowers from the furrows of young tubercles around the apex, large or small, campanulate. Pericarpel naked or with only a few scales, receptacle-tube coloured like the perianth-segments, with ciliate scales. Fruit a globose to oblong, green or red berry with floral remains. Seeds obliquely-hemispherical or ±ovoid; seedcoat black to dark brown, pitted or reticulate. According to Taylor (1983), the genus falls into 4 sections:

Sect. *Pleurantha* N.P. Taylor: Flowers in the axils of grooved tubercles, lateral rather than apical; perianth-segments ciliate. Seedcoat brown, with broad, shallow, pits. 2 species in N Mexico.

Sect. *Escobaria*: Flowers in the axils of grooved tubercles, apical; perianth-segments ciliate; stigmas usually whitish or pink, rarely greenish. Seedcoat pale to dark brown, with conspicuous pits. 6 or more species, 2 of them with numerous varieties, from S Canada to C Mexico.

Sect. *Neobesseya* (B. & R.) N.P. Taylor: Flowers in the axils of grooved tubercles, apical; perianth-segments ciliate; stigmas green or greenish yellow. Seedcoat black, with conspicuous pits. 5 species, 2 of them with numerous varieties, in the USA and N Mexico, and 1 species in Cuba.

Sect. *Acharagma* N.P. Taylor: Flowers arising at the spine-bearing areoles, the tubercles not grooved; perianth-segments not ciliate; seedcoat brown or black, with conspicuous pits. 2 closely related species in N Mexico (Coahuila).

Escobaria vivipara (Nutt.) F. Buxbaum var. **arizonica** (Engelm.) D.R. Hunt ■□ [= **Coryphantha arizonica** (Engelm.) B. & R. (*Escobaria*) □□

Solitary or forming small groups, depressed globose to shortly cylindric stem, 3–12 cm high, tubercles cylindric. Areoles with 16(–22), thin, white or brown, radial spines and 4–6 stouter, brownish central spines 1.5–2 cm long. Flowers 3.5–5 cm long, deep pink, with numerous, long, narrow perianth-segments. Fruit ellipsoid, 2 cm long, 1 cm thick, greenish to red-brown. USA (S Utah, SW Colorado, Arizona and NW New Mexico). *E. vivipara* var. *radiosa* is illustrated on p. 268.

Escobaria emskoetteriana (Quehl) Backeb. (*Escobaria*) □■ □□

Mat-forming, stem 5 cm high and 4 cm wide, dark green, tubercles conical, 1 cm long, 6 mm wide at base, distant, pointing upwards. Areoles sparsely felted, with over 20 tough, needle-like, whitish, sometimes russet-tipped radial spines up to 2 cm long, and 6–8 central spines of similar size, white below, ginger above, axils naked. Flowers 3 cm long and wide, dirty white with greenish-red centre. Mexico (San Luis Potosí).

Escobaria orcutti Boed. (*Neobesseya*) □□ ■□

Solitary or sparsely offsetting, globose to shortly-cylindric, up to 15 cm long and 6 cm wide. Areoles with 20–50 white, bristly radial spines, and 6–22 stouter and longer central spines, often up to 2.5 cm long, usually reddish towards the top or brownish. Flowers 2–3 cm long, pink. Fruit clavate, 1.5–2 cm long, scarlet. USA (SE Arizona, W Texas, S New Mexico).

Escobaria dasyacantha var. **chaffeyi** (B. & R.) N.P. Taylor (*Neobesseya*) □□ □■

Sparsely offsetting, 6–12 cm high and 5–6 cm wide stem, almost completely covered with white spines, tubercles very short, pale green, with numerous bristly white radial spines, and several rather shorter, brown or black-tipped central spines. Flowers 1.5 cm long, 1 cm wide, creamy pink to yellowish-white. Fruit 2 cm long, carmine-red. Mexico.

Escobaria vivipara (Nutt.) F. Buxbaum var. **radiosa** (Engelm.) D.R. Hunt ■■ □□

Differs from var. *arizonica* (see p. 266) in having more numerous, but thinner and paler, central spines, and in the paler flowers with distinctive, narrow perianth-segments. USA (SW Oklahoma, NC Texas and SE New Mexico).

ORTEGOCACTUS Alexander

Globose to short-cylindric, rather small, usually clustering, with tubercles arranged in spirals and numerous spines. Flowers arising in the axils between the upper tubercles, sometimes at the base of a groove extending from the spine-cluster, or the groove lacking; pericarpel immersed in soft woolly hairs; receptacle-tube slender, naked; limb spreading. Fruit globose-ellipsoid, soon becoming dry, seeds nearly globose, with black, pitted seedcoat. 1 species in SW Mexico (Oaxaca).

Ortegocactus macdougallii Alexander □□
[= **Neobesseya macdougallii** (Alexander) Kladiwa] ■■

Globose to shortly-cylindric, 3–4 cm wide stem, usually forming groups, tubercles close-set. Areoles with short wool, with up to 7–8 needle-shaped, black or white radial spines up to 12 mm long, and 1 straight, white, black-tipped central spine 4–5 mm long. Flowers from axils of upper tubercles, 2–3 cm long, up to 2.5 cm wide, funnel-shaped, yellow. Fruit globose, 5 mm thick, orange-yellow to reddish, soon becoming dry, with persistent floral-remains. Mexico (Oaxaca).

MAMMILLARIA Haworth [incl. COCHEMIEA (K. Brandegee) Walton, DOLICHOTHELE (K. Schumann) B. & R., MAMILLOPSIS Morren ex. B. & R., BARTSCHELLA B. & R. NEOMAMMILLARIA B. & R., PHELLOSPERMA B. & R., SOLISIA B. & R., PORFIRIA Boedeker, CHILITA Orcutt, KRAINZIA Backeb., EBNERELLA F. Buxbaum, MAMMILLOYDIA F. Buxbaum, OEHMEA F. Buxbaum, PSEUDOMAMMILLARIA F. Buxbaum, LEPTOCLADODIA F. Buxbaum]

Small to medium-sized, globose to shortly-columnar, upright or decumbent, solitary or clustering by offsets or by dichotomous division of the apex, often with a thick, tuberous root, with or without milky sap. Tubercles arranged in very regular oblique rows, conical, sometimes flattened or cylindric, without a furrow between the spine-bearing areole and the flower-bearing axil. Areoles with very variable spines. Central spines often shaped like a fish-hook. Flowers in profusion in a ring around apex, usually from the previous year's axils, very simplified, large funnel-shaped or small and slenderly campanulate, regular or (*Cochemiea*) somewhat zygomorphic with oblique limb. Pericarpel naked, ±immersed in the body-tissue. Receptacle-tube coloured like the perianth-segments or sometimes greenish. Perianth-segments usually pink to red, more rarely white or yellowish. Fruit berry-like, concealed until shortly before it ripens, then suddenly maturing, oblong, clavate, rarely almost globose, vivid red, purple or greenish, initially fleshy, later drying, with or without floral remains. Seeds almost globose, ovoid or pear-shaped, hilum in some species with large strophiole; seedcoat black or brown, matt or glossy, regularly pitted, with straight or undulating cell-walls or apparently smooth, very seldom verrucose. With about 150–200 species this is the largest cactus genus apart from *Opuntia*. The main area of distribution is Mexico, extending north-westwards through Texas as far as California, eastwards via Cuba and Haiti, to the S Bahamas, and southwards to N Colombia, and Venezuela.

The genus *Mammillaria* is divided into the following 6 subgenera:
Mammilloydia (F. Buxbaum) Moran: Depressed globose to elongate, solitary or clustering, with watery sap. Axils with bristly hairs as long as the tubercles, areoles with dense white sometimes reddish spines. Seeds glossy black, smooth or tessellate or verrucose. 1 species.
Oehmea (F. Buxbaum) D.R. Hunt: Globose or elongated to cylindric, solitary or clustering, with watery sap. Central spines 1 or more, elongate, shaped like a fish-hook. Flowers large, pale orange or yellow. Receptacle-tube fused with the style-base. Seeds few, very large (2–3 mm in diameter), matt black, rugose and pitted. 1 variable species.
Dolichothele K. Schumann: Usually globose with thickened, tuberous root, offsetting from the base to form clumps, soft-fleshed, without milky sap. Tubercles finger-like, sometimes very long, fleshy, dark green. Axils naked or slightly hairy. Areoles usually with a few spines, in some species with a hooked central spine. Flowers mostly large, typically sulphur-yellow, rarely pale yellow. Lower part of the receptacle-tube fused with the style. Seeds large, black to brown, coarsely pitted. 7 species.
Cochemiea K. Brandegee: Slenderly cylindric, often very elongate (up to 2 m) and then decumbent or arching, freely branching near the base, bushy or forming low thickets, without milky sap. Usually at least 1 central spine, hooked. Flowers narrowly tubular, zygomorphic, S-shaped, with oblique limb, scarlet. Perianth-segments in two rows, anthers and style long-exserted. Seeds black, with large, deep pits. 5 species.
Mamillopsis (Morren ex B. & R.) D.R. Hunt: Globose to shortly cylindric, eventually forming large mounds. Tubercles close-set, without milky sap, axils woolly. Areoles with very numerous white or yellowish radial spines and one sometimes hooked central spine. Flowers large, tubular-funnelshaped, bright red or orange. Stamens and style exserted. Seeds black, pitted. 2 species.
Mammillaria Haworth: Solitary or offsetting from the base, globose to elongate cylindric (up to 70 cm long, 6–10 cm thick), with or without milky sap. Axils with wool and bristles or only bristles, seldom glabrous. Radial spines numerous, needle-like or bristly. Central spine straight to hooked. Flowers in a ring near the apex or lower, from older axils, usually without noticeable flower-tubes. Seeds black or brown, pitted or reticulate. The most extensive subgenus with over 150 species.

Mammillaria candida Scheidw.
[= **Mammilloydia candida** (Scheidw.) F. Buxbaum] (*Mammilloydia*)
Solitary or offsetting to form dense, flat clumps, stem globose to elongate, 8–10 cm high, 5.5–7 cm wide, blue-green, densely covered with white spines, tubercles clavate to cylindric, 1 cm long, axils with 4–7 white bristles. Areoles white-felted, with over 50 bristly, white, interlacing radial spines 5–9 mm long, and 5–9 spreading, rather stouter, white, often brown-tipped central spines 4–7 mm long. Flowers solitary or scattered near the apex, tubular-funnelshaped, 2 cm long, 1.5 cm wide, dull rose-red, white-rimmed. Fruit clavate, 18 mm long, 3–4 mm thick, carmine-red. Mexico (San Luis Potosí).

Mammillaria beneckei Ehrenberg
[= **Oehmea nelsonii** (B. & R.) F. Buxbaum] (*Oehmea*)
Offsetting and forming clumps up to 35 cm wide, globose to elongate stems, 6–7 cm wide, tubercles dark green to reddish, thick-conical, 6–7 mm long. Areoles initially white-woolly, with 13–15 fine needle-like, white, brown-tipped radial spines up to 8 mm long, and 4 hooked, ±downward-pointing, dark central spines up to 1 cm long, axils sparsely woolly. Flowers from the axils, broadly funnel-shaped, 3–4 cm wide, yellow. Fruit red. S Mexico.

Mammillaria longimamma DC.

■□
□□

[= **Dolichothele longimamma** (DC.) B. & R.] (*Dolichothele*)
Solitary or offsetting from the base, forming clumps, 8–15 cm high and wide, glossy green stem,w ith somewhat tuberous root, tubercles distant, cylindric, elliptic in cross-section, 2–7 cm long, 1–1.5 cm thick, white-fleshed, axils hairy-felted to glabrous. Areoles with 9–10 subulate, straight or weakly curved, spreading, white to pale yellow radial spines 5–20 mm long, and 1 straight, light brown, black-tipped central spine up to 25 mm long. Flowers numerous near apex, funnel-shaped, 5–6 cm long and wide, canary-yellow. Fruit globose to ovoid, 10–12 mm long, yellowish-green to red. C Mexico.

Mammillaria surculosa Boed.

□■
□□

[= **Dolichothele surculosa** (Boed.) F. Buxbaum] (*Dolichothele*)
Freely offsetting to form mats and mounds, stems small, up to 4 cm high, 3 cm wide, glossy green with sturdy, tuberous root, tubercles distant, shortly cylindric, up to 8 mm long, 4 mm thick, finely white punctuate. Areoles with 15 very thin, straight, translucent white radial spines 8–10 mm long, and 1 straight, nearly erect, hook-tipped, amber-yellow to brownish central spine, 20 mm long. Flowers from older axils near apex, funnel-shaped, up to 18 mm long, sulphur-yellow with reddish tips, stigma yellowish-green, sweet-smelling at night. Fruit club-shaped, green to reddish tinged. Mexico (Tamaulipas).

Mammillaria carretii Rebut (*Dolichothele*)

□□
■□

Solitary, depressed globose, 5–6 cm wide, dark green stem, tubercles cylindric, 7–9 mm long, axils glabrous. Areoles at first sparsely woolly-felted, with 14 subulate, horizontally spreading, weakly curved, yellow radial spines, brown towards the tip, 11–13 mm long, and 1 porrect, hooked, brown central spine 14–16 mm long. Flowers solitary, lateral, 2.5 cm long, 1.5 cm wide, funnel-shaped, whitish with pink midstripe. Fruit slender, green. Mexico (Coahuila).

Mammillaria camptotricha Dams

□□
□■

[= **Dolichothele camptotricha** (Dams) Tiegel]
Offsetting from the base and forming groups, broadly globose stem, 5–7 cm across, deep green, tubercles slender-conical to almost cylindric, sometimes curved, up to 2 cm long, 7 mm thick at the base, axils sparsely hairy and with 2–5 yellowish bristles 10–15 mm long. Areoles with 4 or more thin, curved, pale yellow radial spines 10–15 mm long, interlacing on the apex, central spine absent. Flowers funnel-shaped, 1.5 cm long, barely 1 cm wide, white, scented. Mexico (Querétaro).
Formerly included int subg. *Dolichothele* but recently transferred to subg. *Mammillaria* by Hunt (1981), who includes it in sect. *Mammillaria*, series 8. *Decipientes* (see p. 276).

Mammillaria poselgeri Hildmann　　　　　　　　　　　■□
[= **Cochemiea poselgeri** (Hildmann) B. & R.] (*Cochemiea*)　□□
Cylindric, initially upright, then decumbent or hanging over cliffs, up to 2 m long, 2.5–
5 cm thick stems, branching bushily from the base, blue-green to grey-green, tubercles
nearly erect, conical, rectangular-based, 10–12 mm long, axils with white wool and
rarely bristles. Areoles with 7–10 horizontally spreading, stiff radial spines up to 15 mm
long, deep yellow on new growth or red, later greying, and 1 stouter, protruding, hooked,
darker-coloured central spine 2.5–3 cm long. Flowers lateral, in a ring below the apex,
tubular-funnelshaped with somewhat oblique limb, 3.5 cm long, 2–2.5 cm wide, scarlet.
Fruit pear-shaped, 6–9 mm thick, glossy scarlet. Mexico (Baja California).

Mammillaria setispina Engelm　　　　　　　　　　　□■
[= **Cochemiea setispina** (J. Coulter) Walton] (*Cochemiea*)　□□
Freely-branching and forming dense clusters, cylindric, 3.5–5 cm thick, and up to
30 cm high stems, light grey-green, tubercles distant, somewhat rectangular, 4–5 cm
high, axils initially white woolly later glabrous. Areoles with 9–12 needle-fine, sharp,
spreading, milk-white, dark-tipped radial spines, unequal, up to almost 2 cm long, and 4
central spines, 1 porrect, strongly hooked, up to 3 cm long, and 3 upward-pointing, thin,
black-tipped. Flowers 5.4 cm long, bright vermilion, perianth-segments rolled up
backwards. Fruit club-shaped, 1.7 cm long, dark red. Mexico (Baja California).

Mammillaria halei K. Brandegee　　　　　　　　　　　□□
[= **Cochemiea halei** (K. Brandegee) Walton] (*Cochemiea*)　■□
Forming groups, with 30–50 cm high, 5–7.5 cm thick, upright stems, almost
completely covered with spines, tubercles short, axils initially woolly but without
bristles. Areoles with 10–20 stiff, straight, spreading, at first red-brown, finally grey,
darker-tipped, radial spines up to 1.5 cm long, and 3–4(–6) similarly coloured, very
stout central spines up to 3.5 cm long. Flowers around the apex, 4–5 cm long, slender,
bright scarlet, perianth-segments only partly recurved. Fruit club-shaped, 1.2 cm long.
Mexico (Baja California, S islands).

Mammillaria senilis Loddiges　　　　　　　　　　　□□
[= **Mamillopsis senilis** (Loddiges) F.A.C. Weber] (*Mamillopsis*)　□■
In age offsetting and mound-forming, globose to cylindric stem, 10–18 cm high, 6–
12 cm wide, with white woolly-felted apex, and completely covered in spines, tubercles
rather blunt, conical and close-set, 8–10 mm long, 3–4 mm wide, glossy green, axils
with short white wool. Areoles white woolly with many (40–50) stiff, bristly, white or
yellowish radial spines 8–15 mm long, interlacing, covering the entire body, and 5–6
pale yellow to brownish central spines up to 2 cm long, 1 or more of which with hooked
tip. Flowers lateral from the younger axils, 4.5–6 cm long, 5.5–6 cm wide, somewhat
obliquely funnel-shaped, orange-red to violet with darker midstripe. Fruit rounded, red.
N Mexico at altitudes of 2500–3000 m.

The subgenus *Mammillaria* can be further divided into 3 sections:
Hydrochylus: with watery sap.
Subhydrochylus: tubercles with watery or at most fainly milky sap. Milky sap — only
seasonally if at all — in the whole shoot or the lower part.
Mammillaria: Tubercles with milky sap.
Within these sections 14 series may be distinguished:
Hydrochylus K. Schumann:
Series 1　　*Longiflorae* D.R. Hunt (9 species)
Series 2　　*Ancistracanthae* K. Schumann (35 species)
Series 3　　*Stylothelae* (Pfeiffer) K. Schumann (26 species)

Series 4   *Proliferae* D.R. Hunt (9 species)
Series 5   *Lasiacanthae* D.R. Hunt (11 species)
Series 6   *Sphacelatae* D.R. Hunt (3 species)
Series 7   *Leptocladodae* (Lemaire) K. Schumann (4 species)
Series 8   *Decipientes* D.R. Hunt (2 species)
Subhydrochylus Backeberg ex D.R. Hunt
Series 9   *Heterochlorae* (Salm-Dyck) K. Schumann (13 species)
Series 10   *Polyacanthae* (Salm-Dyck) K. Schumann (12 species)
Series 11   *Supertextae* D.R. Hunt (12 species)
Mammillaria (*Galactochylus*) K. Schumann)
Series 12   *Leucocephalae* (Lemaire) K. Schumann (10 species)
Series 13   *Mammillaria* (*Macrothelae* (Salm-Dyck) K. Schumann) (42 species)
Series 14   *Polyedrae* (Pfeiffer) K. Schumann (10 species)

Mammillaria tetrancistra Engelm.
[= Phellosperma tetrancistra (Engelm.) B. & R.] (Series 1)
Solitary or offsetting from the base or higher up on older growth, globose to cylindric stem, 5–15(–30) cm high, up to 7 cm wide, with long, branching, fleshy root, tubercles distant, ovoid to cylindric, 4–7 mm long, pale green to blue-green, axils initially with somewhat lax wool and a few long bristles. Areoles with 40–60 needle-like to bristly, almost horizontally spreading, white, often brown-tipped radial spines 5–12 mm long, arranged in 2 rows, and 3–4 dark brown to black central spines, the upper ones 3–7 mm long, straight or sometimes hooked, the lower 1 6–9 mm long and hooked. Flowers lateral, funnel-shaped, 5 cm long, 3.5 cm wide, purple with whitish edge. Fruit club-shaped, 6–12 mm long, 4–6 mm thick, scarlet. USA (Arizona, Utah, Nevada), Mexico (Baja California).

Mammillaria theresae Cutak (Series 1)
Usually solitary but also offsetting, conical-cylindric stem, up to 10 cm high, 2 cm thick, olive-green, often flushed with purple, tubercles tiny, slender. Areoles woolly with numerous, whitish, plumose radial spines 2 mm long, and up to 9 central spines. Flowers narrow-tubed, funnel-shaped, 3.5–4 cm long, 3 cm wide, violet-purple, greenish-brown outside. N Mexico (Durango, Corneto Pass).

Mammillaria longiflora (B. & R.) A. Berger
[= Krainzia longiflora (B. & R.) Backeb.] (Series 1)
Usually solitary, rarely offsetting globose, dark green, up to 6 cm high and wide, tubercles close-set, laterally widened at the base, strongly conical towards the tip, 5–10 mm long, axils ±glabrous. Areoles with 20–30 needle-like, radial spines 10–13 mm long, spreading and covering the whole stem, white, rarely yellow, and 4 stouter, yellow or dark red-brown, central spines 10–20 mm long, the lowest 1 porrect and hooked sideways. Flowers numerous towards apex, funnel-shaped, 4–5 cm long, 3–4 cm wide, pale pink. Fruit ±globose. Mexico (Durango).

Mammillaria guelzowiana Werderm.
[= Krainzia guelzowiana (Werderm.) Backeb.] (Series 1)
Solitary or sprouting from the base and forming clumps, depressed globose, up to 8 cm wide, 4–6 cm high stems, green, tubercles almost cylindric, 12–13 mm long, 4–5 mm thick at the base, axils glabrous. Areoles with very numerous (60–80) spreading, hair-like towards the top, white radial spines up to 1.5 cm long, and 1 porrect, hooked, red-brown, central spine 8–10 cm long. Flowers solitary from older areoles near apex, 5 cm long, 6 cm wide, purple-red with lighter edge. Fruit almost globose, 8 mm thick, yellowish. Mexico (Durango).

Mammillaria wrightii Englem. (Series 2)

■□
□□

Solitary, globose to depressed globose, dark green stem, 4–8 cm wide, tubercles cylindric, round, 10–15 mm long, 3–4 mm thick at the base, soft, axils glabrous. Areoles initially white woolly, with 12–14 needle-like, white, darker-tipped radial spines 8–12 mm long, and 1–3 stiff, needle-like, hooked, dark brown to almost black central spines. Flowers funnel-shaped, 2.5 cm long and wide, brilliant purple. Fruit large, ovate-globular. USA (New Mexico and Texas), Mexico (Chihuahua).

Mammillaria sheldonii (B. & R.) Boed. (Series 2)

□■
□□

Solitary or sprouting from the base, globose to cylindric, dark grey-green stem, up to 25 cm high, 5–6 cm wide, completely covered in spines, tubercles small, ovoid, axils naked. Areoles with 10–15 white radial spines 6–12 mm long, and 1–3 initially red, then dark brown, sharp-hooked central spines up to 15 mm long. Flowers broadly campanulate-funnelshaped, near the apex, 2–2.5 cm long, 3–4 cm wide, rose-red with whitish edge. Fruit elongate, up to 2.5 cm long, scarlet. N Mexico (Sonora)

Mammillaria mazatlanensis K. Schumann (Series 2)

□□
■□

Freely sprouting from the base and clump-forming, globose to cylindric stem, 9–12 cm high, 3–4 cm wide, grey-green, tubercles distant, shortly conical, 4–8 mm long, 1 cm wide at the base, axils with small tufts of wool and 1–2 short bristles. Areoles with 13–15 evenly spreading, bristly or needle-like white radial spines 5–10 mm long, and 4 longer and stouter, needle-like central spines 8–15 mm long, bright brown, white at the base, often 1 of them hooked. Flowers funnel-shaped, 3–4 cm long, carmine-red with green stigma. Fruit slenderly pear-shaped, 2 cm long, 7 cm across, reddish yellow. Mexico (Sinaloa and Sonora).

Mammillaria yaquensis Craig (Series 2)

□□
□■

Vigorously sprouting and tussock-forming, slenderly cylindric stem, 6–8 cm high 1.5–2 cm wide, reddish green, tubercles shortly conical, 3 mm long, 5 mm wide at the base, axils with only very little wool. Areoles with 18 straight, fine, needle-like, 5–6 mm long, cream-coloured, light brown-tipped radial spines, and 1 needle-like, strongly hooked, 17 mm long, reddish brown to dark brown central spine. Flowers solitary or several together, campanulate-funnelshaped, 2 cm long and wide, pale pink with long, deep purple stigmas. Fruit shortly clavate, 1 cm long, blood-red. Mexico (Sonora).

Mammillaria blossfeldiana Boed. (Series 2)

Solitary or sprouting from below, globose to shortly cylindric, dark green stem, up to 10 cm high and 3–5 cm wide, tubercles cylindric to conical, firm, 8–10 mm long, 5–7 mm wide at the base, axils naked. Areoles somewhat woolly only at first, with 15–20 fairly stout, needle-like, straight, matt white, darker-tipped radial spines 7–14 mm long, and 1–4 stout, needle-like, dark brown to black central spines 8–15 mm long, the lowest 1 hooked. Flowers campanulate, up to 2.5 cm wide, whitish with pink midstripe. Fruit 1.4–1.8 cm long, red. Mexico (Baja California).

Mammillaria schumannii Hildmann
[= **Bartschella schumannii** (Hildmann) B. & R. (Series 2)

Sprouting from the base and forming clumps of more than 40 heads, cylindric, up to 10 cm high, up to 6 cm wide stem, grey-green to tinged with greyish violet, tubercles rounded-rectangular, short and thick, axils with short wool. Areoles with 12(9–15) sturdy, subulate, straight, white or black-tipped radial spines 6–12 mm long, and 2(–4) central spines 10–15 mm long, white at the base and black above, the upper straight, the lower porrect and hooked. Flowers campanulate, near the apex, 4 cm wide, vivid rose-red. Fruit oblong, 15–20 mm long, scarlet. Mexico (Baja California).

Mammillaria insularis Gates (Series 2)

Sprouting laterally and from the base, depressed globose, 6 cm high and 5 cm wide stem, blue-green, with thick, fleshy, tuberous root, tubercles conical, truncate, 7 mm long and 7 mm wide at the base, axils glabrous or with a little wool. Areoles with 20–30 slender, needle-like, white radial spines 5 mm long, and 1 sideways-hooked, black to brown or yellow central spine 10 mm long. Flowers broadly funnel-shaped, 1.5–2.5 cm long, whitish pink with darker pink midstripe. Fruit club-shaped, 10 mm long, 3 mm thick, orange-red. Mexico (Baja California).

Mammillaria boolii Lindsay (Series 2)

Solitary or occasionally offsetting, globose, blue-green stem, 3.5 cm high and 3 cm wide, tubercles oblong, truncate, axils lightly woolly only when young. Areoles with 20 needle-like, spreading, white radial spines 15 mm long, and 1 porrect, strong-hooked, yellowish or horn-coloured, darker-tipped central spine 15–20 mm long. Flowers 2.5 cm long and wide, pink or purplish-pink. Fruit oblong-clavate, 2.5 cm long and 0.5 cm thick, orange. Mexico (Sonora).

Mammillaria moelleriana Boed. (Series 3)

Solitary, globose, glossy green stem, up to 6 cm wide, completely covered in spines, tubercles ovoid, 8 mm long and wide, axils naked. Areoles only initially with white wool, with 35—40 somewhat spreading, sharp, needle-like, snow-white radial spines 7—9 mm long, and 8—9 central spines, honey-coloured to dark red-brown, lighter towards the base, the lower 4 hooked and up to 2 cm long, the upper ones straight and shorter. Flowers in a ring, 1.5 cm long and wide, greenish white. Mexico (Durango).

Mammillaria mercadensis Patoni (Series 3)

Solitary or only sparsely offsetting, globose, olive-green to dark green stem, 5 cm wide, tubercles conical to shortly cylindric, rounded, 1 cm long, axils naked. Areoles only initially with white wool, with 25—30 thin, needle-like, weakly protruding, white radial spines 5—8 mm long, and 4—7 stiff, needle-like, brown to red or yellow central spines 1.5—2.5 cm long, the lowest, longest 1 hooked. Flowers 1—3 cm wide, yellowish white to pale pink. Mexico (Durango).

Mammillaria pennispinosa Krainz (Series 3)

Solitary, rarely offsetting, depressed globose, 3.5 cm wide and 3 cm high, covered in plumose spines, with thick tuberous root, tubercles cylindric, dark green, 5—7 mm long, 3 mm wide at the base, axils near the apex with some short felt, later glabrous. Areoles with 16—20 straight, thickly plumose-haired, nearly erect, later laterally interlacing, radial spines 5—8 mm long, greyish white or russet towards the tip, and 1(—3) porrect, hooked, reddish central spines 11—12 mm long. Flowers campanulate to shortly funnel-shaped, 15 mm long, 12 mm wide, white with carmine-pink midstripe and pale carmine-pink throat. Fruit cylindric, 2.5 cm long, 3 mm thick, carmine red. Mexico (SW Coahuila).

Mammillaria stella-de-tacubaya Heese (Series 3)
[= Mammillaria gasseriana Boed.]

Sprouting from the base, globose to shortly ovoid, matt grey-green stem, 3—4 cm wide, with fleshy, branching root, tubercles fairly close-set, shortly ovoid, 6 cm long and thick, punctate when young, axils glabrous. Areoles with 40—50 spreading, white radial spines 5—8 mm long, in 2—3 pectinate rows, and 1—2 sturdier, hooked central spines 8 mm long, white, dark brown above. Flowers solitary, campanulate-funnelshaped, small, 7—8 mm wide, cream-coloured with faint brownish midstripe. Fruit very small, club-shaped, vermilion. Mexico (SW Coahuila).

Mammillaria bombycina Quehl (Series 3)

Solitary or offsetting and group-forming, globose, later cylindric, fresh green, 8–20 cm high and 5–6 cm wide stem, with white woolly apex and attractive red-brown to yellow spines, tubercles dense, shortly cylindric, 15 mm long, axils with abundant white wool. Areoles with 30–40, pectinate, radial spines spreading and covering the whole stem, thin, stiff, shining silky white, up to 10 mm long, and 4 central spines, cruciform, white at the base, bright red-brown or yellow above, the upper one 7 mm long, the side ones 10 mm, the lowest one 20 mm, stouter and hooked. Flowers in a ring around the apex, funnel-shaped, 1.5 cm long and wide, light purple. Fruit club-shaped, whitish. Mexico (exact origin unknown).

Mammillaria zeilmanniana Boed. (Series 3)

Solitary or sparsely offsetting from the base or laterally, ovoid to shortly cylindric, glossy dark green stem, 6 cm high and 4.5 cm wide, tubercles close-set, ovoid to shortly cylindric, 6 mm long, 3–4 mm thick, axils glabrous. Areoles initially with short white wool, with 15–18 very thin, needle-like to almost hair-like, white radial spines 10 mm long, and 4 sturdier, needle-like, red-brown central spines up to 1 cm long, the lowest 1 hooked. Flowers in a ring some distance from the apex, bell-shaped, 2 cm wide, carmine-violet to purple-pink. Fruit small, whitish-green. Mexico (Guanajuato).

Mammillaria bocasana Poselger (Series 3)

Sprouting from the base and forming dense, flat or gently domed clumps, individual stems globose to short-cylindric, 4–5 cm wide, light to dark blue-green stems, tubercles slenderly cylindric, 6–10 mm long, 2–4 mm thick at the base, axils naked or with thin white woolly hairs. Areoles with sparse yellowish woolly-felt, with 15–30, bristly white radial spines up to 2 cm long, terminating in hair-fine threads, loosely enveloping the entire stem, and 1–4 subulate, porrect, white to yellowish-brown central spines, the lowest 1 hooked. Flowers funnel-shaped, 16 mm long, 12 mm wide, yellowish-white somewhat reddish striate. Fruit slenderly club-shaped, 3–4 cm long, red. Mexico (San Luis Potosí).

Mammillaria wildii A. Dietrich (Series 3)

Freely sprouting from the base and sides and forming mounds, globose to cylindric stem, 8–15 cm high, 4–7 cm wide, dark green to blue-green, tubercles fairly distant, oblong, up to 13 cm long, 3–6 mm thick at the base, axils with a few long or twisted hairs, sometimes rose-red. Areoles very weakly white-felted, with 8–10 bristly white radial spines 6–8 mm long, and 3–4 somewhat stouter and longer, honey-coloured central spines, 1 porrect and hooked, the others horizontally radiating. Flowers numerous, funnel-shaped, 12–15 mm long, 10–12 mm wide, whitish, outside dull red striate. Fruit club-shaped, brownish-red. Mexico (Hidalgo).

Mammillaria prolifera (Miller) Haworth (Series 4)

Sprouting from the base and above to form dense mats overtopped by longer shoots, globose to shortly cylindric stems, 4–6 cm long, 3–4 cm wide, dark green, tubercles slenderly-conical, 5–8 mm long, 4–5 mm thick at the base, soft-fleshed, fresh green, axils with white hairs. Areoles with numerous (20–40) hair-like, white radial spines 6–10 mm long, and 5–9(–12) radiating central spines 6–8 mm long, initially deep yellow, lighter-tipped, later whitish. Flowers campanulate-funnelshaped, 13–14 mm long, yellowish. Fruit curved club-shaped, 1 cm long, coral red. West Indies, Cuba.

The illustration shows var. *prolifera*, with yellow spines (Cuba). Other varieties are: var. *haitiensis* with rather sturdier body up to 7 cm wide, with pure white central spines (Haiti); var. *texana* (= *M. multiceps*) with whitish central spines often dark brown towards the tip (NE Mexico, Texas; var. *arachnoidea* with soft white spines (E Mexico)).

Mammillaria pilispina J.A. Purpus (Series 4)

Offsetting and forming small mats of a few heads, hemispherical, 4 cm wide, dark green, tubercles fairly close-set, cylindric, rounded on top, 8–10 mm long, 6 mm thick, axils with a few long, curly hairs. Areoles with a ring of very fine, curly, snow-white hair-spines, and 4–5 sturdier, subulate radial spines 6–7 mm long, yellow at the base, white in the middle and brown to the tip, and 1 similar, straight, not hooked, central spine. Flowers 9 mm long, 7–15 mm wide, whitish-yellow. Fruit curved club-shaped, 1.5 cm long, 4 mm thick, pale pink. Mexico (San Luis Potosí).

Mammillaria viereckii Boed. (Series 4)

Small, usually solitary, rarely offsetting from the base, globular, 3–3.5 cm wide, dark green body, entirely enveloped in spines. Tubercles distant, slender cylindric, 8–10 mm long, 2–3 mm thick. Axils light green with sparse white wool, with 8–10 hair-like, twisted bristles, often protruding beyond the tubercle-tip. Areoles with 9–10 fine, needle-like spines 12 mm long, amber or golden-yellow. Flowers appearing singly near the crown, funnel-shaped, 12 mm long, 12 mm wide, cream-coloured with greenish throat. Fruit small, club-shaped, vermilion. Mexico (Tamaulipas).

Mammillaria plumosa F.A.C. Weber (Series 5)

Freely offsetting and forming small, dense cushions. Individual body globular, 6–7 cm high and 6–7 cm wide, completely covered with soft, feathery spines. Tubercles cylindric, 12 mm long, 2–3 mm wide at the base, flaccid, light green. Axils with long white wool. Areoles with up to 40 pinnate, silky-soft, white radial spines 3–7 mm long; central spines not present. Flowers bell-shaped, 1.5 cm long and 1.5 cm wide, yellowish to greenish white. Fruit cylindric, 7 mm long, pale reddish green. Mexico (Coahuila).

Mammillaria carmenae Castañeda & Nuñ, de Cac, (Series 5) ■□ □□

Globose to lightly cylindric, 5–8 cm high, green, offsetting. Tubercles conical, elongate, 6–8 mm long, their whitish-green bases not touching, not firm, axils with white wool and long white bristles. Areoles with more than 100 soft, white or pale-yellow radial spines 5 mm long, central spines absent. Flowers 11 mm long and wide, white, pink-flushed. Fruit ovoid, 6 mm long, 3 mm thick, greenish-white. Mexico (Tamaulipas).

Mammillaria humboldtii Ehrenb. (Series 5) □■ □□

Solitary, or occasionally sprouting from the base, globose to ±elongate stem, pale green, with slightly depressed apex, tubercles cylindric, 12 mm long, 2–3 mm wide at the base, axils weakly white-woolly, with 7–8 straight white bristles, unequal. Areoles with 80 or more very thin, horizontal, snow-white radial spines, unequal, 2–8 mm long, completely covering stem, central spines absent. Flowers 1.5 cm wide, light red. Fruit club-shaped, reddish, without floral remains. Mexico (Hidalgo).

Mammillaria schiedeana Ehrenb. (Series 5) □□ ■□

Sprouting from the base and forming many-headed, low clumps of various shapes, stem globose to cylindric, up to 12 cm high and 6 cm wide, dark green to almost black, almost completely covered with spines, on tuberous root, tubercles slenderly-conical, distant, up to 1 cm long, axils with fairly dense, white to golden-yellow woolly hairs. Areoles with up to 75 horizontally spreading,white radial spines 2.5 mm long, arranged in rows, with numerous hair-spines between them, white at the base, yellow to golden towards the tip, central spines absent. Flowers in a ring around the apex, campanulate-funnel-shaped, 2 cm long, 1.5–1.7 cm wide, whitish. Fruit club-shaped to cylindric, 1.2 cm long, vivid carmine-red. Mexico (Hidalgo).

Mammillaria pectinifera (Ruempler) F.A.C. Weber (Series 5) □□
[= **Solisia pectinata** (B. Stein) B. & R.] □■

Globose to obovoid, up to 6 cm high and 3–4 cm wide stem, in age offsetting, almost completely covered in white spines, with slightly depressed apex, tubercles 3–4 mm high, laterally compressed, with milky sap, axils naked. Areoles elongate, with 40–60, pectinate, pure white to light reddish spines up to 2 mm long. Flowers lateral from the axils of older areoles, 2–2.5 cm wide, bell-shaped, yellowish or pink. Fruit oblong, 6 mm long, red. C Mexico (Tehuacan).

Mammillaria viperina J.A. Purpus (Series 6)　■□ □□

Mat-forming with decumbent stems freely sprouting from the base, slenderly cylindric, up to 20 cm long and 1.5–2 cm thick, completely covered in spines, tubercles shortly cylindric to globose, 5 mm long, light green, axils sometimes with white hairs and bristles almost as long as the tubercles. Areoles with 25–30 fine, snow-white to dark brown, needle-like spines 3–5 mm long, interlacing and pointing on all sides. Flowers 15 mm long and 20 mm wide, light carmine, olive-green outside with purplish-brown midstripe. Fruit clavate to cylindric, 8 mm long, 3 mm thick, carmine red, with floral remains. Mexico (Puebla). (Illustration turned anticlockwise through 90°)

Mammillaria microhelia Werderm. (Series 7)　□■ □□

Solitary, rarely sprouting from the base, cylindric to clavate or somewhat curved, glossy green stem up to 15 cm long, 3.5–4 cm wide, tubercles shortly conical, 4 mm high. Areoles with white wool at first, later glabrous, with up to 50 bristly radial spines 4–6 mm long, pure white at first, later yellow to red, pointing evenly in all directions, and 0–4, usually 1–2 ruby red and dark-tipped, central spines up to 11 mm long, porrect or nearly erect. Flowers in a ring around the apex, broadly campanulate, 1.5 cm long and wide, yellowish white, often with pink tips. Fruit clavate, 11 mm long, 4 mm thick, whitish to pink. Mexico (Querétaro).

Mammillaria elongata DC. (Series 7)　□□ ■□

Growing in dense colonies, slenderly cylindric, fresh green stem up to 20 cm long and 3 cm thick, with conical tubercles. Areoles with 15–20, somewhat recurved, yellow radial spines 8–12 mm long, and 0–1–3 protruding central spines; spine colour very veriable, from white or yellow to dark foxy-red. Flowers below the apex, 1–1.5 cm long, pale yellow. Fruit clavate, dirty red. Mexico (Hidalgo).

Mammillaria densispina (J. Coulter) Vaupel (Series 7)　□□ □■

Solitary, globose or elongate, dark green stem, 8–10 cm high and wide, with conical tubercles 5 mm long. Areoles white woolly, with 20–25 protruding, thin, straight, white to yellow radial spines,unequal 8–13 mm long, and 5–6 straight, rarely weakly curved, foxy-red to brown central spines 10–20 mm long. Flowers in a ring around the apex, funnel-shaped, 2 cm long, 1 cm wide, purplish-red outside, sulphur-yellow inside. Fruit shortly clavate, red. Mexico (San Luis Potosí, Querétaro, Guanajuato).

M. camptotricha, representing Series 8, is illustrated on p.272.

Mammillaria discolor Haworth (Series 9) ■□ □□

Solitary, in age sprouting and forming clusters, globose to cylindric, fresh green to blue-green stem up to 8 cm wide, with depressed apex white woolly-felted, topped with spines, tubercles conical, 6–7 mm long, axils glabrous. Areoles with short, white, woolly felt, soon glabrescent, with 16–20 or more horizontally spreading, thin, snow-white radial spines up to 1 cm long, and 6–8 stouter, straight, spreading, light yellow, later darker yellow to brown, black-tipped central spines up to 1 cm long. Flowers in a ring round the apex, 2 cm long, 1.6 cm wide, rose-red to carmine-red, old-rose ouside, perianth-segments with darker midstripe and white-edged. Fruit clavate, 2.5 cm long, red, with floral remains. Mexico (Distrito Federal, Hidalgo).

Mammillaria durispina Boed. (Series 9) □■ □□

Solitary, oblong-globose to shortly columnar, matt dark green stem, up to 20 cm high and 11 cm wide, with slightly depressed, white-woolly, spine-covered apex, tubercles globose, 8 mm high, with truncate tip, axils at first with white wool, later glabrescent, without bristles. Areoles only white-woolly on new growth, later glabrous, with 6–8 tough, straight, stellate, brownish-grey or russet, darker-tipped radial spines 7–8 mm long (uppermost 10–15 mm long), somewhat protruding, central spines absent. Flowers in a ring around the apex, 15 mm long, 12 mm wide, deep carmine-red with light-green throat. Fruit clavate, 2 cm long, carmine red, green on top. Mexico (Querétaro and Guanajuato).

Mammillaria esperanzaensis Boed. (Series 9) □□ ■□

Stem solitary, globose at first, eventually becoming shortly cylindric, up to 9 cm across, with cylindric-conic tubercles, naked in the axils. Radial spines up to 20, thin, prickly, pale yellow; central spines 4–7. stouter and bulbous at the base, amber-brown, the lowermost longest and down-curved, all spines with metallic sheen. Flowers campanulate, 2.5 cm across, creamy white, the outer segments with broad reddish midstripe outside. Mexico ((Puebla).

Mammillaria matudae H. Bravo (Series 10) □□ □■

Solitary or sprouting from the base, slenderly cylindric stem, up to 20 cm high and 3 cm thick, tubercles conical to weaky rectangular, 4.5 mm long, axils naked. Areoles initially somewhat woolly, with 18–20 needle-like, horizontally spreading, transparent white radial spines 2–3 mm long, and 1 stouter, upward-pointing, transparent white, reddish-tipped, later off-white central spine 4.5 mm long. Flowers funnel-shaped, 1.2 cm long, light purple. Mexico (on the border between Mexico and Michoacán).

292

Mammillaria spinosissima Lem. (Series 10)

■□
□□

Solitary, cylindric, dark green to blue-green stem, 4–10 cm wide, up to 30 cm high, densely covered in spines, apex woolly and with a tuft of erect spines, tubercles conical, weakly angular, 4–5 mm long, axils somewhat woolly and bristly. Areoles at first short-felted, with 20–30 fine, bristly, white radial spines 2–10 mm long, and 7–10 rather stouter, bristly central spines 1–2 cm long, from pure white or yellow to ruby red or dark brown. Flowers in a ring, widely funnel-shaped, 2 cm long, 1.5 cm wide, pink to purple. Fruit clavate, 2 cm long, red. C Mexico.

Mammillaria guerreronis (H. Bravo) Backeb. (Series 10)

□■
□□

Offsetting, columnar, up to 60 cm long and 6 cm wide, light green, densely spiny stem, tubercles small, conical, axils with persistent white wool and 15–20 white bristles. Areoles initially white-felted, with 20–30 straight, bristle-fine radial spines 5–10 mm long, white, orange-yellow at the base, and 4 white to pink-tinted central spines 1.5 cm long, 1 of which is hooked. Flowers whitish-pink. Fruit clavate, 2 cm long, red. Mexico (Guerrero).

Mammillaria eriacantha Pfeiffer (Series 10)

□□
■□

Solitary or offsetting, clavate to elongate-cylindric, light emerald green stem, 15–50 cm high and 4.5–5.5 cm wide, tubercles ±close-set, conical from a rectangular base, 6–8 mm long and 4–6 mm wide at the base, axils with sparse wool. Areoles at first sparsely white-woolly, with 16–25 bristly, spreading and interlacing, hairy, yellowish to golden radial spines 3–6 mm long, and 2 subulate, straight, thick, needle-like, upward or downward-pointing, yellow central spines 8–10 mm long. Flowers below the apex, shortly funnel-shaped, 1.5 cm long and wide, yellow. Fruit clavate, 1 cm long, pink to orange. Mexico (Veracruz).

Mammillaria haageana Pfeiffer (Series 11)

□□
□■

Globose, 5–10 cm high, 5–8 cm wide stem, light green, with somewhat depressed, white-woolly apex, tubercles close-set, ovoid-conical, slightly laterally compressed, 4–5 mm long, axils naked or ±white-woolly. Areoles initially white-felted, with 25–30 stiff, protruding, interlacing, white radial spines 5–6 mm long, and 2 (1–3) upward- and downward- pointing, white, brown-tipped central spines up to 1 cm long. Flowers numerous in a ring, vivid carmine-red. Fruit carmine red. This species, better known under the incorrect name *M. elegans* has numerous forms; the illustration shows a form also known as *M. conspicua* J.A. Purpus. C Mexico.

Mammillaria crucigera Martius (Series 11)

Globose to cylindric, up to 15 cm high and 3–5 cm wide stem, with deeply depressed apex, eventually forming large clumps through dichotomous division, tubercles small, up to 4 mm long, close-set, rectangular at the base, conical above, fresh green to olive grey-green, with watery sap, milky in the growing period, axils with abundant thick white wool. Areoles sparsely white-woolly only when young, with 24 or more fine, needle-like, straight, horizontal, white radial spines 1.5–2 mm long, and usually 4 cruciform, thicker, waxy-yellow to chalk-white, dark brown to black-tipped central spines 2–3 mm long. Flowers small, purple or deep red to violet-pink. Fruit clavate, 10 mm long, 3–5 mm thick, carmine red, with floral remains. Mexico (S Puebla, N Oaxaca).

Mammillaria flavicentra Backeb. (Series 11)

Solitary, clavate to cylindric-columnar, grey-green stem up to 18 cm high, 9–10 cm wide, with level, white woolly apex, tubercles pyramidal, 7 mm long, 6 mm wide at the base, with watery sap, axils with curly wool, without bristles. Areoles glabrous, with 22–24 thin, needle-like, glassy white radial spines 2–4 mm long, and 4–6 fine, thinly subulate, yellowish central spines 5–6 mm long. Flowers 3–4 mm wide, carmine red. Fruit 1.5 cm long, thickly-clavate, whitish-greenish below, merging into pink above. Mexico (N Oaxaca).

Mammillaria sempervivi DC. (Series 12)

Solitary or sparsely offsetting, globose to shortly cylindric, dark grey-green stem, up to 7 cm thick, with somewhat depressed, white-woolly apex, tubercles up to 1 cm long, 4- or more-sided, axils woolly. Areoles with 3–7 white, caducous radial spines up to 3 mm long, and 2 stout, weakly curved central spines barely 4 mm long. Flowers scattered near apex, 1 cm long, off-white to pink. Fruit clavate, 8 mm long, red, with floral remains. Mexico (Hidalgo).

Mammillaria pseudoperbella Quehl (Series 12)

Globose, in age often shortly columnar, bluish-green, completely covered in spines, tubercles close-set, cylindric-conical, weakly rectangular, 6–7 mm long, with milky sap, axils slightly woolly. Areoles with 20–30 white, bristly, pectinate, appressed, radial spines 3–4 mm long, and 2 short, stouter, dark brown, black-tipped, central spines. Flowers 15 mm long, 12 mm wide, white with red midstripe outside. Fruit clavate, 8 mm long, coral red. Mexico (exact origin uncertain).

Mammillaria hahniana Werderm. (Series 12)

Broadly globose, up to 9 cm high, 10 cm wide stem, freely offsetting to form many-headed clumps, with somewhat flattened, sparsely woolly apex, tubercles small, 5 mm long, conical, fresh green, very milky, axils with short white wool and 20 or more white, ±curved bristles up to 4 cm long. Areoles with short white wool, later glabrous, with 20–30 pectinate, laterally spreading, hair-fine, wavy or curly radial spines 5–15 mm long, and usually 1(2–4) porrect, thin, needle-like, white, russet-tipped central spines up to 4 mm long. Flowers in a ring around the apex, small, 12–13 mm wide, purple-red. Fruit shortly clavate, 8 mm long, 5 mm wide, pinkish-red to almost whitish. Variable species. The illustration shows a form with relatively short hairs and longer central spines (*M. woodsii*). Mexico (Querétaro).

Mammillaria zahniana Boed. & Ritter (Series 13)

Solitary, depressed globose, dark green stem, with slightly depressed, somewhat woolly apex, tubercles rectangular to weakly rounded, underside keeled, upperside rounded, broad-based, 2 cm long, axils sparsely woolly, without bristles. Areoles only initially white woolly, with 4 subulate, straight, protruding, whitish to horn-coloured, black-tipped spines, upper ones 3–8 mm long, lowest up to 15 mm long. Flowers somewhat distant from apex, 3 cm long, 2.5 cm wide, sulphur-yellow with lighter edge and darker tip. Fruit clavate, red. Mexico (Nuevo Leon, Coahuila).

Mammillaria zeyeriana F. Haage (Series 13)

Solitary, globose to pyramidal, in age mostly oblong, light blue-green stem, up to 15 cm high and 10 cm wide, with depressed, very sparsely woolly-felted apex, highly-surmounted with spines, tubercles conical, weakly angular, 10–12 mm long, axils sparsely woolly, later glabrous. Areoles slightly woolly-felted, later glabrescent, with 10 straight, fine, needle-like, white radial spines 3–10 mm long, and 4 needle-like, somewhat flexible, ruby-red at first, then chestnut-brown, finally white, very dark brown-tipped central spines 1.5–2.5 cm long, uppermost 1 strongly curved, lower 3 porrect. Inner perianth-segments reddish-orange with yellow edge. Fruit clavate, 25 mm long, 7 mm thick, carmine-red, with floral remains. Mexico (Coahuila, Durango).

Mammillaria coahuilensis (Boed.) Moran (Series 13)
[= Porfiria schwartzii (Frič) Boed.]

Solitary, flattened stem, 4.5 cm wide, containing milky sap, with thick, conical, tuberous root, tubercles distant, up to 12 mm long, triangular and pointed leaf-like, 10 mm wide at the base, 4 mm thick, upper side flat, blue-green, axils with small tufts of wool. Areoles woolly when young, later glabrous, with 16 thin, stiff, horizontally spreading, grey-white radial spines, unequal, up to 6 mm long, and 1 brownish, stouter central spine 6 mm long. Flowers several together near apex, campanulate-funnelshaped, up to 3 cm wide, whitish with pink midstripe. Fruit curved clavate, up to 3 cm long, vermilion. Mexico (Coahuila).

Mammillaria craigii Lindsay (Series 13)

Solitary or dividing dichotomously, pale yellowish to grey-green stem with depressed, woolly apex, tubercles firm, 4-sided, sharply angled towards the top, 6–7 mm long, 9–10 mm wide at the base, axils somewhat white-woolly, without bristles. Areoles with abundant brownish wool, 7–8 fine, needle-like, straight, protruding, golden-brown radial spines 4–12 mm long, and usually 2(1–3) thin, needle-like, stiff, golden-brown central spines 1–2 cm long. Flowers bell-shaped, 1.5–2 cm long, 1–1.5 cm wide, deep pink with darker midstripe. Fruit clavate, 1.2 cm long, red, with floral remains. Mexico (Chihuahua, Sonora).

Mammillaria miegiana Earle (Series 13)

Usually solitary, globose, leaf-green stem, 16 cm high, 10 cm wide, with somewhat flattened apex, tubercles 12 mm long and 4-angled tip, young axils with white wool, later glabrous. Areoles with 10–11 spreading, grey-white radial spines 8–9 mm long, and 2 brown central spines 7–8 mm long, the upper 1 pointing upwards. Flowers in a ring around the apex, 2 cm long, 2.5 cm wide, scarlet, pink in the centre, brownish red outside. Fruit clavate, 2.5 cm long, 1 cm thick, cherry-red. Mexico (Sonora).

Mammillaria canelensis Craig (Series 13)

Solitary, globose to ovoid, light to dark green stem, with somewhat depressed apex, tubercles firm, globose to almost cylindric, 5–8 mm long, 5–8 mm broad at the base, axils with white wool and bristles almost as long as the tubercles. Areoles at first densely white woolly, with 22–25 very fine, needle-like, straight, laterally spreading, white radial spines 5–15 mm long, and 2–4 stouter, straight to curving, orange-yellow central spines 3 cm long, spreading above the apex. Flowers 1.8 cm long, 1.5 cm white, light greenish-yellow. Mexico (SW Chihuahua, SE Sonora).

Mammillaria johnstonii (B. & R.) Orcutt (Series 13)

Solitary, only rarely sprouting from the base, globose, matt blue-green to grey-green stem, 15–20 cm wide, with only weakly depressed apex, tubercles firm, 4-sided, 10–13 mm long, 6–9 mm wide at the base, axils somewhat woolly, without bristles. Areoles only initially weakly woolly, with 10–15 needle-like, straight, white to horn-coloured, reddish-brown or black-tipped, slightly protruding radial spines 6–9 mm long, and 2 straight, subulate, protruding, light purple to black central spines 10 mm long. Flowers around the apex, bell-shaped, 1.5–2 cm long and wide, pink with brownish midstripe. Fruit 2.5 cm long, red to scarlet. Mexico (Sonora, San Carlos Bay).

Mammillaria baxteriana (H. Gates) Boed.
ex Backeb. & F.M. Knuth (Series 13)
[= **M. marshalliana** (H. Gates) Boed. ex Backeb. & F.M. Knuth
Usually solitary, sometimes clustering, deep-seated, depressed-globose, up to 12 cm across, with elongate-conic, angular, bluish-green tubercles, woolly in the axils. Radial spines 8–13, unequal, the lower longer, up to 15 mm long, spreading, white; central spine usually only 1, 1–2 cm long, curving upwards, white with dark brown tip. Flowers campanulate, about 1.5 cm long and 2 cm across, pale yellow, the outer segments with pink midstripe, stigmas pale yellow. Fruit club-shaped,. 2 cm long, bright purplish red; seeds curved pear-shaped, brown, reticulate. Mexico (Baja California).

Mammillaria sartorii J.A. Purpus (Series 14)
Solitary or freely clustering, globose to shortly-cylindric stems, dark blue-green, densely and finely white-punctate, 8–12 cm wide, with slightly depressed apex, with abundant white woolly felt topped with short, dark brown spines, tubercles firm, with rectangular base, turning to conical above, 1–1.2 cm long, with milky sap, axils with abundant, curly, white wool and very small isolated bristles. Areoles with abundant curly, white, woolly felt, and 4–6 whitish or brownish-white, brown-tipped radial spines, unequal, from 5–8 mm long, without, or occasionally with 1 similar central spine. Flowers 2 cm long, light carmine with darker midstripe. Fruit oblong-clavate, 1.5 cm long, carmine red, with floral remains. Mexico (Veracruz).

Mammillaria mystax Mart. (Series 14)
Solitary, sometimes sprouting from the base, globose to shortly cylindric, dark grey-green stem up to 15 cm high and 7–12 cm wide, with depressed, woolly apex completely covered with long, interlacing spines, tubercles close-set, firm, 4–6-sided pyramidal, sharply keeled on the underside, 10–15 mm long, 8 mm wide at the base, axils with sparse white wool and strongly twisted bristles. Areoles somewhat curly woolly-felted, later glabrescent, without or with 1–4 mostly very small, fine, needle-like, white, brown-tipped radial spines 3.8 mm long and 3–4 twisted, 4-sided central spines 1.5–2 cm long, middle 1.5–7 cm long, ruby-red on new growth, later greying. Flowers in a ring around the apex, campanulate-funnelshaped, 2.2–2.5 cm long, 2 cm wide, fiery carmine-red. Fruit clavate, 2–2.5 cm long, with deciduous floral-remains. Mexico (Puebla, Oaxaca). The illustration shows a very short-spined form of *M. mystax*, with poorly developed radial spines and axillary bristles.

Mammillaria collinsii (B. & R.) Orcutt (Series 14)
Offsetting and mat-forming, individual stems equal-sized, globose, 6–8 cm thick, often bronze-coloured to flushed with deep purple, tubercles firm, conical-cylindric, 8–10 mm long, the base 6–7 mm wide, axils strongly white-woolly, with twisted bristles often longer than the tubercles. Areoles initially with white wool, soon glabrous, with 7 needle-like, straight, somewhat protruding, pale, dark-tipped radial spines 5–7 mm long, and 1 stout, needle-like, porrect, dark brown central spine up to 8 mm long. Flowers 1.5 cm long, yellowish and pale pink striate. Fruit clavate, up to 2 cm long, deep red, with floral remains. Mexico (Oaxaca).

COPING WITH DISEASES AND PESTS

The healthier and hardier the cacti, the less susceptible they will be to diseases and pests. Nevertheless, cacti can be attacked by pests, through a newly acquired plant, for example, or through infection from the garden, or one or two plants may sicken, especially in winter.

The major diseases of cacti are wet and dry rot, which are principally caused by fungi. The rot frequently starts in the roots or root-neck, where fungal parasites can most easily invade the plant, and then travels very quickly up the conducting tissues, which usually turn red. The disease can also enter through small points such as, local wounds on the plant, and then spread inwards.

In warm and damp conditions that encourage fungal growth, the disease usually develops so quickly as to be fatal. If noticed in time, the apex of the plant at least can be saved, or further spread limited by cutting out the affected part. When cutting diseased plants, the cut surface must be carefully examined to be certain that no red discoloration still remains on the conducting channels, which are easily recognizable as clear dots; only absolutely healthy pieces can be saved as cuttings or grafts.

Fungal attack is a particular threat to young seedlings, which can often be destroyed by the dreaded 'damping-off' disease within a few hours. Instant attention is required as soon as the first signs of damping-off are noticed; slender threads of fungus on the soil, seedlings becoming glossy and toppling over.

The infected plants must be totally removed and destroyed, any seedlings which still look healthy must be treated with a fungicide and, if possible, transplanted to fresh soil. Further growth of the fungus must be discouraged as far as possible by sunlight and fresh air.

Attacks by animal pests should not be able to cause much damage nowadays if plants are kept under scrutiny. A considerable number of more or less specific products exist, including systemic controls that are absorbed by the plant and are effective against sucking and nibbling insects. There are also contact poisons applied by spray or fumigation which can reach even the most inaccessible crannies.

A warning about the use of chemical pest-control preparations: do not use the same preparation against the same pest for a long period of time, because this can produce a resistant strain against which the remedy becomes ineffective. Rotational use of several different preparations is therefore strongly advised.

The grower may have to contend with the following animal pests:

Red spider mite

This red mite, falsely named 'red spider' because it spins a fine web, can be a particularly troublesome pest. It is so small that it can hardly be seen without a magnifying glass; in dry air it multiplies extraordinarily fast, and devastates the outer layers of plant tissue by piercing the cells, which consequently turn a nasty brown. Since the red spider mite appears in the open-air in summer on fruit trees, beans, and many other plants, an attack must always be expected, especially in a dry summer.

It has a particular predilection for the soft-fleshed cacti such as *Lobivia (Chamaecereus) silvestrii*, *Mammillaria longimamma*, some *Echinocereus* species, Coryphanthas and Rebutias. The first signs of an attack are a silver-grey film or rusty flecks on the green plant stem. Immediate counter-measures are necessary, followed by repeated spraying at intervals to prevent further attack. A good preventative measure is to provide damp air by frequent misting or spraying, since the red spider mite likes dry air.

Mealy bug

This 1–3 mm long, brown, woolly bug is the same shape as a woodlouse and is covered with mealy, white, waxy secretions. It lays its eggs in thick white webbing that looks like tufts of cotton wool and usually lies in inaccessible places. In a limited attack it is enough to remove this invader with a stiff paintbrush, but a subsequent treatment with chemicals is expedient to deal with hidden roots.

Scale insects

These insects move about while young, but the adults cling to the plant like limpets under round shields 1–2 mm across, and thus protected they multiply fiendishly. They can be physically removed with a stiff brush, but a chemical follow-up is necessary.

Root mealy bugs

These root bugs are pure white but otherwise very similar in appearance to the other mealy bugs. They are particularly dangerous and hard to fight because they live around the roots and root-neck of the plant, producing whitish, woolly secretions to build their nests, and are quite invisible from above. They can be dealt with by removing every scrap of earth from the roots of the affected plant and dipping them in a pesticide. This should be followed by repeated watering with a systemic insecticide until no bugs can survive.

The following pests are likely only in frames or greenhouses:

Woodlice

Halved and hollowed-out potatoes placed cut-side down on the ground will generally attract the woodlice. They can then easily be caught and destroyed.

Slugs

Slugs generally betray their presence by leaving slime-trails. Since they only come out of hiding at night, the easiest way is to look for them then using a flashlamp. Slug pellets are also very effective, since they both attract and destroy.

Ants

These can be harmful because they dig under cacti to build their nests; they also often take the seeds from the ripe fruits. They can easily be dealt with by chemical means.

Mice

Mice can harm the plants incidentally by nibbling the ripe fruit and thereby opening the way to other pests.

GLOSSARY

Abaxial Turned away from axis; referring to surface of an organ, such as a leaf, facing away from the main stem (opp. Adaxial).
Acropetal In the direction of the apex, referring to developmental sequence.
Acrotonous Emphasized towards the apex.
Actinomorphic Radially symmetrical; referring to a flower with more than two planes of symmetry (see Zygomorphic).
Adaxial Towards the axis; referring to surface of an organ facing towards the main stem (opp. Abaxial).
Adventitious Said of roots which do not arise from the radicle or primary root system, but from elsewhere.
Aerial root Root arising above ground.
Alternate Of leaves or other parts not opposite or whorled but placed singly at different heights on the stem.
Anastomosing Connecting to form a network, especially veins in a leaf.
Anatropous Inverted, recurved through 180°; said of an ovule bent over against its own stalk, with the mouth or micropyle close to the placenta.
Annulate Ringed or banded.
Anther Male part of the flower that produces pollen, usually borne on a filament. Anther and filament together known as a stamen.
Anthocyanin Blue, violet or purple pigment colouring leaves etc.
Anticlinal Said of cell-walls which cut the surface at right angles (opp. Periclinal).
Apex Tip, highest point.
Apical Located at or constituting the apex.
Appressed Lying flat, pressed closely against a surface.
Areole Highly condensed and modified short-shoot growing in the leaf axil as a felted cushion, unique to cacti, usually hairy and/or spiny; from them flowers and offsets arise.
Aril Outer covering or merely an appendage of a seed formed from the funicle; may be pulpy or hard.
Ascending Nearly erect.
Axil Notch or angle between the axis and any organ, e.g. leaf, arising from it.
Betalain Nitrogen-containing pigment found only in the group of families, including *Cactaceae*, known as *Centrospermae*.
Caducous Falling off early.
Cambium Layer of tissue that gives rise to secondary growth in stems and roots by cell division.
Campanulate Bell-shaped.
Campylotropous Said of an ovule curved back on itself so that the

micropyle is near to the hilum, as in *Cactaceae*.

Carpel Female reproductive structure of flower, usually comprising ovary, style and stigma; carpels may be solitary or grouped or fused with others, as in *Cactaceae* (see Gynoecium).

Centrifugal Tending outwards from the centre or axis.

Centripetal Tending inwards to the centre or axis.

Cephalium Modified flowering zone of some cactus stems, often marked by copious development of hairs and/or bristles. A distinction is sometimes made between the 'true' cephalium of *Melocactus*, for example, where vegetative growth ceases when the cephalium forms, and various kinds of 'pseudocephalium', where vegetative growth can continue.

Chalaza Basal zone of ovule where nucellus and integuments join.

Ciliate Fringed with hairs.

Clavate Club-shaped.

Cleistogamous Of flowers that do not open; self-pollination occurring within the closed flower.

Collenchyma Living tissue providing support and with characteristic unevenly thickened walls.

Cortex Layer of tissue between epidermis and vascular tissue, or external layer such as bark or rind (adj. Cortical).

Cotyledon Embryonic leaf; first leaf or leaves of a seedling after germination.

Crenate With notched edges.

Cristate Crest-shaped or crested.

Cultivar Assemblage of plants originated or selected and propagated artifically.

Cupule Cup-shaped structure.

Cuticle Thin, waterproof layer that covers the epidermis.

Cutin Waxy, water-repellent substance impregnating cell walls.

Deciduous Shed periodically or annually.

Decumbent Lying or growing along ground but turning upward at or near apex.

Decurrent Running downward.

Dehiscent Splitting or bursting open.

Deliquescent Becoming liquid.

Diaphragm Membranous protrusion in floral tube of some cacti which more or less closes the nectar chamber.

Dichotomous Forking equally; as when the stem divides into two equal branches.

Dimorphic Having two forms (opp. Monomorphic).

Druse Mass of needle-like crystals contained in a cell.

Endosperm Nutritive tissue formed within the embryo sac.

Epicotyl Portion of the stem of an embryo plant or seedling lying above the cotyledons (see Hypocotyl).

Epidermis Outermost cell-layer.

Epiphyte Plant that grows on another plant without drawing nutrients from it (adj. Epiphytic).

Exine Outermost layer of the pollen grain (see Intine).

Exserted Sticking out; said of stamens and/or style which extend beyond the perianth.

Fascicle Bundle or cluster.

Filament Stalk of stamen supporting anther.

Funicle Stalk of the ovule attaching it to placenta.

Glabrescent Becoming glabrous.

Glabrous Smooth, without hairs or excrescences.

Globose, globular Globe-shaped, spherical.

Glochids Barbed spines or hairs, mostly small and brittle, often in tufts, characteristic of *Opuntioideae*.

Growing-point Group of cells capable of division at the tips of the growing shoots and roots, which produce new tissue.

Gynoecium The female organs of the flower, as a whole.

Hilum Scar left on the seed where the funicle was attached.

Hypocotyl Portion of the seedling axis below the embryonic leaves or cotyledons (see Epicotyl).

Hypodermis Layer(s) of cells immediately under the epidermis.

Imbricate Overlapping.

Inferior Said of the ovary when positioned below the insertion of perianth and stamens.

Inflorescence Flower-cluster or clusters.

Insertion Attachment, for example, of stamens in a flower.

Integuments Outer and inner coats of the ovule.

Intercalary Inserted between already differentiated tissue regions.

Internode That part of a stem which lies between two nodes.

Interstitial pits Depressions between (rather than within) testa cells.

Intine Inner layer of the pollen grain or spore (see Exine).

Isodiametric Having the same diameter in all directions.

Keel V-shaped ridge on one side formed by channel on the other surface.

Mamilla Nipple-shaped tubercle or podarium with the areole at its tip.

Margin Edge of plant organ, such as a leaf.

Median Situated in the middle; lying in the axial plane.

Medulla Soft internal tissue, pith of stem or root (adj. Medullary).

Medullary rays Bands of parenchyma between pith and cortex.

Meristem Growth tissue; groups of cells capable of repeated division to form permanent tissue.

Micropyle Opening in the integument of the ovule through which the pollen tube enters.

Monomorphic Having a single shape or form (opp. Dimorphic).

Monopodial With single axis extending at apex, producing successive lateral structures beneath it.

Node Point on stem where a leaf or leaves arise.

Nucellus Central structure of ovule containing the embryo sac.

Obconic Inverted cone-shaped.

Obovoid Inverted egg-shaped, narrower nearer point of attachment.

Offset Side-shoot, often easily detached for propagation; offsetting = sprouting.

Ontogenesis Development of an individual through its various stages.

Orthostichy Arrangement of nodes, areoles and so on in a vertical row (see Spirostichy).

Ovoid Egg-shaped, broader nearer point of attachment.

Ovule Outgrowth of a seed plant's ovary that develops into a seed after the egg cell it contains is fertilized.

Panicle Lax inflorescence or flower cluster.

Papilla Small, rounded protuberance on any part of plant.

Parastichy Secondary spiral in phyllotaxis.

Parenchyma Basic living cell-tissue.

Pectinate Comb-shaped.

Pedicellate zone Portion of flower beneath the ovary.

Pendent Hanging.

Perianth Calyx (sepals) and corolla (petals), taken together. In *Cactaceae*, the sepals and petals form an intergrading series, termed perianth-segments, 'tepals' or 'sepaloids' and 'petaloids'.

Pericarp The pericarpel at the fruiting stage.

Pericarpel That part of the floral axis surrounding the ovary.

Periclinal Said of outer or tangential cell-walls (opp. Anticlinal).

Periderm Secondary protective tissue with cork cells.

Perisperm Nutritive tissue in the seed formed outside the embryo sac.

Petaloid Petal-like.

Phyllotaxis Mode of arrangement of leaves in relation to axis.

Pistil Female organs of flower, usually consisting of stigma, style and ovary.

Placenta Part(s) of ovary which bear ovules.

Placentation Arrangement of ovules within the ovary.

Podarium Nodal swelling, corresponding to the leaf-base.

Pollen tube Tube formed by protrusion of intine which penetrates style to convey pollen for fertilization.

Polyhedral Many-faceted.

Porrect Sticking straight out forwards.

Primary root The first root which develops as a continuation of the radicle.

Primordium Rudimentary outgrowth consisting of tissue capable of giving rise to, for example, a leaf.

Proliferous Bearing offsets; also said of flowers or fruits which produce further flowers from receptacular areoles, thus sometimes forming strings of fruits.

Prophyll Rudimentary leaf or bracteole at base of leafy shoot.

Pruinose Frosted appearance, with white powdery coating.

Pseudocephalium An apparent cephalium of wool and/or bristles (see Cephalium).

Pulp Juice or flesh which fills cavity of fruit.

Radicle Embryonic root.

Raphe Strand or ridge of vascular tissue in ovule connecting base of nucellus with the placenta.

Receptacle-tube Elongate-tubular part of the floral axis situated above the ovary, supporting the floral organs; sometimes taken to include the pericarpel.

Reticulate Net-like or criss-crossing.

Rostrate With a beak-like projection (noun: Rostrum).

Rotate Wheel-shaped; said of a flower in which the petals or perianth-segments radiate horizontally like the spokes of a wheel.

Rugose Wrinkled.

Serial Said of buds that arise sequentially.

Sessile Stalkless.

Shrub Plant usually branching from base rather than with a single stem or trunk and branching higher up (see Tree).

Sinuate Wavy-edged.

Spination Spine characteristics and distribution.

Spines Sharp-pointed, hard or woody structures, derived, in cacti, from leaves.

Spirostichy Arrangement of nodes, areoles and so forth in spiral rows (see Orthostichy).

Stamen Pollen-bearing male organ of flower, consisting of anther and filament.

Staminode A sterile, usually reduced stamen.

Stigma Surface or structure at apex of style, receptive to pollen.

Stolon Sucker or runner; a prostrate basal branch, above or below ground, which can root and produce new stems or plantlets.

Stoma Minute pore in epidermis through which gaseous exchange occurs (pl. Stomata).

Striate Marked with lines on the surface, sometimes with slight ridge or furrow.

Strophiole Swollen excrescence or appendage of the hilum of a seed.

Style Structure, usually slender, connecting ovary and stigma(s).

Subtending Said of a leaf in whose axil there is a bud, areole and so on.

Subulate Awl-shaped, slender and tapering.

Succulence Juiciness, fleshiness.

Succulent Juicy, fleshy, water-retaining; succulent plants store water in specific organs, for example, stem-succulents, leaf-succulents.

Superior Said of the ovary when the perianth and stamens are inserted below it on the receptacle.

Taxonomy The principles and practice of classification.

Terete Rod-like, rounded and smooth, often tapering.

Tessellate Patterned like a mosaic or pavement.

Testa Seedcoat.

Throat Of a flower, the visible portion between limb and tube.

Transverse Across; at right angles to the vertical.

Tree Plant with usually single, distinct trunk between ground and first branching.

Tribe Group ranking between genus and subfamily.

Truncate Ending abruptly as if cut off.

Tuber Swollen underground stem with storage capacity.

Tubercle Small, rounded prominence (adj. Tuberculate).

Tuberous root Swollen root with storage capacity.

Turbinate Shaped like a top or an inverted cone.

Umbilicus Navel-like formation; depression (adj. Umbilicate).

Vascular bundle Group of conducting channels and associated tissues.

Verrucose Covered in wart-like excrescences.

Verticillate Arranged in whorls.

Whorl Cluster of three or more parts such as leaves radiating from a single node.

Xerophyte Plant adapted to dry conditions.

Zygomorphic Bilaterally symmetrical; divisible in symmetrical halves in one plane only (see Actinomorphic).

INDEX

Bold figures refer to illustrations.

315

Q

R